HISTORY OF
International Perspectives

ROBERTO DELL'ORO and
CORRADO VIAFORA, Editors

HISTORY OF BIOETHICS
International Perspectives

ROBERTO DELL'ORO and
CORRADO VIAFORA, Editors

International Scholars Publications
San Francisco - London - Bethesda
1996

Library of Congress Cataloging-in-Publication Data

    Vent'anni di bioetica. English
    Bioethics : a history / Roberto Dell'Oro and Corrado Viafora,
    editors.
      p. cm.
    Includes bibliographical references and index.
    ISBN 1-57309-049-2 (cloth : alk. paper). -- ISBN 1-57309-048-4
    (pbk. : alk. paper)
    1. Medical ethics. 2. Bioethics. I. Dell'Oro, Roberto, 1959-
    . II. Viafora, Corrado, 1950- . III. Title.
    R724.V4413 1996
    174'.2--dc20   96-21552
                                                        CIP

Copyright 1996 by Lanza Foundation (Italy)

Original title

VENT'ANNI DI BIOETICA
IDEE PROTAGONISTI ISTITUZIONI

CORRADO VIAFORA (ed.)
Lanza Foundation, Padua (Italy)

English Translation
by

ROBERTO DELL'ORO
Center for Clinical Bioethics
Georgetown University

TABLE OF CONTENTS

ANALYTIC TABLE

II

IV

FOREWORD

by

Roberto Dell'Oro

History of Bioethics: International Perspectives is a collection of different voices on the birth and development of biocthics. Originally published in Italian as a result of an international symposium organized by the Lanza Foundation of Padua, it makes available to an English speaking audience the reflections of scholars from different linguistic and cultural traditions. Such a broad horizon can not only shed a different light on the foundational underpinnings of bioethics as a discipline, but also and foremost, provide some important bibliographic material for a cross cultural approach to the specific issues at stake. Since this material is introduced by the authors in their respective languages it has been virtually impossible, and perhaps even useless, to provide any reference to the original version of books when it exists in English, let alone the translation in English of each bibliographic entry. In this sense, the possibility of retrieving the material quoted by the authors does not rule out the ability to read in different languages, but rather confirms its importance. Yet, the task of providing some information on bioethics from the point of view of an Italian, French, Spanish, Dutch and German audience remains a first step toward a more serious cultural dialogue. Lanza Foundation, which has sponsored the English translation and edition of this text, represents an important factor in this direction. Therefore, some words on the nature and work of the Foundation are in order.

The Lanza Foundation was founded in the mid Eighties. Its specific goals were to enter into the delicate debate between faith and culture; to face an ever urgent necessity to recuperate the meaning of religious values and ethical principles; to reply to the compelling progress of science and technology, as well as to the massive changes in the economical and social realm. For this reason the Lanza Foundation envisages its own specific goal as an important one for the whole of society. The common search for ethical principles and values stands as a focal point in the private and public arena thus assuring the life and dignity of each human being in a free and fair society.

In light of these programmatic intentions the Lanza Foundation set down its constitution, as well as the basic guidelines for its activity in July 1988. The Foundation creates annual and pluriannual projects which are supervised by the members of its Scientific Board and by external experts. One of its prime objectives is to collect and process material from the internal and external archives in order to understand and analyze more deeply those aspects which influence decision making in the pastoral field and in the economical, social, and political sphere. Four different working groups have been established within the Foundation: "Ethics, Philosophy and Theology"; "Ethics and Medicine"; "Ethics and Environmental Policy"; "Ethics and Economics".

The project called "Ethics and Medicine" was inaugurated in the course of 1988. Paolo Benciolini, a Professor of Medical Law at the University of Padua, is the head of the project, while the research activities are coordinated by Prof. Corrado Viafora. The main objectives of the project have been the analysis of trends and directions in contemporary bioethics, and the creation of a "Bioethical Laboratory" for educational workshops and academic training. It is from the International Conferences of Bioethics that the book *Vent'anni di Bioetica* originated under the direction of Corrado Viafora who was the editor of the book in the Italian version. It is now offered to the English speaking audience with the title *History of Bioethics: International Perspectives*.

PREFACE

by

Warren Thomas Reich

It is a privilege to present to the U.S. reading public and bioethics scholars this volume on bioethics in several parts of the world. It offers a distinctive collection of culturally and intellectually diverse perspectives that are of mounting importance as the field of bioethics becomes more and more internationalized.

It is widely acknowledged that the field of bioethics had its start in the United States, where it has also acquired an impressive standing in academia, public policy and public education through the media. What is not so widely known in the United States is that bioethics has emerged and advanced in other countries and languages to a remarkable degree, especially during the past decade. The international developments in bioethics are not widely known in the United States due to the foreign language deficiencies of so many U.S. scholars, a shortcoming that has an isolating effect on U.S. scholarly dialogue. This volume will help to remedy that deficiency.

The essays are not designed to offer a substantive advancement of bioethical scholarship, but to present a rich portrayal of this field of learning in a variety of mentalities and cultures, and in this way to promote international and intercultural dialogue in bioethics.

Bioethics outside the United States deals with a somewhat different range of issues and methods. It offers critique of the initial U.S. orientation on bioethics, while utilizing some of the same rule-based analysis so common in the U.S. More significantly, one finds in the bioethics that has been developed in other countries distinctively different moral mentalities and intellectual approaches that are instructive for the rethinking of bioethics in the U.S.

For example, millennia of traditions in the Mediterranean basin have created a strong orientation to virtue, character, and moral anthropology as the matrix of ethics. By contrast, the "virtue ethics" that is being pursue by some scholars in the United States often lacks sustained links to an understanding of the nature of the human being as a moral being. In the area of political philosophy, the notion of solidarity found in Northern Europe offers a corrective to the excessive individualism that has characterized much of bioethics in the United States. These examples are found in chapters by Gracia and Malherbe, who explain approaches to bioethics that are firmly rooted in deep intellectual and moral traditions significantly different from those found in the United States.

This volume offers a very useful range of topics, settings, and analyses. Viafora, the editor of this volume, explains the cultural context, the moral methodologies, and points of agreement and disagreement in the field of bioethics viewed from an international perspective. Roy examines the contours of bioethics in international perspective: the past and emerging trends of thought and issues against a rich background of ideas in science, medicine, philosophy, and practical ethics. The origins and developments of bioethics in the United States are presented by Reich.

The chapter on bioethics in the Spanish language-area not only describes distinctive features of bioethics in Spain and in Spanish-American countries; its author (Gracia) also offers an insightful analysis of bioethics as civil ethics, as pluralistic ethics, as autonomous ethics, and as rational ethics. Malherbe's chapter gives an account of the rise of bioethics in French-speaking countries, while delineating a continental philosophy of medicine. Among many issues regarding bioethics in Italy, Bompiani discusses two different elements that may be of special interest to U.S. readers: the emergence of a new subjectivity centered on the "rediscovery of the body" and the underlying debate between theological (i.e. Catholic) and "lay" approaches to bioethics in Italy.

A distinctive feature of bioethics in German-speaking countries is the deep-seated problem of how to find a foundation for practical ethics: in Marxist thought? in sectarian (presumably adversarial) religious thought? in a highly speculative philosophical system of thought? in the experience-oriented hermeneutical approach? Bondolfi discusses these foundational questions in German-speaking countries, while also summarizing developments in many practical bioethics issues. The Netherlands are perhaps best known in the field of bioethics for their controversial law and practices regarding euthanasia. The origins and elements of that bioethical debate are presented by the leading Dutch bioethicist de Wachter.

In my view, the Lanza Foundation and Professor Viafora were correct in referring to the two decades of 1970-1990 as the first twenty years of the field of bioethics. (The original title of this book was *Vent'anni di Bioetica*, Twenty Years of Bioethics.) It was around 1970 that public reaction to biomedical abuses galvanized a gradually developing interest in the ethics of the life sciences in the United States. Perhaps more significantly, the very word bioethics, which was first coined by Van Rensselaer Potter in 1970, was a major factor in stimulating development of the new field of bioethics. As the two parts of that word indicate, the initial promoters of that term (Potter, André Hellegers, Daniel Callahan and others) were attempting to promote a synthesis of -- or at least a dialogue between -- a knowledge of the life sciences and of ethics in response to the problems that were being experienced and foreseen in mid-century United States (see Warren Thomas Reich, "The Word 'Bioethics': Its Birth and the Legacies of those Who Shaped It," *Kennedy Institute of Ethics Journal*, Vol. 4, No. 4, 319-335; and "The Word 'Bioethics': The Struggle over Its Earliest Meanings," *Kennedy Institute of Ethics Journal*, Vol. 5, No. 1, 19-34).

The word functioned like a magnet in the United States: It became the rallying-point of new intellectual initiatives, of new interdisciplinary research and teaching, of new research centers, and of new federal and private funding.

Furthermore, the word bioethics strongly influenced public acceptance of ethics as a secular field of learning related to the humanities.

Consequently, there are good reasons for claiming, as this volume does, that 1970 marked the principal historic starting-point of the field of bioethics as a publicly recognized field of learning. Nonetheless, bioethics also embraces the previous twenty years of the "pre-history" of bioethics, when the first interdisciplinary dialogues stimulated a renaissance of medical ethics.

Although the word and the field of bioethics were first spawned in the United States, their cousins in other countries are clearly a distinctive and forceful branch of the family that deserves to be better known in the country of origin. Thus it will be helpful to U.S. scholars to have available to them in English translation the essays found in this volume on bioethics in French-speaking, German-speaking, Dutch-speaking, Spanish-speaking, and Italian-speaking countries, placed in dialogue with chapters on bioethics in English-speaking countries.

Introduction

BIOETHICS TODAY: AN HISTORIC AND SYSTEMATIC ACCOUNT

Corrado Viafora

The goal of this introductory paper is to provide an historic as well as systematic account of the development of bioethics. Attention will be given to the most significant scientific literature in order to highlight the different approaches of diverse linguistic domains. The paper was conceived on the occasion of the "International Bioethical Meetings", and within the activities coordinated by the Project "Ethics and Medicine" of the Lanza Foundation. Three questions will be addressed: 1) the cultural and interdisciplinary context from which bioethics was initially born and eventually developed; 2) the most important points of agreement within the field as well as issues still open to discussion; 3) the systematic frame which makes possible a productive confrontation between different bioethical approaches.

1. The Origins and the Development of Bioethics

Bioethics is now twenty years old. Stimulated by perplexities and hopes, fueled by the extraordinary biomedical progress, bioethics was initially conceived as a reflection on the conditions for dealing responsibly with the power of modern medicine; it was to be a reflection altogether original and systematic. Meantime, bioethics has taken root and developed into a "movement" defined by many initiatives, *i.e.*, bioethical centers and committees, and specific teaching programs. Moreover, bioethics has been increasingly receiving the attention of public opinion because of the ethical concerns it raises. The request for an ethical reflection is particularly clamored in the "new"[1] field of biomedical technologies concerning the initial and the terminal moments of life. At the level of daily practice, the demand for a more humane medicine[2] faces the reality of very complex phenomena, *i.e.*, scientific development, socialization of health care, and increasing dependence of life upon medicine.

Some approaches to these phenomena generate only moralistic pronouncements. Yet, some aspects characterizing today's medical practice and health care show the urgency of an ethical reflection. Of special concern are: the de-personalization of health care in hospitals, the systematic marginalization in health care services of particular categories of patients, the reduction of health care to a technical fact, and finally the fragmentation of medical intervention which causes a dilution of responsibility and deprives the physician-patient relation of its consistency.[3]

1.1. Context of the Discipline: from Medical Ethics to Bioethics

From an historical perspective, philosophers and moral theologians have contributed most to the formation of bioethical reflection.[4] The interest of moral philosophy, in particular, for bioethics is part of a wider phenomenon. The beginning of the seventies signaled a turning point in ethical reflections from metaethics to applied ethics.[5] In more general terms, this turn can be expressed as a "rehabilitation of practical philosophy".[6] During the last century, practical philosophy has been expropriated of its prescriptive function, and had been moving toward providing a ground for criteria and norms of human praxis.

On the other hand, the attitude of medicine toward ethics has been quite ambivalent. In spite of the increasing relation between medicine and ethics, the former still shows some resistance[7] toward the latter. Applied ethics is suspiciously seen as introducing into medicine a specific ideological point of view. Such a stand arises from the theoretical presupposition that medicine as a science deals with facts alone, and prescinds from any ideological perspective.

Indeed, the suspicion underlying biomedical developments simply makes evident the reality of a deep and old difference which prevails between science and ethics.[8] According to some, scientific research should be independent from any rule extrinsic to scientific method. Not only does the need to know deserve absolute priority, but it also must be pursued independently of any other value. Even if the tension between science and ethics is still very evident, its becoming clear that such a tension should be overcome: ethical concerns must be understood as intrinsic to scientific research. Without it, science is deprived of any reference to ethical values, and inevitably falls in the hands of power and ideology.[9]

Responsibility is normally thought as an issue concerning the application of science alone, thus leaving pure science directly involved in research, and free from every ethical consideration. Indeed, ethical judgments usually refer to technical applications of science. Yet, it would be naive to think that ethical issues arise only when technology is applied.[10] Pure research, also, should be confronted with the question of the morality of means. Ethical issues have emerged acutely precisely in the biomedical and biogenetic field since, in this case, the "material" to be researched is the human being itself.

Consider for instance the question, still open in Italy, of research and experimentation on human embryos. Granting the embryo the dignity of a human being, the question becomes: is it right to use such an embryo for the purpose, in itself very noble, to know the laws of life's development? Is the respect due to an embryo less important than the desire to know and the possible use of this knowledge?[11]

Bridging the gap which separates the world of scientific facts and the world of ethical values has been, perhaps, the most important accomplishment of bioethical reflection in the last two decades. Twenty years ago, when Van Potter first introduced the word "bioethics" the title of his book *Bioethics: Bridge to the Future*[12] had a prophetic meaning indeed. If confronted with the object of traditional medical ethics, the novity of bioethics consists in widening very much the field of inquiry. This is true not only for the area of scientific research, but for the socio-political and ecological dimensions as well.

There is little doubt that the area of scientific research offers a wide scope where new problems inevitably emerge. Given the massive introduction of biomedical technologies in medical practice, the task of contemporary bioethics becomes one of trying to discern when human beings have power over science and technology and when the opposite occurs.

A second direction in the broadening of traditional medical ethics has been the awareness that general health is, by and large, dependent upon factors which are not inherently medical: *i.e.*, nutrition, hygiene, housing, work conditions, lifestyle. This awareness generates new urgent questions for applied ethics. First, there is the issue of a more fair distribution of wealth which, in turn, determines the allocation of health care resources. Second, how to frame -- in light of the perspective of social justice -- public policy guidelines concerning both a fair distribution of health care resources and research priorities? The dramatic situation of the Third World where malaria alone affects 250 million people challenges any ethical reflection. Biomedical research must make it a priority to pursue the goal of preventing two thirds of humanity from falling into these devastating endemic diseases.

Ecological sensibility has stimulated a third area of development in traditional medical ethics. This sensibility has pointed out that life is a unity, and will be lost or saved as a whole. An ethics of common solidarity among all living beings emerges. Bioethical reflection has to revise traditional ethical categories in order to verify their fitness to interpret new dimensions of human responsibility toward life in the present situation.

The broadening of bioethics in the areas of scientific research, health care policy and ecology, provides an account for the development of important issues in today's reflection. This fact does not yet explain the repercussion and the profound impact of bioethics on public opinion during the last twenty years. One explanation springs from the fact that bioethics has spoken the language of rights;[13] a language quite familiar to the Western cultural context. Indeed, without the support of a general human rights movement it would be impossible to account for patient's rights movement[14] as well as for the bioethical movement in general.

The language of rights applied to the biomedical field is a real novity, and it can be traced back to the beginning of the seventies.[15] During these years there began, in the West, a process of patient's emancipation which was to find expression and recognition in the right to informed consent. Especially in its first phase, bioethical reflection was strongly influenced, beyond any doubt, by the new language of rights rather than by the old language of virtues and duties which characterized the Hippocratic ethical tradition.[16]

1.2. The Operative Context: Bioethical Centers

The ground where bioethics is implanted is, so to speak, the context defined by the relation between ethics and biomedical progress, or the relation human rights-medicine.

From an operative perspective however, the important role played by a particular type of institution must be mentioned, *i.e.*, bioethical centers. The contribution of the centers during these two decades is so relevant that it goes hand in hand with the very progress of bioethics itself. Beginning in 1970 in America and the early eighties in Europe, other institutions together with the Centers, have given great impulse to this new area of research: research groups on emerging bioethical problems, didactic and formative programs, specialized periodicals and informative dossiers, bibliographical repertoires, archives and centers of documentation.[17]

All these institutions have been particularly important in promoting a real dialogue between the human community in general and the community of experts in biomedical science in particular, as well as scholars involved in the creation of adequate ethical and legal guidelines.

Among the centers which have contributed the most to the development of bioethics, the following must be mentioned: the "Hastings Center" (New York) and the "Kennedy Institute" (Washington); the "Institute of Medical Ethics" (London) and the "Instituto Borja de Bioetica" (Barcelona).[18] A brief presentation of the activity of these centers may serve the purpose of verifying concrete issues, methods and organizational aspects of bioethical reflection.

The "Hastings Center", or "The Institute of Society, Ethics and Life Sciences", was founded in 1969 by the philosopher D. Callahan and the psychiatrist W. Gaylin. During the same year, D. Callahan worked on an ambitious project on the medical, ethical and legal aspects of abortion. The book was published in 1970 with the title *Abortion: Law, Choice and Morality*.[19] In 1969 Callahan published two other works; *The Catholic Case for Contraception*[20] and *The Sanctity of Life*.[21] The latter is a synthesis of moral philosophical arguments, themes from Protestant ethical thought, and Catholic moral theology.

The center founded by Callahan and Gaylin was meant to be an independent research institute, that is, a research community which was not committed to any specific ideology or religious denomination. The goal of the Center was to analyze issues emerging from the biomedical field: *i.e.*, to advance research in ethics as applied to the biomedical field; to stimulate the teaching of ethics in universities, medical and nursing schools; to make information on health care issues available to institutions and to the general public. Interdisciplinary research groups were to work on projects in different fields of inquiry. These were to form the basic structure for the activities of the center. The purpose of the research was to provide objective information and at the same time to formulate guidelines for medical practice and scientific research. Together with the experts invited, each work-group is composed of scholars chosen among non-resident members of the center. The groups are coordinated and guided by the resident staff of the Hastings Center. These group leaders include scholars of different disciplines such as social science, law, biomedicine, as well as philosophers, moral theologians and public administrators. The research promoted on the basis of this interdisciplinary approach deals with different issues like death, suffering, genetics, ethics of social sciences, behavior's control, health care policy, foundations of ethics, ethics of the profession. Since 1971 the center has been publishing a bimonthly periodical entitled *The Hastings Center Report*, and it is one of the best in the field of bioethics. Other publications include *A Review of Human Subjects Research*, and several books with the material produced by the research groups of the center.

The founder of the "Kennedy Institute of Ethics", Dutch born Andre Hellegers, was a Professor of obstetrics and a specialist trained in fetal physiology. The decision by Hellegers to create a permanent research institute on biomedical ethics had an important effect the discussions triggered by the encyclica "Humanae Vitae".[22] Hellegers had not only participated since 1964 in the work of the Pontifical Commission of study on family, population and natality problems, but also played a major role as a member of the Executive Committee. When on July 29, 1968, Pope Paul VI issued the encyclica reaffirming the traditional opposition of the Catholic Church to contraception -- and rejecting the recommendation signed by the majority of the Commission -- Hellegers was deeply disappointed.

The contribution of the Protestant theologian Paul Ramsey -- whom Hellegers had chosen as a collaborator and interlocutor -- was decisive in laying down the foundations of the Kennedy Institute. Ramsey remained at Georgetown University Medical School for a year as a "Visiting Professor in Ethics of Genetics". The results of his research was published in 1970 under the title *The Patient as Person: Explorations in Medical Ethics*.[23] This book was especially influential in bringing biomedical ethics to the attention of a wide academic and professional public. The fruitful collaboration between Ramsey and Hellegers succeeded in bringing together a group of scholars of Christian ethics. In the period 1971-75, the Catholic theologians C. Curran, B. Häring, R. Mc Cormick, W. Reich and the Protestant theologians R. Branson, F. Carney, S. Hauerwas,

L. Walters, all came to Georgetown University. Because of the direct contact with the Medical School, these scholars began working on bioethics with an interdisciplinary and ecumenical approach which has remained so far the characteristic feature of the Institute. The Institute intends to promote a conception of bioethics in light of a "moral anthropology", that is in light of what is universally human.

The "Kennedy Institute" made possible the publication of two important bibliographical tools: *New Titles in Bioethics* and *Scope Notes Series*. Also born in the Institute was the *Encyclopedia of Bioethics* edited by W.T. Reich. Finally, the "Intensive Bioethics Course" which takes place every year, and is directed to health care professionals, university and government administrators is another achievement of the Institute.

The first European initiatives took place during the years when the two American Centers were activating important research tools. The *Journal of Medical Ethics*, a prestigious periodical of medical ethics, began its publication during 1975 in London. Directed by R. Gillon, the Journal represents the official publication of the "Institute of Medical Ethics". The Institute has replaced the "London Medical Group" in promoting a wide program of lectures and symposia on ethical issues within medical practice since 1963. Analogous groups are associated with other institutes operating within medical clinics in England. The "Institute of Medical Ethics" was constituted in "Society for the Study of Ethics", and is an independent organism. It sponsors research programs on different ethical issues and publishes the materials of these programs. Past research includes the issue of resource allocation, death and dying, and since 1986-87 clinical research also focuses on children and pre-natal life.

The "Instituto Borja de Bioetica" was also created in 1975. During its first years, the "Institute" was part of the Theological Faculty of Barcelona. Since 1984 it has been an autonomous research institute, and it is the first bioethics center on European continent. The primary goals of the institute are the following: to reflect on ethical questions raised by biomedical progress giving particular attention to the dialogue between christian faith and scientific world; to provide a service to society in general and to the church in particular. The themes for the research are functional to requests coming from the church, the government or the hospitals. Research is done both at a personal level and through the creation of *ad hoc* commissions. So far, issues that have been explored are: family planning, the protection of mother and child in the early age, ethics and legislation of abortion, the treatment of chronically ill patients, patients' rights, euthanasia and the right to die with dignity, the code of nursing ethics, and diagnosis of cerebral death of children. The institute has formulated protocols to be followed in cases where blood transfusion are to be administered to Jehovah's Witnesses, as well as prenatal diagnosis. The institute publishes a series of notes: *Horitzons de Bioetica.*

During the eighties Bioethics has become popular in other European countries as well.[24] Many recently established centers show the growing vitality of bioethics.

2. Achievements and Open Questions

So far we have been outlining the genetic context and the operative development of bioethics. The next step will be to point out the most important achievements of bioethics during these two decades of life. At the same time, questions should be addressed concerning the character of bioethics as a field, and the development of its epistemological foundations.[25]

The basic achievements of bioethics seem to be the following:

a) the awareness that medicine -- especially in its present phase of scientific and technological development -- needs an ethical reference point in order to remain, at the service of the whole human being and for all human beings;

b) the need for a rational foundation of ethics on the presupposition that ethics is, first of all, a matter of plausible arguments. Ethical judgements do not rely upon authority, but upon their intrinsic rational strength;

c) the need to engage ethics in a constant dialogue with law so that the recognition of a distinction between the two does not exclude, but rather makes possible their reciprocal influence. Far from being relegated to the domain of private conscience, ethics should constitute a critical element in shaping normative systems of public policy;

d) the importance of ethical committees to solve recurring conflicts in the application of new medical technologies so that physicians, patients, and relatives are not left alone in their decision.

Nevertheless, new and complex questions emerge in light of these fundamental achievements. These should be carefully addressed since they ultimately constitute one of the central theoretical knots of contemporary moral philosophy. The task ahead is to determine what makes practical rationality unique.

2.1. Which Ethics?

We are initially confronted with different interpretations on the nature of ethics and its functions.[26] Such a problem, although very radical, is seldom sufficiently reflected, thus creating misunderstandings and ambiguities. Can ethical issues be really understood when treated as matters of strategy and procedure? Do they not constitute, first of all, questions of meaning and values? If, as it is claimed in this paper, ethical issues are primarily concerned with meaning and values, then ethics or bioethics is impossible without reference to an anthropological paradigm. Such a bold statement certainly is in need of deeper reflection.[27] On the other hand, it is immediately clear that different interpretations of the relation between ethics and anthropology undoubtedly play an important role in framing bioethical issues.[28]

The question of the relation between ethics and anthropology is reflected in the counterposition of two different paradigms within contemporary bioethical reflection: ethics of principles[29] and ethics of virtues.[30]

The ethics of principles has been, so far, the dominant model for two major reasons. First, this model seems more practical in the solution of issues of justice toward which modern conscience is particularly sensitive. Secondly, bioethical issues in recent years have been especially dealing with the advance of biomedical technologies. The appeal to experience, intuition, or moral sensibility doesn't seem enough in the solution of these issues. What is needed instead is an impartiality conducive to clear and fair moral judgements. Impartiality means acting according to principles so that moral judgements in any given circumstance can be applied to analogous cases in other circumstances, and independently of the subject involved. Impartiality is beyond any doubt an important feature in ethics, and yet it is not everything. Moral experience cannot simply be reduced to issues of justice and fairness. Attention should be focused on the moral subjects involved in the situation: their personal and relational identity cannot be liquidated as purely irrelevant. In spite of positive aspects inherent to the ethical paradigm based on principles, a new paradigm based on virtues has emerged as a possible alternative.

2.2. Which Rationality?

Another achievement of contemporary bioethics has been to evidence the need for a rational foundation of ethics. Yet, many questions seem involved in such an achievement. The ethical theories available are numerous, and each one of them differs from the other precisely with respect to the place assigned to reason in ethical evaluations.[31]

Within contemporary bioethical reflection it is possible to distinguish different approaches to the question of the place of reason in ethics.[32]

For the *analytic approach*, the place of reason in ethics consists in analyzing the coherence between general principles and concrete norms.[33]

For the *contractualistic approach*, the function of reason is to make possible an agreement on procedures which give to everyone equal opportunities.[34]

For the *clinical approach*, moral reasoning in bioethics has to avoid introducing general principles which make impossible any agreement, rather, it has to concentrate upon particular cases.[35]

For the *utilitarian approach*, the function of reason in ethics and particularly in bioethics is reducible to a costs/benefits analysis for the individuals involved in a particular situation in order to guarantee the welfare of the greater number.[36] For the *personalistic approach*,[37] the function of reason in ethics is to elaborate moral norms in light of the personal nature of the human being: nature provides the direction for the self-realization of the human being. Differences can be found within the personalistic approach according to the different emphases on the *ontological*,[38] the *relational*,[39] or the *hermeneutical* dimension of human nature.[40]

The most original contribution of the personalistic position is the strong relation it establishes between ethics and anthropology. Within this perspective, ethical values are seen as conditions for the realization of the human being *qua* human being. Therefore, ethical issues are not reducible to purely strategic questions which aim at social functionality, agreement, or maximization of happiness. Rather, ethical questions are, first of all, questions of meaning and value. Consequently, practical reason can become a normative instrument because it is capable of interpreting the human meaning of choices. An ethical issue is defined by the fact that, in any given situation, what is at stake is the realization of the human being.

The anthropological approach moves from the interpretation of the human structure as an original datum: the human being is and ought to be human, but he is at the same time a fact and a task. This task requires the analysis of what is human and the search for the values upon which the human dimension of our existence is grounded. It is within this perspective that ethics constantly refers to an anthropological dimension, thus striving unceasingly to understand the "truth which makes us human".

One of the issues raised by the personalistic approach is the relation between nature and person. This issue is particularly acute in the bioethical reflection related to the Catholic tradition. For some, the intrinsic natural order provides the ethical principle in the form of an immediate determination of action guides.

For example, the natural structure of sexual relations and procreation provides the norm for the right determination of actions in the field of sexuality. To violate natural laws -- separating in this case the unitive from the procreative aspect of conjugal sexuality -- would imply at the same time to violate the will of God manifested in these very natural processes.

The question of the relation between nature and person can be resolved differently by taking into account another anthropological perspective.[41] That it to say, to define human being as an open structure, or the biblical understanding of man and woman as created in the "image of God", *i.e.*, God's partners and collaborators with Him in the work of creation. This perspective seems to give a better account of human structure as fact and task. Human nature means to be a person; to become self-conscious and capable of an autonomous answer to the call of God which is directed to the totality of the person. On the other hand, this self-realization of the human being as person ought to take place according to the very nature of all the aspects which define the reality of a human being: the nature of sexuality, the nature of language, etc. These aspects possess in each person a particular nature: they are a given reality, and yet the process of their discovery presupposes at the same time an act of interpretation.

A conclusion can be reached from the evaluation of different approaches to the place of reason in ethics and bioethics. None of the approaches introduced above exclusively exhausts the meaning of reason in ethics: to analyse, universalize, calculate, discern, and to interpret are operations in which practical reason is legitimately engaged. The question becomes: is it possible to elaborate an argumentative model which is capable of bringing together different ways of understanding the place of reason in ethics? The third part of the paper deals with this very question.

2.3. What Kind of Law?

The third relevant acquisition in contemporary bioethical reflection concerns the relation between ethics and law,[42] or more specifically, between bioethics and law.[43]

The law does not and ought not to coincide with ethics: this is a common distinction agreed upon almost universally. At the same time concrete policy -- such as social, ecological or health care policy -- ought to be ethically inspired. Thus the question: given the necessity of a relation between ethics and law, how can this relation be articulated in a strongly pluralistic society? If even a pluralistic and democratic society cannot avoid referring to a "minimum of ethics" within law, which are the principles defining this "minimum"? The paradigm of human rights seems to provide an adequate solution to the problem.[44] But how to refer to such a paradigm when, in spite of a general claim to it, the possibility of grounding a list of human rights appears to be highly questionable?[45] Isn't the reference to human rights generic and ambiguous when deprived of an adequate foundation?

Consider for example, the case of the right to die with dignity. This very right is claimed by both those who are in favor of euthanasia, and by those who consider the legitimization of euthanasia a clear sign of death without dignity. Therefore, isn't the right to die normatively generic and ambiguous?

Indeed it's not only a particular ethical or juridical category which constitutes a problem. The very nature of legal intervention in bioethics as such seems problematic. If, on one hand, the legal gap in the area is pointed out with great concern, the intervention of the law is denounced, on the other hand, as inopportune. According to the latter position, it is impossible for the law to define permanent guidelines for new problems given the rapid development of the biomedical field. According to some, the law not only cannot, but ought not to intervene. In the long run, the intervention of the lawgiver would cause harm to a professional activity which requires taking responsibility, sense of initiative and constant concentration on research. Within this viewpoint, bioethics is seen as an alternative to law: more responsibility should be granted to those directly involved in the biomedical field at the expense of external intervention of public powers.

It seems more fruitful to identify the specific functions of legal intervention in bioethics rather than dwell on sterile counterpositions. David Roy points out three functions of law:[46]

a) to control abuses. The need for social control in order to prevent possible abuses seems undeniable in a context where biomedical progress concentrates enormous power in the hands of few people;

b) to assure continuity. The rapidity with which new discoveries unfold in the biomedical field suggests the need for a continuity with the past. Since certain ethical categories are deeply rooted in our culture, it is necessary to establish a relation with tradition in order to assure continuity;

c) to establish priorities. Bioethical issues can generate conflicting counterpositions because of their great emotional impact upon society. Therefore, an important and specific function of legal intervention is the establishment of priorities in order to assure a minimum of consensual ethics. What kind of legislation will be able to absolve such functions?

No one doubts the importance of conveying morality through the law, and yet in many cases it is better for the legislator not to intervene. Some of the issues within the biomedical field should be left unregulated. That is, they should simply be considered the object of moral decision of patients, their families and the medical staff. The discussion of the relation between ethics and law cannot, at this point, leave out such institutions as ethical committees which are typical of contemporary bioethical reflection. It is precisely at the level of these institutions that ethics and law can be brought together. This last statement intends to offer an hypothesis of reflection which has to be confronted with different legal traditions. It is clear however, that the necessity of a common decision between patients, family members and medical staff has stimulated the creation of ethical Committees in hospitals.[47] Many and new conflicting cases in the application of recent biomedical technologies require that physician, patient and families are not left alone in the decision process as in the cases of organ transplant, artificial sustaining treatments in terminally ill patients, suspension of reanimation efforts, therapeutic interruption of pregnancy, artificial reproduction. The support provided by physicians, psychologists, lawyers, philosophers, theologians and hospital administrators within ethical committees represents, under certain conditions, a valid instrument to analyze problems and find adequate solutions.

2.4. Ethics Committees in the Hospitals: Which Functions? Which Consensus?

Three types of ethics committees are internationally known:

a) ethics committees for scientific research. Promoted by the "International Medical Association" in 1964 at Helsinki, their function is to control the respect of human subjects involved in research and experimentation projects (see Reich's article);

b) national ethics committees. These are composed of groups of experts delegated by national governments to express arguments on biomedical practices which are ethically problematic. Their suggestions and positions are taken into account in framing legal decisions (see Bompiani's article);

c) hospital ethical committees. These committees deal with ethical issues within hospitals at the level of clinical practice and research (see Gracia's article).

The international, and now also the Italian, debate on ethics committees in the hospital has been particularly concentrated on defining the functions of an ethical committee, and in creating strategies for consensus. It is necessary however, to premise some important remarks before entering into the discussion of the two points. The specific nature of the committees is ethical. They are formed by physicians, lawyers, psychologists, philosophers and moral theologians. Their function is to make an ethical evaluation on the rightness of some interventions.

Yet, ethics committees are not the only agency dealing with ethical issues in hospitals. Other institutions should regularly deal with ethical issues, thus functioning -- at times -- like ethics committees. These are: administrative committees for resources allocation, committees for studying the frequency of diseases and mortality in hospitals, work groups on human conditions within hospitals, committees responsible for issuing guidelines on certain practices such as pre-natal diagnosis, the reanimation of PVS patients, etc. Even if it is still too early to determine the precise features of ethics committees in hospitals, it is possible however, to point out some of the tendencies in the international bioethical movement concerning their institutional functions. Two of them seem to be predominant, *i.e.*, a consulting function and a formative function.

There is agreement on the fact that ethical committees in hospitals should have a consulting function. The power to decide on issues of general management belongs to the hospital administration. Physicians are responsible for issues arising out of their relation to the patient. Ethics committees therefore, are neither a system for controlling the decisions of physicians, nor a group in charge of ethical questions, nor finally, an instrument of defense against legal suits. Ethical committees are consulted in the following areas:

a) clinical and pharmacological research. The specific function of the committee in this area is to monitor the respect of the subjects involved in experimental protocols;

b) analysis of conflicting ethical cases. The function of ethics committees at this level is: to highlight the ethical aspects of a particular medical practice, to clarify the ethical issues at stake in a given situation, to provide arguments in favor of a solution, to determine the degree of disagreement among different solutions, and to elaborate strategies of intervention for analogues cases in the form of general guidelines.

Ethics committees have also a formative function. Even if today medical practice deals increasingly with complex ethical issues, the education of medical students still ignores ethics as a fundamental condition of the medical profession.

The indifference toward the ethical dimension of medicine generates two inadequate attitudes: technicism and paternalism. According to the former, anything possible is therefore also permissible, whereas according to the latter, the criterion of good medicine is purely based on knowledge and conscience. Both technicism and paternalism signify the crisis of practical reason in medicine. Ethical committees may provide an important contribution for overcoming this crisis.

A general consensus on the functions of ethics committees has finally been reached. Skepticism however, still exists toward the possibility of bringing together different ethical points of view into a real dialogue. Furthermore, such a task, which is not without ambiguities, seems impossible to achieve.[48]
The question of reaching a consensus within ethics committees has to be carefully addressed. In a way, it highlights a fundamental problem in bioethics. The temptation within committees, as in ethical reflection in general, is to adopt a purely "strategic" kind of consensus as a method. The success of such a temptation however, would cause the end of ethics and would deprive the committees of their ethical consistency. In order to prevent this outcome, the work in the committees has to be based upon the following conditions:

a) the committees should not be considered a self-referential system, that is, a system defined by a logic of strategic rationality whose goal is to negotiate an agreement among particular interests;

b) on the other hand, the committees are not an ideal community of communication defined by practical rationality whose goal is the universalization of rights and duties.[49]

The birth of the committees can make an important contribution toward a clearer understanding of the ethical implications of biomedical practice.

3. The System of Bioethics

So far, we have given an account of the major achievements and the open questions in the development of contemporary bioethics. A productive approach to this development however, requires a systematic frame in which all the data can be arranged. In the absence of such a frame of reference it is still possible to list different positions on concrete issues, but undestanding the meaning of possible conflicts and establishing a common ground of communication and dialogue becomes difficult.

Indeed, to determine correctly such a systematic account is an arduous task. The common risk is leaving out part of the overall bioethical experience. On the other hand, it is impossible for any theory as such, to provide an exhaustive account of ethical experience. This awareness suggests an attitude of deep listening to the ethical experience in which the human being is originally involved. Ethics in general and bioethics in particular cannot prescind from this original experience. Reason must be conceived primarily as a means for understanding and interpreting ethical intentionality which is an original part of human conscience, or any normative system becomes a construction without foundations. In other words, what constitutes the starting point of rational reflection in ethics is not a pretended neutrality, detached from practical engagement and involvement. The phenomena of obligation, responsibility, indignation and shame all are inconceivable without a living ethical conscience. This conscience is what constitutes the undeniable presupposition of real moral life even if it is denied at the level of a rational reflection.

The attempt to give a systematic account of bioethics based on these premises, appears to be a methodological requirement, and this is particularly important when trying to determine the epistemological structure of a new field of inquiry. Bioethics, like ethics in general, is not defined by the simple juxtaposition of normative statements arranged in hierarchical order. Rather, the field of bioethics can be structured in different areas which have specific meaning and function within the general ethical system. It is important to recognize and underline the meaning and the function of each area. Moreover, it seems indispensable to define these areas in the clearest way possible in order to distinguish and legitimize different uses of reason in ethics and bioethics.

3.1. Regulatory Function of Ethical Principles

Principles represent the fundamental area of ethical systems. In essence they all share a characteristic feature which is known, since Kant, by the name of universalizability. The categorical imperative for Kant is universal. That is to say, any norm is valid for a single person or a group only insofar as it can be applied to any person or group in the same situation.

This principle, although only formal, carries out an important regulative and orienting function. It prescribes that, under the same conditions, everyone act according to the same rule. In order to avoid discrimination, the principle recognizes every human being as a subject entitled to equal consideration and respect.

Nowadays, it is of paramount importance to adequately underline the area of principles. Principles should direct reason toward the ethical truth especially within the biomedical field. Otherwise, instead of the power of truth, the truth of power will triumph: power propitiated by the massive introduction of technology. The risk implicit in this phenomenon is the shift from an ethical understanding of medicine, as it has been developed through the entire history of medicine, to a pure technological one. This shift would make any ethical concern purely indifferent to the biomedical field. The principles invoked in the literature -- almost as a canonical framework of bioethics -- are the principle of autonomy, beneficence, and justice. From a theoretical perspective all these principles could be reduced to one fundamental ethical principle. The principle of autonomy prescribes acting in such a way as to treat the patient always as an end and never as a means; that is, according to his nature of autonomous subject. The principle of beneficence prescribes acting so that the consequences of every action are for the benefit of the patient and for the integral good of his person. The principle of justice prescribes acting so that the benefits and harms resulting from a given situation be equally distributed, and without making differences unless differences are relevant for the kind of treatment in question.

From a practical point of view the originality and strength of these principles has to be found in their ability to adapt to the needs of all the subjects involved in the physician-patient relationship, *i.e.*, the physician, the patient, and the society. The principle of autonomy pertains to the first component of the relation, *i.e.*, the patient. The principle of beneficence pertains, in turn, to the physician, the health care personnel in general, and to the family. The third component should be referred to all the other social agents who intervene in the physician-patient relation, *i.e.*, society, and the general interests of the community to which individuals belong, and for whose good they participate. An adequate normative frame can be provided only on the basis of all these three principles.

Within the bioethical movement a consensus has been reached in considering these principles to be a framework for a rational bioethics. Nevertheless, differences emerge in the interpretation of the univocal meaning of each principle and in the solution of conflicts among them. The question is twofold. First: how to interpret the principles univocally? Which is the source to be referred to in order to give a more precise content to autonomy, beneficence and justice? Second: what to do in the case of a conflict among the principles? How to establish an effective hierarchy among them?

3.2. The Interpretative Function of the Anthropological Paradigm

Although ethical principles such as autonomy, beneficence and justice represent a fundamental orientation for actions they remain formal in substance. A system of values according to a particular anthropological paradigm alone can provide the source from which the univocal content of these principles can be drawn. The anthropological paradigm represents a particular conception of what the human being is, an image which implicitly or explicitly grounds everyday choices, thus determining models of behavior, criteria of evaluation and motivations for action.

The anthropological paradigm brings about a system of values which shapes the meaning of life, suffering, death. Other relevant concepts in the biomedical field such as health, therapy, healing and finally the very concept of health care profession as service, vocation or simply as a job are also addressed. It is this axiological content which defines the concrete understanding of autonomy, beneficence and justice. Conceiving life as a gift rather than a pure consumer's good makes a great deal of difference. So does refusing suffering as a radical evil to be avoided at any cost rather than accepting it as a test which reveals something about human life and its constitutive fragility. Finally, it is different to think of death as a shameful reality to be kept out of our daily discourse than to integrate it as part of our existence.

In other words, while the foundation of ethical principles remains at a transcendental level, the practical use of them is never pure. Rather, it has to be articulated through the value system defined by the anthropological paradigm. Therefore this paradigm represents the necessary pre-comprehension for understanding the meaning of ethical principles and for determining their practical use. If this is the case, it's easy to understand why the nature of many conflicts and counterpositions within bioethical reflection is anthropological rather than normative. The counterposition between sanctity and quality of life, for instance, most clearly represents the clash among different anthropological conceptions in our society. According to some, this conflict simply manifests the opposition between the old pre-modern mentality and the modern one. But from such a perspective it seems impossible to provide adequate solutions for new biomedical issues without, at the same time, questioning the sanctity-of-life-conception in favor of a new criterion based on quality of life. In our opinion, both criteria become ambiguous when assumed in an absolute way. The emphasis on the sanctity of life ultimately leads to the sacralization of mere biological processes. On the other hand, the modern and post-modern emphasis on quality of life might impoverish our anthropological conception, especially if humanity is defined on the basis of purely quantitative and functional parameters. Biological life is not sacred in itself. Yet, beyond our cultural schemes based on efficiency and functionality, the life of every human being at every moment of its development has to be respected as an end, and never treated as a means. The quality-of-life-criterion is a symbol of the modern mentality, and it expresses a positive attitude in our outlook toward life. Nevertheless, it is necessary to be aware of the risks implied by a univocal understanding of such a criterion.

The sanctity-of-life-criterion normally identifies the Christian understanding of life as God's gift. Since life is God's gift, it has to be accepted and preserved at any cost and under any circumstance as inviolable and undisposable. The concept of sanctity-inviolability can be fully maintained within a Christian understanding of life. Yet, this concept cannot be attributed to mere biological life. If the concept of sanctity of life must be interpreted literally, then how is it possible to justify the moral-theological tradition when it allows certain actions like killing in war, capital punishment, and killing for legitimate defense? Aren't these exceptions at odds with the moral obligation of the sanctity-of-life-principle? It is certainly difficult to put the Christian meaning of life within a framework. Consequently, the anthropological paradigm inspired by the Christian conception of life as God's gift needs to be carefully interpreted when applied to the solution of bioethical issues. Life is a gift of God, and only he has absolute and exclusive authority upon it. Therefore, man cannot dispose freely of his life. This is the basic understanding of Christian conception of life. It follows that:

a) we don't own our life, but rather life owns us. Through creation and redemption the human being participates in God's life;

b) the biblical message presents God as life. Yet the Christian conception of life does not allow reversing the terms by saying that life is God. In other words, the sacralization of life is not a Christian idea. Some values may be more important than life;

c) if life is God's gift, than every human being is defined by his/her relation with God the Creator, and the source of life. Every human being is somebody before God. Therefore, contingent determinations are not essential in determining the value of the life of every human being;

d) the life of human beings has to be respected not only when it is innocent, strong or healthy. According to the "new justice" of the Gospel, the commandment "Thou shalt not kill" assumes a radical interpretation: it becomes part of a new logic of non-violent love. Love goes to the extreme of accepting the enemy and making him the neighbor.

Some consequences derive from this conception of life as gift. Two in particular should be pointed out since they concern those areas where the meaning of Christianity has been often misunderstood. These are, suffering -- where Christianity has seemed to justify a mentality of sorrow and pain -- and the area of sexuality where Christianity has been accused of having a negative attitude toward the body and sexuality. The Christian message about suffering states that life is a gift, but that this gift is constantly being threatened. Eliminating suffering, limitations and contingency from the human condition is pure illusion. Neither can avoiding suffering be considered an achievable goal. If Christianity recognizes the necessity of living with suffering, it does not consider this threat a fatality. But this doesn't mean that suffering as such increases morality, or promotes a pathological need to suffer. This is not the Christian approach. Rather, it is defined by other motives, i.e., the awareness that the real threat against life is the fact of being cut off from God who is the source of life. The invitation to suffer with Christ and in Christ and to make one's suffering an element of communion with Christ's cross is rooted and justified in the deeper invitation to love like Christ and with the same measure.

The Christian message about sexuality stresses that life is a gift, and not a fall. Therefore, the Christian vision of life cannot inspire any inferiority of the flesh toward the spirit. In fact, according to Biblical anthropology, flesh and spirit imply different ways of looking at the human being. The whole human being is flesh, and therefore finite. But the whole human being can also be said to be spirit, and defined by the relation to God. Precisely the presence of God to man's life both physical and spiritual, contributes to the unity of his living being. The philosophical tradition inspired by Christianity has expressed this unity with the concept of person.

In light of the concept of person it is possible to understand the human meaning of the body and of sexuality in particular. In opposition to a biological reduction of human anthropology, the human meaning of the body cannot be immediately determined by the biological structures of organic body. On the contrary, the anthropological model provided by Christian personalism tends to understand the human meaning of the body from the very fact that the body we are referring to is the body of a person. The human meaning of the body as well as the meaning of that particular kind of language which is sexual, can be understood only when the totality of the person is taken into account.

It might be asked whether, in light of these synthetic statements about the Christian conception of life, the principle of life as a gift is capable of providing the meaning of human dignity. It would seem that such a principle cannot be proposed, especially in light of certain aspects characterizing modern culture, *i.e.*, the refusal of suffering, the ability to control one's own death, the selection of the quality if life. In order to make this principle meaningful it is necessary to show its ability to interpret the reality of the human being. This is possible only through an understanding of the attitude toward life which characterizes our culture. Generalizations are often arbitrary, and yet it becomes increasingly widespread to think of life as a weak reality without a meaning in itself. A "weak" approach to life means that life does not have a value (value would denote a "strong" approach to life), but it appears to contemporary conscience as a neutral fact. Further specifications make up the conditions upon which life can be said to be worth living. Consequently, the right attitude toward life as a whole becomes a mentality of verification and adaptation to logical schemes.

Functionality discriminates according to usefulness, between what is to be considered meaningful and what is not.[50]

The danger of such an interpretation of the quality of life according to exclusive functional values is the introduction of a new conception of social normality which is utterly discriminatory. From a historical point of view, this conception clashes with the mentality prevailing at the end of the sixties. Its main merit was to promote the dignity of cultural and social diversities, and to defend the particular abnormalities of individuals. What has happened to the passionate claim for the respect of diversity? Only a cultural model based on a strong interpretation of the value of life can successfully validate such a claim. Therefore, can the Christian conception of life as a gift be considered null and void?

3.3. The Operative Function of Moral Norms

Ethical principles cannot determine the right action for particular situations even when interpreted in light of a particular anthropological conception. More concrete and operative criteria are necessary in order to pass from the level of principles and values to the level of concrete ethical norms. Indeed, ethical problems in modern medicine are strictly related to particular cases situated in unique circumstances. Although principles define criteria to which we can refer, they alone are not adequate in deciding concrete cases. Principles need to be completed with specific norms which only make them operative. Without norms, principles remain mute with respect to what ought to be prescribed, prohibited or allowed. Elaborating norms for particular ethical judgements is essentially an interdisciplinary work. What operations are required in order to pass from principles to norms, thus formulating the ethical judgement for a particular issue?

According to the current mentality, while the scientific judgement is based on reasoning, the ethical one would be exclusively the result of intuition. The complexity of ethical problems which derive from biomedical developments clearly challenges the present mind set. Rather, biomedical issues confirm the inadequacy of the attempt to solve problems on the basis of intuitions by pointing out the need to turn to ethical reasoning. Let us try to explain the rational operations used in this area of the bioethical system by simply referring to a concrete example: the issue of experimentation on human subjects.

3.3.1. Verifying the Use of Terms

The first operation in shifting from principles to norms is to verify the use of terms. The aim of this task is to avoid using terms which are purely descriptive as if they were valuative. Ethical judgements would be compromised if certain terms were prejudicially referred to. A serene evaluation of the term experimentation, for example, is excluded at the outset, by attributing to it a negative meaning. Experimentation is often associated with the idea of a cavy, and therefore with utilization and instrumentalization. Yet, the experimental component is essential for medical practice. Pharmaceutical products and new treatments, for instance, inevitably require experimentation on human subjects.

3.3.2. Identifying the Situation

The second task is identifying the situation. The function of this second moment is to know with precision all the relevant data which are important in a particular biomedical problem, and to identify through an interdisciplinary approach all factors pertinent to the ethical decision. In the case of clinical experimentation this second operation consists in distinguishing the type of experimental activity according to its own specific feature: e.g. a therapeutic attempt is different from a therapeutic protocol.

In the case of a therapeutic attempt the physician ascertains that any improvement would be impossible with normal treatment, and therefore decides for the application of a treatment which has not been tried yet for the pathology in question. In the case of a therapeutic protocol there is an explicit experimental intention. It is taken for granted that the patient will undergo treatment and cures which present the same or better chances than traditional treatments. Both therapeutic attempt and protocol are part of the same medical activity which aims specifically at improving the patient's health.

The case of a non-therapeutic experimental activity is different. Its goal is to acquire new information without contributing to the patient's health. Informed consent and a detailed description of empirical data constitute an important condition for the ethical legitimacy of this experimental practice. The ethical issue at stake will be different depending on the kind of experimentation:

a) therapeutic attempt does not require informed consent;

b) therapeutic protocol may sometimes justify only partial disclosure of information for the consent

c) non-therapeutic experiment requires informed consent.

3.3.3. Identifying the Ethical Issue

In an ethically problematic biomedical situation the issues at stake may be manifold. It is important to identify these issues one by one, and with precision. Experience suggests framing every situation in the form of a question in order to make problematic terms immediately evident. Thus, each question should identify a possible course of action. Referring again to the area of experimentation and to the distinction already made between therapeutic experimentation (T) and non-therapeutic experimentation (nT) we can point out some problematic aspects.

Concerning (T) let's examine the following problematic aspect (T 1): in order to be an active part of the therapeutic process the patient is informed of risks and benefits, as well as of collateral effects and conditions necessary for the positive outcome of the treatment. The question is: must the information be always complete? In particular: must the information be always complete even when the disclosure of a given therapy will make the patient aware of a disease which he/she is yet not capable of accepting?

With reference to (nT) let's examine the following problem (nT 1): the informed consent of the patient is always necessary, but is it also in all cases sufficient? Is it allowed to transform a living and feeling human being, even when consenting, into an experimental tool? In particular the question becomes: can a terminally ill patient accept to become a cavy for experimental treatments which will not benefit him only out of a sense of human solidarity toward other patients who might in future benefit of this same treatment?

3.3.4. Formulating the Ethical Judgment

Obviously the most important operation is to formulate the ethical judgement since it establishes what has to be concretely done. The first moment consists in referring a particular situation to general values-principles. Often this is enough in deciding what to do. For instance, during every moment of illness the patient remains an autonomous personal subject with a right of choice. The patient also has the right to actively participate in the therapy. Therefore every effort has to be made in order to adequately inform the patient. The principle of autonomy prescribes *prima facie* this course of action. Personal awareness and maturity in one's own existence is the value which the respect of this principle secures. This can be accomplished only if the patient's right to the truth is respected. Lying cannot be justified even to hide the nature of an experimental treatment which would thereby make the patient aware of the gravity of his situation. If there is no solution to a disease the patient does not loose the right to his own fulfillment through a conscious acceptance of death. A particular solution might be good, *i.e.*, the solution coherent with universal values-principles, and yet not necessarily the right one in a particular situation. It is therefore necessary in some cases to go through a second moment of reflection. In the case (T 1) there are two possible courses of action:

a) one might claim that knowing the truth is the indispensable presupposition of self-realization. It is, therefore, prohibited to manipulate the information no matter what the contingent circumstances might be;

b) another might decide to modify the evidence because the patient cannot bear the complete information; in this case awareness and participation in the therapy would simply mean depression and desperation.

The same situation can be found in (nT 1):

a) one might claim that a living and feeling human being, even when consenting, cannot be transformed into an experimental tool;

b) another might envision situations where a patient accepts to be a cavy for reasons of solidarity.

How to establish the right solution in these conflictual situations? What is the concrete operative norm in these cases? The situation (T 1) can be solved without telling the truth. The argument for this solution can be said to be teleological since the consequences of the action are taken into consideration. According to this judgement beneficence comes before autonomy. The situation (nT 1) in turn, can be solved by allowing the terminally ill patient to be available for the benefit of others. This solution presupposes a personalistic understanding of the principle of autonomy according to which the human being is defined by his relation to others and for others. This interpretation has to be seen within a particular anthropological paradigm, and it establishes a hierarchy in which the principle of justice-solidarity comes before beneficence.

In sum, the two emblematic cases (T 1) and (nT 1) show how the hierarchy among ethical principles in a given conflictual situation is established by reference to two different sources: the interpretation of the principles on the basis of a particular anthropological paradigm and the evaluation of the consequences of alternative courses of action.

3.3.5. Identifying Responsibilities

Identifying responsibilities has always been central in the production of the norms, but it appears to be problematic for at least two reasons. First, the division of responsibility for the medical act makes it more difficult to identify who is in charge. Second, the extreme segmentation of biomedical knowledge makes it problematic to identify the subject toward whom the responsibility is directed.

In the past, medical needs where fulfilled on the basis of a personal relation between physician and patient. Nowadays, many people have become part of this relation and the physician acts through mediators, technological equipment and medical exams. The reduction and the segmentation of personal sharing in the physician-patient relationship does not necessarily imply less responsibility and care. On the other hand, the various operators who intervene can easily become pieces of an impersonal process, and these factors might lead to a pervasive sense of non-responsibility.

Non-responsibility could be the result of another phenomenon which characterizes science and particularly biomedical science: the extreme specialization and segmentation of scientific knowledge. Basic concepts are shattered and divided among different disciplines without it ever being possible to reconstruct them through various interdisciplinary attempts. This renders the totality and the consistency of the person unthinkable. Non-responsibility inevitably results because a scientific practice without any reference to the whole human and personal subject cannot deal with anything but genes, cells, organs. This process will certainly lead to complete blindness.

3.4. The Motivating Function of Virtues

Principles, together with the interpretative anthropological values and norms applying them to particular situations are fundamental in directing and orienting ethical life. However these do not suffice in giving an account of the way ethics and bioethics work. Normative criteria (such as principles and norms) are valid only insofar as they are assumed at a personal level. Hence, virtues seem to offer the possibility of providing personal motivations for the accomplishment of right actions.

The restoration of the concept of virtue is, indeed, one of the most important aspects of the contemporary ethical debate. Modern ethics had dissolved the very concept of virtue by questioning its genealogy (Nietzsche) and pointing out the many forgeries and adulterations in the most beautiful virtues.

Freud, in turn, has made us more aware of unconscious elements which surreptitiously invade the reality of virtues.

The suspicion of ethical conscience in general and the paradigm of virtues in particular is based, according to Freud, on the apparent inconsistency of the "ego" and of its autonomy within psychic dynamics. Being conditioned by the impulses of the "id" on one hand and tyrannized by the oppressive authority of the "super-ego" on the other, the "ego" cannot provide for itself any direction. Even if Freud envisions a strong "ego" capable of directing its own development, in practice he restricts such a possibility to few persons only. A fundamental pessimism still remains.

Some of the disciples of Freud have presented a more positive evaluation of ethical conscience, thus bringing to completion the theory of a strong "ego" which the Master had only foreshadowed.

Among the disciples of Freud, E. Erikson[51] had an important place in moving toward a theory of a strong "ego" and in presenting an original approach to the concept of virtue. Even if Erikson's approach is not philosophical but rather psychological, his perspective might contribute to the contemporary recovery of virtues, especially in bioethics. Rethinking the development of the "ego" led Erikson to a positive recognition of ethical conscience. The "ego" is conceived as an interior principle and therefore activates -- in each moment of development -- a specific energy which allows it to accomplish the task required at that moment. Along the stages of development ethical reflection follows closely the history of the "ego" which, in turn, acquires the virtues for the activation of its autonomy, and overcomes the crises proper to each stage. According to Erikson, the basic principle in the evolutionary process is called "epigenetic"; a term which expresses an analogy with the principle governing the fetal development. Everything grows according to a basic plan, and the parts are derived in established times out of this basic plan. Erikson is particularly convincing in grounding a developmental model of a strong "ego" capable of self-realization within the framework of the epigenetic principle. Contrary to Freud's position, ethical development is nourished and supported by the energy intrinsic to the "ego"; an energy of interior good which constitutes the basis of ethical education.

Erikson's theory seems to offer valid arguments against the Freudian suspicion model, and one which had contributed much to the discrediting of the concept of virtue. Nevertheless, different sorts of difficulties remain for a virtue ethics. The reproposition of a virtue ethics seems problematic in light of changes which concern society, the modern practice of medicine, and ultimately the relation between physician and patient.

First, the social and cultural context which made the paradigm of virtue ethics possible appears to be worn out. This is not without repercussions on medical ethics and health care ethics in general. In fact, the quality of care provided by health care services is not independent from the dominant ethos of society. How to express solidarity in a society defined by indifference and anonymity? Or how to be caring in a society dominated by apathy?

The culture of indifference may have great impact especially upon the educational process. Indeed, the education of new health care professionals should be given special consideration in the acquisition of attitudes and virtues which qualify the medical practice. Yet, the current curriculum doesn't seem to grant any dignity to the formation of virtues. Rather it only requires from the health care professional the ability to perform certain functions or, in the case of the physician, to repair the ill organ. No place is given to the professional as a person, to his human skills, or to the meaning of health care profession. The education of health care professional today is based upon the belief that all these dimensions are purely superfluous.

Given such a cultural context, what meaning does the reference to a virtue ethics have? The difficulty of a virtue ethics today depends not only on the gulf which separates the dominant ethos from the attitudes of health care professionals. It also depends upon the concrete condition -- sometimes really degrading -- of health care services as well as on the present character of scientific medicine.

The insistence on caring for the patients, and being solicitous toward them might be taken as a mystification if the institutional context lacks sufficient space, treatment and adequate structures. Yet, a virtue ethics might be a mystification in opposite cases as well, *i.e.*, in a context of high technology and extreme functionality. Insisting on personal virtues when the patient is detached and objectified simply means setting the seal upon the gap which separates medicine and health care assistance. In spite of all the difficulties however, there is a growing conviction that it is possible to go beyond the counterposition of paternalism and autonomy only by means of an ethics of virtue.

Conclusion

Knowledge and power can desecrate anything, at least in intention: the embryo, the sick, the idiot, the aging. Even a young body and a strong spirit can be desecrated. But whatever has a heart cannot be profaned, for the presence of a heart can only be revealed to another heart (L. Lombardi Vallauri).

The goal of this introductory essay was to provide a historic and systematic framework within which to situate the development of bioethics in the different linguistic areas. Only essential observations were devoted to the historic moment, because the different sections of the book will offer a more profound and well documented analysis. More attention was given to a systematic account, thus contributing to the understanding of these two decades of bioethics, and to the creation of an argumentation model. Such a model should be able to determine the specific functions of practical rationality in relation to various areas of application (the area of principles, anthropological paradigms, norms and virtues).

Yet, even when an argumentation model has been established, another task is still ahead: to give an account of the way in which ethical criteria operate at a social level, and how they form a culture. Indeed, only culture can perform the function of transforming ethical criteria into values and ethical evidences commonly shared. Sometimes these motivations can shape an organic symbolic system. Given the motivational and synthetic power of the symbolic system within a culture, bioethics today cannot avoid reflecting upon the serious impoverishment of the symbolic system which defines the reality of life. Fecundity as blessing, illness as trial, death as passage, life as gift, are all traditional symbols which seem to be definitely worn out.

In reference to death, for example, many important studies show that our culture is lacking, in terms of social participation, and in general deprived of symbols which are capable of conveying the social meaning of such an important event. In his book *The Loneliness of the Dying*, N. Elias[52] points out the current attitudes of our society concerning death. We disguise it -- especially in the case of children -- or we feel embarrassment in the presence of a dying person. These attitudes spring from the fact that our social tradition no longer provides an adequate symbolic language to articulate the meaning of death. Without common symbols, the possibility of dialogue and reciprocal understanding gets lost. In such a situation ethics becomes increasingly abstract to the extent that it presents itself in the form of a scientific and impersonal exercise.

It is therefore necessary for bioethical rationality to recover a symbolic dimensions.[53] Although important for ethics in general, this recovery seems urgent in bioethics since it deals with the reality of life. The language of life is laden with dimensions transcending the level of formal logical rationality. The composition of reason and feeling, essential for understanding moral experience, is possible only through the recovery of a symbolic outlook on life. Events like birth, suffering, and death cannot be experienced without symbols because they go beyond the grasp of reason.

The collapse of a symbolic system of reference reduces events like birth and death -- in themselves not pathological -- to pure medical facts deprived of further meaning.

ENDNOTES

1. G. Berlinguer introduces a distinction between a bioethics of borderline cases ("bioetica di frontiera") and an ordinary bioethics ("bioetica quotidiana"). In a recent paper he states: "A debatable emphasis can be noted in the scholars' interest as well as in the public information. While attention is being given to borderline cases, moral and scientific problems involving millions and even billions of people in daily life are completely neglected. For instance, some cases of euthanasia or "good death" are publicly discussed, but no mention is given to millions of "bad deaths", i.e. to premature and undeserved deaths caused by lack of prevention and treatment. Moreover, scientific energies and moral reflection are rightly dedicated to artificial fertilization, whereas little work is done at the level of research as well as practice on the common reality of sterility for which artificial insemination can rarely provide a remedy. Finally, while concern is raised toward pharmaceutical and genetic control of behavior, scientific research fails to recognize other forms of human manipulation which are very common", G. Berlinguer, "Bioetica quotidiana e Bioetica di frontiera," in *Bioetica*, ed. A. Di Meo and C. Mancina (Bari: Laterza, 1989), pp. 6-7.

2. An authoritative analysis of the question can be found in G. Giunchi, "Luci e ombre della Medicina del Duemila," *Fondamenti* 5, (1986): 107-118.

3. For an interpretation of ethics as an instance of humanization see C. Viafora, "Umanizzare la nascita, la malattia e la morte. Problemi e prospettive," *Credere oggi* 6, (1987): 92-112. From a medical perspective G. De Sandre, "A servizio di chi sono i servizi sociali e sanitari," in *Il rispetto delle persone nei servizi sociali e sanitari*, ed. Fondazione Zancan (Padova: 1986). On the question of "formation" in order to acquire the ability to relate to others, useful indications can be found in S. Spinelli, "Il contributo delle scienze umane nell'opera di umanizzazione del personale sanitario," in *Per un ospedale piu' umano* (Milano: Paoline, 1985), pp. 91-118. In spite of public outcry a global study on the phenomenon of dehumanization in the hospital remains to be done. Since the Seventies, public opinion has led to the creation of a movement -- like that of workers or the women's movement -- which deals directly with the hospital. The "patients' rights movement" has been stimulated in Italy by the "Tribunals for the

44

Patient's Rights" (Tribunale per i Diritti del Malato). See G. Quaranta, *L'uomo negato* (Firenze: Nuova Guaraldi, 1980): this book has inspired the formation of the "Tribunals".

4. L. Walters, "Religion and the renaissance of medical ethics in the United States: 1965-1975," in *Theology and Bioethics*, ed. E.E. Shelp (Dordreck: Reidel Publishing, 1985), pp. 3-16. Walter's paper concentrates on the derivation of medical ethics in the United States from moral theology. According to the author an important role was played -- particularly from 1965 to 1975, the first phase of this development -- by theologians and by religious questions. The fact is proven by the important role played by theological ethics in the works of the "National Commission for the Protection of Human Subjects of Biomedical and Behavioral Research". Since 1975 moral philosophers have been increasingly involved in the discussion on medical ethics.

5. The relevance of the turning point from metaethics to applied ethics -- particularly for the field of medicine -- has been shown by S. Toulmin, "How Medicine saved the Life of Ethics," *Perspective in Biology and Medicine* 25, (1982): 736-750. According to Toulmin medical ethics has contributed to "save the life" of moral philosophy. Especially in the Anglosaxon context, moral philosophy was languishing in arid metaethical debates. An interesting overview of the development from metaethics to "normative" ethics in Anglosaxon moral philosophy during the Seventies, is provided by E. Lecaldano, "Analisi filosofica, utilitarismo e razionalita' pratica," *Il Mulino* 6, (1986): 971-993. For an acute theoretical analysis of the problems in "applied ethics" see K. Steigleder, "Problemi di etica applicata," *Concilium*, no. 5 (1989): 112-123. The following questions are analyzed: problems of relation between applied ethics and fundamental ethics, the object of applied ethics and its acquisition, the question of responsibility, different levels of discourse in applied ethics.

6. For a complete description of motives and themes of the so called "Rehabilitation of practical philosophy" (Rehabilitierung der praktischen Philosophie) see E. Berti, ed., *Tradizione e attualita' della filosofia pratica* (Genova: Marietti, 1988), pp. 111-135. The rebirth of practical philosophy constitutes an important element of novity and interest in the contemporary philosophical debate. This "rehabilitation" or "rebirth" characterizes German culture in particular. It expresses a reaction toward the inability -- which can be clearly seen in our culture and it was recognized by the sociologist Max Weber -- to provide an adequate foundation of ethics and politics. For a more general overview of this "rediscovery" of ethics in contemporary thought see Fondazione Lanza, ed., *Etica oggi: comportamenti collettivi e modelli culturali* (Padova: Gregoriana, 1989) and Fondazione Lanza, ed., *Problemi di etica: fondazione norme orientamenti* (Padova: Gregoriana, 1990).

7. Some physicians refuse the idea of an ethical reflection in medicine in the name of professional deontology. According to them, only the respect of professional laws and deontological norms of health care defines the normative area of medicine. The need for a philosophical and theological reflection is, therefore, denied from the outset. Rather, what is needed is an adaptation of professional deontology to the new cultural sensibility. This position is shared, for example, by G. Canepa, "Bioetica e Deontologia Medica: aspetti problematici e conflittuali," *Rivista italiana di medicina legale*, no. 1 (1990): 3-6. The position of this author who is a professor of Legal medicine at the University of Genova not only expresses the mind of the periodical in question (*Rivista italiana di Medicina Legale*), but also characterizes a radical critique of the "so called bioethics". According to Canepa bioethics is not only useless, but also a source of confusion, misunderstanding, conflict, and lack of respect for the law. Instead of contributing to the solution of problems bioethics makes them even worse and difficult to resolve. Only medical deontology should be regarded as competent to deal with the new problems created by the development of biomedicine. A more rational and balanced perspective -- from the legal point of view -- is expressed, for example, by M. Barni, "La deontologia e l'etica professionale oggi," *Notizie di Politeia* 16, (1989): 17-22. The author pleads for a "serene dialectics" between deontology and bioethics: "Legal medicine ultimately contributes to the research on those values which are part of bioethics. Bioethics constitutes, therefore, an interdisciplinary field of inquiry" (p. 21).

8. For the different ways of understanding the relation between science and ethics during the twenty year life span of bioethics see L. Battaglia, "Responsabilita', potere, ragione: la questione dei limiti nella Bioetica," *Notizie di Politeia* 18, (1990): 7-11. The thesis of the paper is summarily the following: "The parable of bioethics -- in its pendular motion between hopes and fears -- seems to follow the course of the interdisciplinary relation science-ethics. This relation, defined in its first phase by the project of making ethics sensitive to science, developed later on to that of making science more sensitive to ethics" (p. 9).

9. Those are the conclusions of the International Colloquium: *Scienza ed etica nella centralita' dell'uomo* (Milan, 7-10 April 1988). The acts of the Colloquium are published under the same title by P. Cattorini, ed. (Milano: Franco Angeli, 1989). There were two emblematic positions expressed in the Colloquium: the first goes back to Edgar Morin, the second to the German-American philosopher Hans Jonas. According to the former, the new scientific developments -- especially in the biogenetic field -- push toward a redefinition of the traditional concept of science. The latter asserts the need to redefine he traditional concept of ethics in the face of the "cosmic" dimension of science.

10. See the enlightening essay of F. Böckle, "Ethos e scienza," in *L'etica tra quotidiano e remoto* (Bologna: Dehoniane 1984), pp. 313-330.

11. The Catholic moral Magisterium has given an evident contribution in framing bioethical reflection in terms of the relation between scientific/technological power on one hand, and ethical responsibility on the other. Two among the most significant documents on matters of bioethics denounce the dynamics of the domination involved in new biotechnologies applied to human reproduction. These are the Pontifical encyclica *Humanae Vitae* of 1968, and the instruction of the Congregation for the Doctrine of Faith *Donum Vitae* of 1987. By means of techniques of artificial insemination, for example, the origin of life is no longer seen as the fruit of a "conception", but rather of a "production". These techniques can eventually generate disturbing abuses by controlling human life at its inception. A question emerges from such a negative perspective: is it really impossible to consider the technological power involved in a technique such as homologous artificial insemination in a more positive way? Or is it simply another manifestation of human arrogance toward life? Independently from considerations of merit, it can be said that the Catholic Magisterium has played, during the last twenty years, an historical role for believers and non believers alike, by unequivocally highlighting the questions at stake in bioethical progress.

12. V.R. Potter, *Bioethics: Bridge to the Future* (Englewood Cliffs: Prentice-Hall, 1971).

13. This is the thesis of R.R. Faden and T.L. Beauchamp, *A History and Theory of Informed Consent* (New York: Oxford University Press, 1986), p. 6.

14. On the origin and the meaning of this movement G. F. Annas, "Patient Rights Movement," in *Encyclopedia of Bioethics*, ed. W.T. Reich (New York: The Free Press, 1978), Vol. 3, pp. 1201-1205.

15. From the perspective of history of medicine see the reconstruction provided by D. Gracia, *Fundamentos de Bioética* (Madrid: Eudema, 1989), and especially the pages dedicated to origin and development of the patient rights movement, pp. 173-182. See also: "Los derechos de los enfermos," in *Dilemas éticos de la Medicina actual*, ed. J. Gafo (Madrid: Publicaciones de la Universidad Pontificia Comillias, 1986), pp. 43-87.

16. Such a change of perspective is seen as "revolutionary" by R.R. Faden and T.L. Beauchamp, *A History and Theory of Informed Consent*, p. 94.

17. The presentation of the institutions given in this volume by some of their founders offers a sufficiently clear idea of their activities and features.

18. Information on these Centers has been acquired by an exchange of documentation with the project "Ethics and Medicine" of the Lanza Foundation. The project has sponsored research activities and formation as well as the exchange of documentation and information.

19. D. Callahan, *Abortion, Law, Choice and Morality* (New York: Macmillan, 1970).

20. D. Callahan, ed., *The Catholic Case for Contraception* (New York: Macmillan, 1969).

21. D. Callahan, "The Sanctity of Life," in *The Religious Situations*, ed. D.R. Cutler (1969), pp. 297-339.

22. A. Hellegers, "A Scientist's Analysis," in *Contraception: Authority and Dissent*, ed. C.E. Curran (New York: Herder and Herder, 1969), pp. 216-223.

23. P. Ramsey, *The Patient as Person* (New Haven: Yale University Press, 1970).

24. See "Medical Ethics in Europe," *Theoretical Medicine* 3, (1988): this special issue contains papers dealing with the situation of medical ethics in countries like Great Britain, France, Germany, Finland, Sweden, Norway, Poland. See also: S. Le Bris, "L'enseignement, la recherche et la pratique de la bioéthique," in *L'Europe et la bioéthique* [Actes du le Symposium du Conseil de l'Europe sur la Bioéthique, 5-7 décembre 1989] (Strasbourg: 1989), pp. 133-152. This report gives a broad account of European initiatives which aim at the creation of institutions in bioethics (teaching programs, centers and committees).

25. The epistemological concern, i.e. the need to frame bioethical reflection in a coherent ethical theory, has been given a growing attention. Until recently, bioethical literature had been dealing almost exclusively with cases and special issues. However, the increasing number of publications -- both "manuals" and "monographs" -- has led progressively to the creation of guidelines, governmental and professional recommendations, thus making explicit theoretical differences in the various positions. For this reason, many scholars feel at this moment the need of working on the foundations of bioethics.

26. The "status questionis" of contemporary philosophical reflection is given by A. Poppi, "Il problema dell'etica nella filosofia del Novecento," *Verifiche* 8, (1979).

27. On the possible interpretations of the relation ethics-anthropology within contemporary debate on practical philosophy, see A. Da Re, *L'etica tra*

felicita' e dovere (Bologna: Dehoniane, 1986); in particular the fourth chapter: "Etica ed esperienza", pp. 165-202. In the specific field of bioethics J.F. Malherbe seems particularly aware of the need to stress the importance of the relation between ethics and anthropology. See for example, his reflections on "anthropological foundations of ethics" in the second chapter of the book *Pour une éthique de la médecine* (Paris: Larousse, 1987).

28. The term "anthropology" can be applied to different sciences. It often refers to "cultural anthropology" or to human sciences such as psychology, sociology, pedagogy. But "philosophical anthropology" refers to that particular area of philosophy which deals with the reality of the human being. Unlike the disciplines which study the human being from a particular point of view, "philosophical anthropology" considers the human being as a "personal subject" in its totality.

29. The work which provides the dominant bioethical model based on principles is, beyond any doubt, T. Beauchamp and J. Childress, *Principles of Biomedical Ethics* (New York: Oxford University Press, 1989).

30. A. Jonsen and S. Toulmin, *The Abuse of Casuistry. A History of Moral Reasoning* (Berkeley: University of California Press, 1988); R. Zaner, *Ethics and the Clinical Encounter* (Englewood Cliffs: Prentice-Hall, 1988); J.F. Drane, *Becoming a Good Doctor: the Place of Virtue and Character in Medical Ethics* (Kansas: Sheed and Ward, 1988); A. MacIntyre, *After Virtue* (Notre Dame: University of Notre Dame Press, 1983).

31. An overview of contemporary Italian moral philosophy is provided by P. Zecchinato, *Il punto archimedeo. Ragione ed etica nella filosofia italiana dal '45 ad oggi* (Padova: Liviana, 1986). For the question within the field of "applied ethics" see E. Lecaldano, "La sfida dell'etica applicata e il ragionamento in morale," in *Questioni di Bioetica*, ed. M. Mori (Roma: Editori Riuniti 1988), pp. 37-71. On the problem of the place of reason in ethics see C. Viafora, "Quale uso della ragione in Bioetica?" in *Fondamenti di Bioetica* (Milano: Ambrosiana 1989), pp. 25-56.

32. For an exhaustive account of the question within Italian bioethics see C. Viafora and M. Mori, "Bibliografia sulla bioetica in Italia," *Centri di Bioetica in Italia. Orientamenti a confronto*, ed. C. Viafora (Padova: Gregoriana, 1993), pp. 359-386; A. Bompiani, *Bioetica in Italia. Lineamenti e tendenze* (Bologna: Dehoniane, 1992), with ample bibliography.

33. In the Italian context this position is held by U. Scarpelli, "La bioetica alla ricerca dei principi," *Biblioteca della Liberta'* 99, (1987): 7-32.

34. For the Italian context see S. Maffettone, *Valori comuni* (Milano: Il Saggiatore, 1989). More in general S. Veca, *La societa' giusta. Argomento per il contrattualismo* (Milano: Il Saggiatore, 1982).

35. Such an approach -- little known in Italy -- can be found in: C. Iandolo, *Introduzione all'etica clinica* (Roma: Armando, 1990). For this approach see also the monographic issues of the series directed by P. Benciolini and C. Viafora *Quaderni di etica e Medicina*, published by Gregoriana Libreria Editrice, Padova.

36. In Italy, a utilitarian approach to bioethics is offered by M. Mori and E. Lecaldano. See: M. Mori, "Bioetica. Nuova Scienza o Riflessione Morale?" *Mondo operaio* 1, (1990): 123; E. Lecaldano, "La sfida dell'etica applicata e il ragionamento in morale".

37. For an overview on this approach: C. Viafora, "La prospettiva personalistica in bioetica per risignificare le parole della vita," in *Centri di bioetica in Italia*, ed. C. Viafora, 323-355. See also the monographic issue "Bioetica e persona", *Per la Filosofia. Filosofia e Insegnamento*, maggio-agosto (1992), with papers of C. Vigna, F. Botturi, E. Agazzi, E. Berti, V. Possenti; C. Viafora, ed., *La Bioetica alla ricerca della persona negli stati di confine* (Padova: Gregoriana, 1994).

38. E. Sgreccia, *Manuale di Bioetica* (Milano: Vita e Pensiero, 1988).

39. A. Autiero, Temi di bioetica. Nascere, vivere, morire (Roma: Dehoniane, 1990); C. Viafora, *Fondamenti di bioetica*; S. Spinsanti, *Etica biomedica* (Roma: Paoline, 1987).

40. K. Demmer, *Interpretare e agire. Fondamenti della morale cristiana* (Milano: Paoline, 1989)

41. On the polarity nature-person see the lucid essay of J. Fuchs, "Natura e cultura in bioetica," in *Etica cristiana in una societa' secolarizzata* (Casale Monferrato: Piemme, 1984), pp. 78-87.

42. On the relation between ethics and law from a general perspective see *Ordine morale e ordine giuridico. Rapporto e distinzione tra diritto e morale* (Bologna: Dehoniane, 1985).

43. An interesting approach to the question is provided by A. Bondolfi, "Aspetti etico-giuridici ed etico-politici delle biotecnologie," *Testimonianze* (1989): 66-105.

44. For all these questions see P. Donati, "Il contesto sociale della Bioetica: il rapporto tra norme morali e norme di diritto positivo," in *Bioetica. Un'opzione per l'uomo* [Atti del I Corso Internazionale di Bioetica, Bologna 15-15/29-30 aprile 1988] (Milano: Jaca Book, 1989).

45. On the foundations of human rights: E. Berti, "Per una fondazione filosofica dei diritti umani," in L. Corradini, A. Pieretti, and S. Serio, eds., *I diritti umani. Presente e futuro dell'uomo* (Cosenza: Edizioni Pellegrini, 1986), pp. 61-72.

46. D. Roy, "La bioéthique et les pouvoirs noveaux," *Cahiers de bioéthique*, no. 1: "La Bioéthique", pp. 81-102.

47. For an evaluation of the activity of ethical committees, their development at an international level, their features and problematic aspects, see: S. Spinsanti, ed., *I comitati di etica in ospedale* (Milano: Paoline, 1988). This book is a collection of the papers presented at the International Symposium of Milan on may 23-25, 1986; P. Cattorini, "I comitati di etica negli ospedali," *Aggiornamenti Sociali* 6, (1988): 423 clarifies summarily functions and organizational problems of ethical committees. An international overview is presented in: "Ethics Committees: How are they doing?" in *Hastings Center Report* 3, (1986): 9-24. Another important point of reference is *Scope Notes Series*, no. 3 (1987).

48. Perplexities are raised by E. Sgreccia, "L'etica: presupposto di affidabilita' dell'ospedale," *Sanare Infirmos* 1, (1987). Sgreccia raises some perplexities concerning the possibilities of solving conflicting positions through dialogue. If this were their role, "ethical committees would simply become instrument for the creation of "social consensus". However, such an interpretation of the function of ethical committees presupposes that there isn't an absolute ethics, and the conviction that society is the source of morality", p. 14.

49. Such conditions can be justified in light of a "practical rationality" according to the model of an "ethics of communication", as suggested by Apel and Habermas. See M.J. Bertomeu, "La ética en los Comités de ética," *Quiron*, Vol. 19 (1988), pp. 82-84.

50. For an analysis of the contemporary attitude toward life, see the acute observations in the Pastoral Document of the Italian Bishops: "Evangelizzazione e cultura della vita umana", in *A servizio della vita umana* [Atti della Conferenza Nazionale per la cultura della vita] (Roma: AVE, 1990), pp. XI-LVI.

51. E. Erikson, *Infanzia e societa'* (Roma: Armando, 1972); *Introspezione e responsabilita'* (Roma: Armando, 1972); *Gioventu' e crisi di identita'* (Roma: Armando, 1974).

52. N. Elias, *La solitudine del morente* (Bologna: Il Mulino, 1985).

53. Some hints on the "symbolic" dimension can be found in L. Lombardi-Vallauri, "Le culture riduzionistiche nei confronti della vita", in *Il valore della vita. L'uomo di fronte al problema del dolore, della vecchiaia, dell'eutanasia* (Milano: Vita e Pensiero, 1985), pp. 41-74. See also his "L'uomo non contemplato (diritto, etica, bioetica)," *Il Mulino*, No. 4 (1987), 601-611. On the "symbolic dimension" in relation to an ethical paradigm inspired by personalism see C. Viafora, "Per un nuovo modello di razionalita' pratica," in *Fondamenti di Bioetica*, pp. 49-52.

Chapter 1

ORIENTATIONS AND TENDENCIES IN BIOETHICS
1970-1990

David Roy

Bioethics is one of society's attempts to manage new and far-reaching powers over life, powers coming from quite recent advances in medicine, genetics, molecular biology, reproductive biology and other specializations in the life sciences.

The most extensive developments and applications of these sciences have occurred in pluralistic societies, *i.e.*, those composed of a number of communities holding different moralities and philosophies of life. These communities differ on questions of right and wrong and often take conflicting positions on how advances in the life sciences may, should or should not be applied.

The conflict may arise from differences about governing beliefs and assumptions concerning human life (ethos), fundamental and dominant values (morality) or the norms and methods to be used in resolving value conflicts (ethics). Such moral and ethical issues may arise in any domain of activity; however, those created by developments in the life sciences have been most prominent in attracting public attention and mobilizing societal reflection over the past twenty years.

The principal issues have come from questions about research involving experimentation on human subjects; withholding or withdrawing various forms of life-support treatment for critically ill patients; euthanasia; abortion;

sterilization of the mentally handicapped, birth control, artificial insemination, in vitro fertilization and surrogate motherhood, transplantation of organs and implantation of artificial organs; the definition of death; psychosurgical, psychopharmacological and conditioning approaches to the control of human behavior; recombinant DNA technology, genetic engineering and genetic therapy; and finally the just distribution of limited resources.

Institutes and committees for bioethics represent a societal effort to mount and maintain systematic reflection on the ethical uncertainties, dilemmas and conflicts raised by advances in biomedical science and technology. Innovations in genetics, human embryology, fetal medicine, geriatrics, gerontology, immunology and the neurosciences and the appearance of new epidemic diseases such as AIDS, will add new challenges to the agenda of those working in bioethics in the coming decades. The goal of interdisciplinary, international and intercultural research and reflection in bioethics is to clarify the content of policies designed to harmonize individual rights and welfare with the common good of present and future generations.

1. The Paper's Mandate

Anyone involved seriously and professionally in the work of bioethics over the past several years will have more or less extensive experience in identifying, analyzing, and devising solutions for the ethical issues raised by the biomedical advances and activities mentioned above. I have not been invited to discuss how a specific ethical dilemma in clinical medicine or biomedical research might be analyzed and resolved: for example, whether and why one might justifiably discontinue assisted hydration and nutrition for a person in persistent vegetative state; for example, whether one can establish an ethically justifiable policy of non-resuscitation for very low birthweight babies (newborn children with less than 750 grams and gestational age less than 25 weeks); for example, whether one is ethically justified in changing traditional clinical research methodology to allow persons with AIDS to have freer access to new drugs that have not yet passed rigorous examination for safety and efficacy. It is not my mandate today to analyze and reach a practical judgement in specific questions such as those just mentioned.

I have been invited, if I correctly interpret my mandate, to carry out a task of second-order reflection: to identify, describe, and to consider critically past, present, and emerging directions and trends of thought people are pursuing as they attempt to resolve the many ethical dilemmas mentioned summarily in the introduction.

2. The Context of Bioethics: Human Nature as Project

"We have not yet seen what man can make of man".[1]

Human nature, once a guiding principle for ancient and medieval cultures, has become a question, an as yet unanswered question, and a project in our culture.

Major discoveries launch new directions of inquiry and of cultural, philosophical, or scientific activities. These serve as a "locus anthropologicus" when they generate new fundamental questions about the origin, status, structure, behavior, goals, potential, limits, and destiny of human beings. The Copernican revolution, Darwinian revolution, and the Freudian discovery of the unconscious profoundly transformed our understanding of the human condition. Each of these theories, originating in observations of fact and strengthened with accumulating evidence, set in motion a train of questions and new insights. Each has served as a "locus anthropologicus". Each has modified and enriched the anthropological project, that massive inter-cultural undertaking to understand what and who we really are.

2.1. Greek Medicine and Paideia

Some have dared to say of ancient Greeks: "Other nations made gods, kings, spirits: the Greeks alone made men".[2] "Making", though, had the sense of transcendental education, a process of shaping men into their true form, into real and genuine human nature. That process was called *paideia*. Its primary agents, the "people shapers" of ancient Greece, were the poets, musicians, orators, philosophers, legislators, gymnastic trainers, and doctors.

Paideia was a process of transcendental education, a process governed by the ideal of "humanitas": to shape people according to the universal laws of human nature common to all human beings. "Above man as a member of the horde, and man as a supposedly independent personality, stands man as an ideal; and that ideal was the pattern toward which Greek educators as well as the Greek poets, artists, and philosophers always looked. But what is the ideal man? It is the universally valid model of humanity which all individuals are bound to imitate".[3]

The Greeks viewed medicine as a paradigm of *paideia* because it offered a model of how to meet *paideia*'s central challenge: the concrete realization of a universal pattern or standard in highly individual and varied lives. "Nature" for the Greeks was a dynamic concept, a universal pattern expressing an immanent purpose, a "logos" in the universe for all beings of a kind. Medicine was a process of education as much as it was a science and an art. Medicine was seen as governed by the same objective as paideia: to bring human beings into harmony with the "logos", or purpose of human nature. Human nature, then, served as a normative principle for the practice of medicine and Plato modelled method in ethics and philosophy upon method in medicine.

Medicine for the ancient Greeks was a "locus anthropologicus". In the view of the Greeks: "Medical science does more than give the intelligent public some inkling of medical problems and medical thought. Through its concentration on one realm of human life, that of the body, it makes discoveries of the most vital importance to philosophy in its task of working out a new picture of human nature, and thereby it assists in molding the individual more closely to the ideal of humanity".[4]

2.2. Modern Biomedicine: a Locus Anthropologicus

Modern medicine has again become a "locus anthropologicus", but with a difference. While remaining a profession and an art, modern medicine, hand-in-hand with advanced specializations in biomedicine and the life sciences, has amplified the modest scientific initiatives of Greek medicine into a massive project of research. Human nature, once the normative principle of "homo medicus", is now increasingly the object of "homo quaerens", the target of evermore precise, penetrating, and aggressive methodical inquiry. The human body, from the molecular structure of the genes to the structure and functioning of the brain; the human psyche, from emotions, through perception, to intellectual activity and decision; human behavior, individual and social, all reveal their laws, as partial dimensions of human nature, across thousands of specialized discoveries.

We now know too much to settle for a fixed philosophical synthesis of what human nature is. But we also know too little. We have taken the route of scientific inquiry. Such inquiry continually widens and deepens into increasing branches of specialization. Because that inquiry is light-years away from its end-points and a definitive synthesis, we do not know, nor can we definitely and comprehensively say, what being human means. Human nature, once a principle for ancient cultures, is for ours a question, an as yet unanswered question. Will we, far down the road, circle back, rich in specialized and synthetized knowledge, to a reaffirmation, scientifically founded, of the ancient idea, ideal, and standard: one nature, identical in all human beings across the rich variety of individual and cultural uniqueness? Perhaps this question is too Platonic. If human nature is an emergent reality, modern science may well be an agent of Aristotelian finality. One interpretation of this principle would state: real human nature still has to manifest itself.

One should not be too sure that we are, anthropologically, just passing through a lengthy and necessary, though ultimately temporary, phase of cognitive fragmentation and pluralism. Moreover, can we really, after Darwin's heightening of our consciousness of evolution, hold the simple thesis that the branching specializations of modern methodical inquiry are, however innovative the discoveries, little more than an exercise of scientific hermeneutics, the unfolding of the scientific interpretation of the one and same human nature affirmed in a more global fashion by the philosophers of old? The disappearance of some and the emergence of new natures, mutation and adaptive change to master new challenge, rather than homogeneous constancy, seem to mark the history of natures subjected to the laws of evolution.

Furthermore, science today, biomedicine and the life sciences included, is closely interlocked with the development of technology and power. The objective of science is to know, that of technology to change things. However, as McLaren has pointed out for embryological studies, things have to be changed to be understood. "To achieve even a glimmer of causal insight, we must modify development, either by experimental manipulation or by genetic means".[5] Science and technology, theory and practice, are interlocked "in the very heart of science itself".[6] Scientific discovery rapidly triggers a technological innovation and the technological application stimulates a new turn in the spiral of scientific inquiry.

What does this say about medicine, biomedicine, and the life sciences as a "locus anthropologicus"?

The first implication is that knowledge alone of human nature no longer defines the vocation of human intelligence. Technology has gained ascendancy. The "vocation of man" and the "consummation of his destiny" is increasingly conceived in terms of achieving maximal control over things and himself.[7]

The second implication is that passionate commitment to an ascendant technological ethos, in promoting the expansion of one dimension of man's nature over all others, brings about a profound change in the human knower. "Thus the triumph of *homo faber* over his external object means also his internal constitution of *homo sapiens*, of whom he used to be a subsidiary part".[8]

Modern medicine has only become the center of a massive project of research. In combination with many specializations in biomedicine, the life sciences, and engineering, modern medicine is likely to achieve the power to match an extensive and profound agenda for technological control over life. For example, the development of recombinant DNA technology and evermore sophisticated experiments in genetic engineering have motivated the claim that "man will have a dramatically powerful means of changing the order of life. I know of no more elemental capability, even including the manipulation of nuclear forces. It should not demean man to say that we may now be able to manage successfully a capacity for altering life itself".[9]

The conclusion is that within biomedicine today "man himself has been added to the objects of technology. *Homo faber* is turning upon himself and gets ready to make over the maker of all the rest".[10] Human nature, once the guiding principle of human activity has now become its project. Science and technology are as much an environment for human evolution today as was the biosphere in the past. Human intelligence creates an environment for the human organism and both are "in a constant state of becoming, mutually determining each other".[11]

Modern medicine, as high science and technology, now occupies center spot on our cultural stage. The drama is marked by hope, but by fear, anxiety, and uncertainty as well. The uncertainty is most manifest in the ethical dilemmas we face on a daily basis in hospitals and laboratories. Now that much can be done, many decisions have to be taken. Value conflicts are common. We frequently are uncertain about what is right and what is wrong. Down the road, we may face the most difficult questions of all. If the "logos", the purpose immanent in human nature that guided the ancients, may fall subject to human power and control, where shall then we turn to discover a second "logos" of a higher order of guidance?

3. Bioethics: Conflicts and the Structure of an Ethical Issue

Differences of perspectives, horizon, perception, assumptions, beliefs and values shape the context of bioethics. These differences are not static. They motivate, inspire, arouse, and mobilize people. They generate opposite courses of action on concrete matters that affect every day living, at the level of individual welfare and of the common good. However, the conflicts arising from these differences are not all of one kind. These conflicts, seen together, reveal the complex structure of issues in bioethics.

3.1. Conflicts Based on Insufficient Experience

Conflicts of a first kind are those that can be settled only by an accumulation of fresh data, decisive evidence, or the weight of experience that supports one view, shows other to be mistaken or exaggerated, or eliminates still others from serious discussion.

Years of experience with artificial donor insemination, for example, has produced no evidence that this approach to human reproduction causes greater stress on marriages or greater distortion of the child's development than can be documented in families using natural insemination. Years of experience with many safe recombinant DNA experiments have substituted a base of assurance for the uncertainty and sharply polarized views on biohazards that dominated debate on molecular biology in the early 1970's.

When the social consequences are difficult to foresee and are uncertain, new developments need a monitored trial run until a sufficient accumulation of knowledge and experience reveals the limits and protections that have to be established. The new reproductive technologies offer abundant examples.

3.2. Conflicts Based on Partial Perceptions

A second type of conflict arises when persons with only partial experience, like the fable's blind man touching different parts of the elephant, make judgements about the whole of the phenomenon. Conflicting views or judgements that are based on partial perceptions and limited experience are rarely intractably opposed. A synthesis or integration of these partial perceptions will diminish or eradicate earlier conflicts. Achieving this integration presupposes the insight that no one human mind or community has a monopoly on knowledge, interests, or values.

3.3. Conflicts when Perceptions Are out of Phase

A conflict of perceptions may arise because one or more views are out of phase with current state of question. For example, the view emphasizing the freedom of scientific inquiry from outside preference can no longer rest on outdated claims about the theoretical purity and practical innocence of scientific inquiry and achievements. Even if the goal of science is to understand the world, and the goal of technology is to change the world, the lag time between science and technology is now very short. The closer science moves to the power of changing things, the more surely and the more justifiably will demands be made for public participation in negotiating how that power will be used.

3.4. Conflicts Based on Restricted Value Focus

A fourth kind of conflict arises when individuals or groups restrict their attention and allegiance to one value. During the early period of debate on recombinant DNA in the 1970's, some scientists where concerned with protecting the scientific enterprise as a whole from the destructive meddling of outside influences. Others feared that the way science was proceeding could be detrimental to mankind as a whole and, specifically, to future generations.

Restricted focusing on one value causes another to appear as a threat. The objective is to achieve a balanced commitment to different values.

3.5. Conflict on the Level of Ethos

Conflicts that appear intolerant of any resolution are the most difficult to handle. This is often the case with conflicts that are rooted profoundly in governing, and often unexamined, beliefs and assumptions about the status, destiny, and meanings of human life or about the purposes and roles of society's various institutions in maintaining human community. This is the level of *ethos*.

Some of the prominent ethical issues in clinical practice and clinical research do arise from divergences of views at this fundamental level. Abortion and research with the human embryo illustrate how difficult it is to resolve issues of this kind, if resolution means the achievement of widespread consensus.

3.6. Conflicts on the Level of Morality

An ethos is a foundation for moral life. It partially determines a hierarchy of values and a related set of positions about what human behaviors are imperative, permissible, tolerable, or are to be prohibited. We do not all share identical hierarchies of values in our highly pluralistic societies. We often do differ quite sharply about what is of greater or lesser importance, even if we are not always able to express clearly why we differ. The issue involves a conflict on the level of morality, a conflict about which values may be sacrificed and which may not.

3.7. Conflicts on the Level of Ethics

Ethics works out the judgements that have to be made, the compromises that have to be struck, and the guidelines and policies that have to be devised when individuals and groups in a pluralistic society clash at the levels of ethos and morality. But there is conflict about how these judgements, compromises, guidelines and policies are to be attained.

There is still a tendency in biomedical circles to turn to law, to conventional expressions of public opinion, to authoritative statements from religious, ecclesiastical, or professional sources, and finally, to simple unexamined spontaneous reactions and biases as the basis for distinguishing right from wrong.[12]

Bioethics, whether as clinical ethics, or research ethics, or the social ethics of public policy, represents a process of interdisciplinary and intercultural discourse to reach tolerable resolutions of the issues posed by developments in the biomedical sciences. Work in each of the three above-mentioned domains raises even more difficult and encompassing questions regarding the foundations of bioethics and the growing need for a transnational or planetary ethics.

4. Bioethics as Clinical Ethics

Clinical ethics, first of all, covers the decisions to be made, and the uncertainties, value conflicts, and dilemmas to be resolved at the bedside of individual patients. The outcome of clinical ethics is a practical judgement about what should be done now to help this particular sick person live or die in a fashion that honors her dignity. All too frequently, these decisions and judgements have to be reached rapidly. Often they are decisive for a patient's future and their consequences are just as often irreversible. These are highly focussed decisions, bounded as they are by the unique biology, clinical condition, needs, desires, life-plans, hopes, sufferings, strengths and limitations of particular human beings.

Value conflicts at the bedside frequently arise from uncertainty about how best to care for the gravely ill and dying when available treatments affect patients' clinical needs and total-life interests in quite different ways. These conflicts are inextricably bound up with the unique circumstances of particular cases. Though general principles define moral perimeters, they do not of themselves decide concrete cases. The specific norms required for such cases are not prefabricated and available for deductive application. They have to be constructed slowly and inductively from discriminating judgements about individual patients. Without these specific norms, general principles remain mute about what they command, permit, tolerate, or prohibit.

4.1. The Patient Is the Norm

In clinical ethics, the patient is the norm governing the decisions and practical judgements to be made. In general, beliefs offer the grounding for basic principles, and norms render basic principles operational in specific contexts. Norms are the operational apparatus of conditional ethics. They specify the conditions under which decisions and actions are morally commanded, permitted, tolerated, or prohibited. But there are general primary norms and specific ultimate norms. In clinical ethics, the patient is the specific ultimate norm governing the ethical justifiability of clinical decisions and actions. The patient's biography -- his or her clinical course, relationships, life-plans, and total-life interests -- constitute this ultimate norm.

Clinical ethics works with patients' biographies to interpret the meaning of principles, that is, to determine what principles command, permit, tolerate, or prohibit at the bedside of this particular patient. As such, clinical ethics is a particular kind of inductive ethics. In terms of clinical ethics, we do not know what our philosophical and moral traditions mean until we test them on a range of particular cases. We cannot simply pass each individual case through a grid of philosophical and religious moral principles to reach a clinical ethical conclusion. We simultaneously have to pass these principles through the grid of individual cases to arrive inductively at a reconstruction of these traditions, a reconstruction mediated through a range of personal histories confronting the suffering of multiple loss, as well as the threat of personal disintegration and death.

4.2. Clinical Ethics: an Integral Part of Clinical Judgement

Clinical ethics, then, is not applied philosophy or theology. Clinical ethics is an original, distinctive intellectual activity, not a derivative one. This thesis does not imply that the philosophical work of identifying and criticizing assumptions, clarifying concepts, and evaluating arguments is irrelevant for clinical ethics. Quite the contrary. Clinical ethics needs this work in controlling and reviewing critically the practical judgements it produces. But clinical ethics is not a philosophical or theological enterprise.

A second point is that clinical ethics is an integral part of clinical judgement and of a clinician's work. Ethical dilemmas at the bedside will be misconstrued if the clinical situation is not understood in all its subtle medical and human complexity. Achieving that understanding is an intrinsic component of the physician's clinical mandate. The thesis that clinical ethics is a doctor's work does not imply the paternalistic idea that the doctor resolves the issues of clinical practice by deciding in solitary eminence what is best for patients. Quite the contrary. A clinician regularly has to seek and orchestrate the contributions of many specialized persons in the diagnosis, treatment, and care of patients. Ethical competence presupposes the skill and sensitivity to seek, and the ability to orchestrate, the contribution of many persons to arrive at an adequate understanding of the patient and of what constitutes the patient's best interest. This is particularly true when patients cannot speak for themselves.

Of course, we cannot isolate clinical practice from clinical research, nor can one isolate the patient, doctor, clinical team, whether in treatment or in research, from the larger society of which they are a part.

5. Bioethics as Research Bioethics

The idea of ethics as a process of intelligent inquiry merits emphasis. The notion that research ethics is an integral part of scientific judgement, very much as clinical ethics is of clinical judgement, is fundamental. Many of the ethical issues, and ethical abuses, that have arisen in research with human subjects have been due to a failure to think as rigorously about the conditions for ethical consistency of research as one is presumed to do regarding the conditions for scientific validity of research. Both sets of conditions are demands on intelligence. But that intelligence has evolved slowly.

5.1. The Protection of Human Subjects

Respect for human beings and the protection of their dignity, autonomy, rights, needs, and interests have formed the core of the many codes and guidelines governing the ethics of research since World War II. The Nuremberg Code marks a turning point. It crystallized the essential characteristics of consent required to protect the autonomy of human beings in medical research. Their consent has to be competent, voluntary, informed, and comprehending.[13]

These are basic demands. They arose from the crushing evidence of experiments in which human beings had been treated as objects, or with less solicitude than one would treat animals, during the Nazi period. Of course, the inhuman treatment of human beings in research both preceded and followed the practices of medical researchers under the Nazi regime. At the turn of the century, the Russian physician Veressayev worried that "it is high time...for society to take its own measures of self-protection against those zealots of science who have ceased to distinguish between their brothers and guinea pigs...".[14] Henry Beecher's 1966 publication on ethically careless medical research projects in the United States,[15] as well as reports on the Tuskegee syphilis study,[16] the Willowbrook hepatitis experiment, and the Jewish Chronic Disease Hospital (Brooklyn, New York) project utilizing injections of a suspension of live cancer cells to study the role of the immune system in defense against cancer,[17] made it painfully clear that the basic requirements of the Nuremberg Code had failed, twenty years after the trial, to penetrate the consciousness, and to guide the behavior, of scientists in medical research.

Since the revelations and warnings of Veressayev,[18] Nuremberg,[19] Pappworth,[20] Beecher,[21] Barber,[22] and Gray,[23] one would have to be quite obtuse to remain insensitive to the past facts and the continuing possibility of abuse. In response to reports of abuse, the "National Commission for the Protection of Human Subjects of Biomedical and Behavioral Research", produced a comprehensive review of ethical issues and sets of guidelines for research with human beings. The National Commission placed great emphasis on institutional review boards (IRBs) as instruments of review designed to diminish the blinding of ethical judgement arising from conflicts of interests. This emphasis implies that the Nuremberg Code expresses a necessary but insufficient condition for ethical adequacy when it states that the duty and responsibility for ascertaining the quality of the consent rests upon each individual who initiates, directs, or engages in the experiments.[24]

5.2. Controlled Clinical Research: An Ethical Imperative

The need to emphasize protection of human subjects in research delayed full recognition of the status of clinical research as an ethical imperative.

A physician's moral obligation to offer each patient the best available treatment cannot be separated from the twin clinical and ethical imperative to base that choice of treatment on the best available and obtainable evidence. The tension between the interdependent responsibilities of giving personal and compassionate care, as well as scientifically sound and validated treatment, is intrinsic to the practice of medicine today. The tension arises prior to, and as a moral reality distinct from, any conflict of interests. It is not merely the expression of an individual physician-investigator's disordered intentions, but is a structural part of the medical profession's covenant with the human community.

Controlled clinical trials -- randomized and multiply blinded, when randomization and blinding are feasible, ethically achievable, and scientifically appropriate -- are an integral part of the ethical imperative that physicians and surgeons should know what they are doing when they intervene into the bodies, psyches, and lives of vulnerable, suffering human beings. The ethical requirement of precise and validated knowledge gather force with the likehood that clinical intervention will exert decisive and irreversible impacts on patients' futures and on future patients. Future patients have faces; they cannot be simply lumped together as part of society and then set in opposition to patients occupying hospital beds today.

The standards of good medicine, determined by professional consensus based upon reliable methods of achieving validated knowledge, enter into the inner structure of the doctor-patient relationship. At the very least, this means "that what doctor and patient choose is not the untrammeled expression of the knowledge and values of each. It is limited by the professional norms that constrain the doctor's judgement and constrain it in the name of good medicine generally".[25]

When there is uncertainty or definite doubt about the safety or efficacy of an innovative or established treatment, this position supports the strong view that there *is*, not simply *may be*, "a higher moral obligation to test it critically than to prescribe it year-in, year-out with the support of custom or of wishful thinking".[26] When large numbers of innovative treatments are continuously introduced into clinical practice, as is the case today, rigorous testing of these is ethically mandatory both for the protection of individual patients and for the just use of limited resources. This holds true with even greater force in light of the evidence that many innovations show no advantage over existing treatments when submitted to properly controlled study.[27] They may even be less effective or harmful.[28]

The goal of distinguishing useless, even dangerous, treatments from safe, effective therapies, and of developing such therapies for currently untreatable high-mortality and high-morbidity diseases is not, as has been claimed, "melioristic" and optional.[29] It may be true that the advance and purification of clinical knowledge is not necessary or mandatory for the "good of society" because society, though fragile in the presence of some threats, can surely survive the deaths of individual patients from cancer, cardiovascular disease and genetic anomalies. However, the covenant of the medical profession with the human community is not precisely for the survival of society, but for the survival of the biologically weak and of those threatened with disintegration. Medicine, as Jerome Lejeune has seen, "is essentially and by nature working against natural selection".[30] Resignation, however benignly motivated, to maintaining the status quo of medical knowledge would work against that purpose. It would also betray both the efforts and the heritage of past generations.

The thesis that controlled clinical investigations constitute an ethical imperative can only be maintained if, and to the extent that, it is possible to conduct such trials in an ethically justifiable way.

5.3. The Ethics of Research

If the practice of medicine is both morally mandatory and inherently experimental,[31] controlled clinical trials cannot be inherently unethical. Clinical trials, whatever the tactics used to control for bias, will be unethical only to the extent that they fail to meet a set of necessary and interrelated conditions.

"Ethical justifiability" means consistency with the ethos and morality of the human community. Human communities vary from one culture and society to another, not only in their customs and art, but also in their governing perceptions and values regarding the body, health, disease, suffering, death and a host of other realities affecting the practice of medicine. The conditions for ethically justifiable research with human subjects arise from the requirements for consistency along each of these dimensions. These conditions are structured. They range from fundamental principles of science, medicine, and philosophy across more specific norms, procedures, and regulations to encompass the tailored ethical judgements required for the unique characteristics and designs of individual clinical trials.

Working out the ethics of research requires the exercise of critical intelligence and judgement by a community of human beings engaged in the check and balance of attentive and mutually corrective discourse rather than in isolated monologues. The combination of interdisciplinary dialogue with the study of specific cases, whether of clinical practice or clinical research, acts as a counterforce to moral atomism, rampant relativism, and what Stephen Toulmin has called the tyranny of principles.[32] Principles, guidelines, and codes alone do not decide concrete cases. Principles will fail to reveal their meaning -- what they command, permit, or prohibit -- until they are interpreted in the light of specific research situations.

The ethics of clinical research is open-ended, cumulative, and unfinished. A continual process of feedback is at work between tailored ethical judgements on specific trials and the principles, norms, procedures and regulations required for the ethical conduct of clinical research. Our knowledge of right and wrong is as subject to the process of evolution and cumulative growth as is our knowledge of fact and truth in science.

The concept of conditional ethics, so understood, implies that ethical justifiability is a graded, not a binary, characteristic of clinical trial. The rheostat rather than the on-off switch suggests an appropriate image.

Although due regard must be maintained for the utility and necessity of institutional review boards, ethics committees, and participation of the general public in the ethical evaluation of protocols for research with human subjects, it is a mistake to view ethics as an external authoritarian imposition of regulations or constraints, perhaps even arbitrary in nature, on the process of clinical research. The design and the practice of research ethics should be primarily, though not exclusively, a matter of self-consistency and self-governance within clinical investigation. It must be emphasized that ethical judgement is an integral component of clinical and scientific intelligence; clinical investigators are expected and entitled to perform as integrated human beings and professionals.

6. Bioethics: Expressing Social Ethics in Public Policy

Many of the ethical issues, dilemmas, and uncertainties that appear at the bedside and in the laboratory reach out beyond these confines into society at large. This is obviously the case with the reproductive technologies; with prenatal diagnosis and selective abortion; with HIV infection and AIDS; with patient's requests for active euthanasia; with proposal for research with the human embryo; and with recent experimental treatments for Parkinson's disease, treatments that utilize dopamine producing neuronal cells from the brains of aborted human fetuses.

When ancient wisdom and maxims fail to deliver unambiguous moral guidance people inevitably enter a period of moral transition. We live in such period now. Some would consider it a time of crisis. Perhaps it is. But crisis must not mean catastrophe. Quite the contrary. A crisis is a time for new judgements, decisions, and choices; a time to chart a new course. At such a time the values that silently govern a society in peaceful everyday life come to vibrant public expression in television and radio programs, in a continuous stream of newspaper and magazine articles, and in the report of more formal and systematic discussion carried out in committees and working groups convened by associations and administrations in countries throughout the world.

This high-profile public communication depicts societies locked in the intense kind of moral discourse provoked by the simultaneous presence of potential danger and powerful opportunity, indeed, in a context of considerable uncertainty about how to act effectively, behave rightly, and legislate wisely. No wonder if, initially at least, the passion of public discourse is directly proportional to the vigor of our uncertainties.

A society comes to know itself, and to demonstrate its character, not only by the values it maintains and affirms, but also by the values it sacrifices and the opportunities it forgoes. It is also a marker of our human condition that we are never continually in conscious and comprehensive possession of the beliefs, perceptions, and values that constitute the foundation of our community together. The search, in a period of moral transition, to formulate and reset this foundation is also often a struggle, as we discover in open discourse that we do not all believe alike, or share the same way of seeing things, or hold the same basic values. These are the marks of a pluralistic society, the kind of society in which we live.

In the face of deep divisions on important matters there is no viable substitute in an open society for the long process of civilized argument and persuasion. Compromises have to be struck; guidelines have to be drawn; policies have to be formed; and judgements have to be made about the choices that are consonant with a society's identity, about behaviors that can be tolerated, even if not endorsed, about where limits have to be set to liberty, and about which rights and values have to cede to others when all cannot be honored and maintained.

This process of interpersonal, interdisciplinary, and intercultural dialogue is the real principle of ethics. It is the source of all the particular rules and policies we devise. These may last only for a time and then give way to more comprehensive and equitable norms as our experience matures through social experiment and social discourse.

Prohibitions and commands are not the only outcome of ethical inquiry. It is just as significant that we learn what ethics a pluralistic society permits and tolerates. This process is an integral part of professional responsibility to contribute to the maturation of our public discourse on matters that touch individuals and society as profoundly as do the new biomedical technologies.

Bioethics is not just an enterprise for a new cadre of experts in clinical ethics and the ethics of biomedical research. Bioethics is also at work in the process of reasoned social discourse exemplified in the many working groups, professional committees, and governmental commissions that have come into existence over the past twenty years to confront the challenges of the biomedical revolution. The best achievement of bioethics in these situations of deep moral conflict is often an accommodation that maintains the coherence of a society, fosters the process of moral discourse, supports autonomy of conscience, and protects moral minorities from subjection to the dictates of moral majorities without justifying cause.

7. Toward a Planetary Ethics

Hans Jonas has asked: "What force shall represent the future in the present?".[33] And Mo-ti, the Chinese philosopher, after observing that where standards differ there will be opposition, asked: "But how can the standards of the world be unified?".[34] Both questions bear upon the need to develop a planetary ethics.

7.1. Responsibility for Future Generations

Hans Jonas' question would be irrelevant if the actions, negligence or omissions of current generations were to have no effect on the world of generations of people decades ahead of us in history. But that is not the case. It is not the case for nuclear technology nor for the powerful new biotechnologies and communication technologies. It is not the case for industrial activity and other activities that destroy the ecology of our planet. It is not the case for the HIV epidemic. All these activities set up interlocking chains of consequences that will profoundly determine the mode, and even the possibility, of life of future generations.

The Jonas question is urgent and inescapable, and particularly difficult, if Jonas is correct in claiming that the conditions for the effective exercise of responsibility for future generations reveal "the insufficiency of representative government to meet the new demands on its normal principles and by its normal mechanics. For according to these, only present interests make themselves heard and felt and enforce their consideration".[35]

What is the process and institutional form that could conceivably sustain the sense and international reality of responsibility for future generations?

7.2. Towards a Global Ethics

If we focus attention on standard of care, we must ask what the principles of distributive justice demand when they are directed to the human community across the planet. The right to health care means at least a claim in justice to a fair share, and to a decent standard of health, medical, and hospital services. Everyone recognizes that this standard cannot be identical in all places, nor identical at all times in the same place. Historical and geographical differences are part of the human condition. Yet, some disparities in the share people enjoy within local communities, and within nations, are clearly recognizable as so unfair that the inequities are morally intolerable.

7.2.1. International Inequity

Clearly, there are terrible international inequities marking the shares of food, hospital care, and medicines that people receive within the global community. But how do we perceive these inequities? How do we judge them? Simply as facts, tragic indeed, but still as facts deriving from presumably unchangeable behavioral laws, based on national interest that govern the relationships between nations? Are we really capable of perceiving and judging these inequities as morally intolerable? Are we capable of seeing these inequities as totally incompatible with the relationships we in the developed world should have to people in developing countries?

7.2.2. Global Solidarity

The 1980 report on the North-South commission, chaired by W. Brandt, former Chancellor of West Germany, repeatedly stresses its cardinal premise that the survival of mankind is a global challenge, an imperative powerful enough to create a bond of global solidarity.[36] But we haven't grown up yet into a mature consciousness of global community, and we remain wishy-washy, indeed even doubtful, about the extent of our moral imperative to work mightily for the survival of others and for assuring them standard of sustenance that are essential for human dignity. Indeed, it is far from clear to us "that everyone in the world has a claim on everyone else, simply because we are all human beings, or that rich nations have an obligation to share their wealth and technology. One has obligations to provide for the well-being of one's own children, for example, but not necessarily for the children of others".[37]

7.2.3. Are Our Societies Ready for a Global Ethics?

Our liberal democratic societies of the developed world, if the late Macpherson's analysis is correct, harbor an inherent contradiction between two freedoms. Liberal "can mean freedom of the stronger to put down the weaker by following market rules; or it can mean equal effective freedom of all to use and develop their capacities. The latter freedom is inconsistent with the former".[38] Capitalistic market freedom supersedes, when it does not outrightly contradict, the effective freedom of all for self-development.

Democracy, within the equilibrium or pluralist elitist model of liberal democracy prevailing in affluent Western societies since the middle of this century, has been judged in the Macpherson analysis, of being little more than a market mechanism for registering the desires of people as they are, or as they are seen to be by power elites within the dominant oligopolistic economic market. Democracy has failed to be a transforming principle advancing people towards what they might be or might wish to be. The ethos of equilibrium democracy perpetuates the image of human beings as consumers, as maximizers of their own satisfactions, and of the benefits and utilities that flow to them from society.

Society in this ethos is little more than a collection of individuals constantly seeking power and possession over and at the expense of each other.[39] If R. Descartes grounded human existence in the power of thought, "cogito, ergo sum", this prevailing ethos grounds human existence in the power of possession, "habeo, ergo sum".[40] It is unlikely that international inequities, even terribly tragic inequities, will be seen as morally intolerable when perceptions, judgements, and policies are shaped by an ethos that presents human beings as maximizers of their own consumer interests in a society that requires an equilibrium of inequality.

A global ethics for AIDS, hunger, and poverty will require an epochal change in consciousness, a change that will lead to a preference for community over affluence.[41] But a new consciousness, as Jean Gebser has explained, cannot arise within human beings only on the force of interpretations and sermons.[42] The consciousness of human global solidarity, with its implication that human beings do have a claim on us just because they are human, needs to be realized in particular concrete endeavors before it expands to become the ethos and the foundation for a new global ethics.

8. Bioethics as Anamnesis

Bioethics does not only stand for moral theory and moral decision-making which takes account of biological and biomedical knowledge. Nor is bioethics just a more complicated term for traditional medical ethics. Bioethics stands for interdisciplinary concern with the total range of conditions necessary for a responsible stewardship of life, particularly human life, in a context of rapid and complex biomedical development.

The challenge is to face both the promises and the perils of new knowledge releasing new power over human beings, power of a depth and duration not really encountered before in human history. Meeting these challenge means advancing effectively towards wisdom. That advance starts as we begin to devise new frameworks of value to balance choices and decisions, and new networks of communication to heighten the participation of the entire human community in the design and the realization of the common good.

How can this challenge be met? Surely not only with the construction of ever more precise codes of medical and biomedical ethics. For the problem that constitutes the challenge is the problem of emancipation. The solution to that problem "is not to discover a correct philosophy, ethics, or human science. For such discoveries are quite compatible with the continued existence of the problem. The correct philosophy can be but one of many philosophies, the correct ethics one of many ethical systems, the correct human science an old or new view among many views. But precisely because they are correct, they will not appear correct to minds disorientated by the conflict between positions and counterpositions. Precisely because they are correct, they will not appear workable to wills with restricted ranges of effective freedom".[43]

If persons are the root of ethics, then an orientation and emancipation of persons is required that permits performance to match the reach of aspiration. The problem of liberation "lies in the incapacity for sustained development".[44] Sustaining development is a process of transcendence. Transcendence occurs with the recurrence of the dynamic structure expressed in the transcendental imperative: be attentive, be intelligent, be reflective, be responsible.

The problem of liberation occurs when this structure fails to recur. On one level the problem appears as a "succession of ever less comprehensive viewpoints".[45] On this level the solution has to be the attainment of a higher viewpoint.[46] On another level the problem appears as a break-down of the process of on-going communication. How could it be otherwise? On the level of the mind transcendence occurs when an unconditioned is realized, made real. Human communication reaches its full scope in such an achievement, the achievement of unconditioned acceptance and unconditioned gift. However, when one can or will no longer grasp the unconditional in the level of the mind, how can one achieve the unconditional in human living? So on this level the solution to the problem of liberation "has to be a still higher integration of human living".[47]

A higher viewpoint surely is needed to devise codes of biomedical ethics that can resolve value conflicts capable of tearing apart the human community. But higher values have to be grasped, chosen, made the effective basis for decision and action. If higher viewpoints condition the grasp of higher values it nevertheless remains true that such viewpoints are "a concrete possibility only as a consequence of an actual higher integration".[48]

If such an integration has occurred as an historical event, then appeal to that event and the elaboration of codes, guidelines, and policies in light of that event is surely as much a function of bioethics as it is the interpretation and application of ancient and recent ethical documents. The appeal will achieve little if it is only a recall. The appeal has to take place as an appropriation, as a realization.

Dialogue is the method of bioethics. An on-going process of communication that tumbles determinism and frees from the bondage of bias has to be real. This is why bioethics fails if, at its limits, it is not the communication of the historical verification that all human beings have been accepted unconditionally by the Unconditioned. Communication, precisely as the realization of the unconditioned, is at the root of bioethics. This appropriation of the historical communication of unconditioned acceptance and unconditioned gift is *anamnesis*. To the extent that bioethics functions as *anamnesis* it will find the higher viewpoint required to illuminate what man can make of man.

ENDNOTES

1. B.F. Skinner quoted in Vance Packard, *The People Shapers* (Boston: Little Brown and Co., 1977), p. 3.

2. W. Jaeger, *Paideia: The Ideals of Greek Culture* (New York: Oxford University Press, 1945), vol. I, p. XXIII.

3. Ibid., p. XXIV.

4. W. Jaeger, *Paideia*, vol. III, p. 26.

5. A. McLaren, "Embryogenesis," in *Physiology and Genetics of Reproduction*, ed. E. M. Coutinho and F. Fuchs (New York: Plenum Press, 1974), p. 307.

6. H. Jonas, "Freedom of Scientific Inquiry and the Public Interest," *Hastings Center Report* 6, no. 4 (1976): 16.

7. H. Jonas, "Technology and Responsibility: Reflections on the New Tasks of Ethics," in *Philosophical Essays* (Englewood Cliffs, NJ: Prentice-Hall, 1974), p. 11.

8. Ibid., p. 11.

9. Livermore Shaw, quoted in: Bennet William and Guerin Joel, "Science that Frightens Scientists. The Great Debate over DNA," *The Atlantic Monthly*, no. 2 (1977): 59.

10. Ibid., p. 59.

11. R.C. Lewontin, "The Corpse in the Elevator," *New York Review of Books*, January 10 (1983): 37.

12. D. Callahan, "Normative Ethics and Public Morality in the Life Sciences," *The Humanist*, Sept/Oct (1972): 5.

80

13. R. Levine, *Ethics and Regulation of Clinical Research* (Baltimore: Urband Schwarzenberg, 1986), p. 96.

14. V. Verassayev, *The Memoirs of a Physician* (New York: Knopf, 1916), p. 366.

15. H. K. Becheer, "Ethics and clinical research," *New England Journal of Medicine* 277, (1966): 1354-1360.

16. T. G. Benedek, "The 'Tuskegee Study' of syphilis: analysis of moral versus methodologic aspects," *Journal of Chronic Disease* 31, (1978): 35-50.

17. R. R. Faden and T. L. Beauchamps, *A History and Theory of Informed Consent* (New York: Oxford University Press, 1986), pp. 161-167.

18. V. Verassayev, *The Memoirs of a Physician*.

19. Nurember Code, *Trials of War Criminals before the Nuremberg Military Tribunals under the Control Council Law no. 10* (Military Tribunal I, 1947; Washington, D.C.: U.S. Government Printing Office, 1948-49).

20. M. H. Pappworth, *Human Guinea Pigs: Experimentation on Man* (Boston: Beacon Press, 1967).

21. H.K. Beecher, "Ethics and Clinical Research".

22. B. Barber, J.J. Lally, J. Loughlin Mukaushka and D. Sullivan, *Research on Human Subjects* (New York: Russel Sage Foundation, 1973).

23. B.H. Gray, *Human Subject in Medical Experimentation* (New York: John Wiley and Sons, 1975).

24. Nuremberg Code, *Trial of War Criminals*.

25. P. Morgan, "Randomized clinical trials need to be more clinical," *JAMA* 253, (1985): 1782-1783.

26. A.R. Feinstein, "Clinical Biostatistics: XXVI. Medical Ethics and the Architecture of Clinical Research," *Clinical Pharmacology* 15, (1974): 316-334.

27. J.P. Gilbert, B. McPeek, and F. Mosteller, "Statistics and ethics in surgery and anesthesia," *Science* 198, (1977): 684-689.

28. W.A. Silverman, "The lesson of retrolental fibroplasia," *Scientific American* 236, (1977): 100-107.

29. H. Jonas, *Philosophical Essays. From Ancient Creed to Technological Man* (Englewood Cliff, NJ: Prentice-Hall, 1974), pp. 114-118.

30. J. Lejeune, "General Discussion," in *Ethical Issues in Human Genetics*, ed. B. Hitton et al. (New York: Plenum Press, 1973), p. 19.

31. C. Bernard, *An Introduction to the Study of Experimental Medicine* (1949).

32. S. Toulmin, "How Medicine saved the Life of Ethics," *Perspectives in Biology and Medicine* 25, (1982): 736-750.

33. H. Jonas, *Philosophical Essays*, p. 19.

34. Quoted in E.B. Sellon, "Introduction to an Endeavor," in *Main Currents in Modern Thought. Retrospective Issues*, ed. H. Margeneau and E. B. Sellon, Vol. 32.

35. H. Jonas, *Philosophical Essays*, p. 19.

36. Nord-Sud Kommission, *Das Überleben sichern* (Köln: Kiepenheuer, 1980).

37. C. Levine, "Ethics, justice and international health," *Hastings Center Report* 7, (1977): 5-7.

38. C. B. Macpherson, *The Life and Times of Liberal Democracy* (New York: Oxford University Press, 1977), p. 1.

39. Ibid., pp. 77-92.

40. C. Smith, "The legacy of U.S. interests," *The Globe and Mail* (March 18, 1989).

41. C. B. Macpherson, *The Life and Times of Liberal Democracy*, p. 91.

42. J. Gebser, "The foundations of the aperspective world," in *Main Currents in Modern Thought*, ed. H. Margeneau and E. B. Sellon.

43. B. Lonergan, *Insight: A Study of Human Understanding* (New York: Lonyman, 1958), p. 631.

44. Ibid., p. 630.

45. Ibid., p. 231.

46. B. Lonergan, *Insight: A Study of Human Understanding*, (New York: Lonymann, 1958), p. 234.

47. Ibid., p. 633.

48. Ibid., p. 633.

Chapter 2

BIOETHICS IN THE UNITED STATES

Warren Reich

The emergence of the remarkable phenomenon known as bioethics in the United States around 1970 is traceable, in large part, to morally disturbing events that occurred in three areas -- human experimentation, the social uses of medicine, and the advent of high-technology in medical practice.[1]

It is important to trace the origins of bioethics, in narrative forms, to morally disturbing experiences, for all practical ethics, it could be argued, has its origins in the experience of human moral suffering and moral outrage caused by moral abuses.

1. Origins of Bioethics: Human Experimentation

Three now-classic cases of abuse in human experimentation -- cases that were subjected to public scrutiny for the first time around 1970 -- were instrumental in provoking the rise of bioethics in the United States.

One occurred at Willowbrook State School, an institution for severely mentally retarded children on Staten Island in New York City. It was at Willowbrook that a physician-consultant in pediatrics and infectious diseases began studies in an attempt to develop an effective prophylactic agent against hepatitis. Between 1956 (when the studies began) and 1970 (when the research came to the public's attention), the medical staff deliberately infected newly

84

admitted patients with isolated strains of the virus, for a total of seven to eight hundred children.[2]

Critics claimed that the study increased the subjects' risk of later developing chronic liver disease, since those patients did not receive protective doses of gamma-globulin, as the other children had. The consent forms were misleading; and it appeared that parents were coerced into "volunteering" their children by the implicit threat that the children would not be admitted to the hospital for treatment unless they were made part of the research project. The research unit was closed but no charges were brought against the physician, his associates, or the institution.[3]

Another widely publicized case of abuse in human experimentation occurred in 1964 at the Jewish Chronic Disease Hospital in New York City, where twenty-two elderly patients were injected with live cancer cells. The physicians assumed that they could perform any action so long as the research stood to benefit scientific inquiry. The main charge brought against the researcher and the director of the hospital was that the patients had not been given sufficient, accurate information to grant properly informed consent. The New York Board of Regents, the medical licencing board, found the medical professionals guilty of "unprofessional conduct" and of "fraud and deceit in the practice of medicine".[4]

These two were just a few of the many ethical abuses that occurred in U.S. biomedical and clinical research. In 1966, a highly respected physician-scholar, Henry K. Beecher of Harvard Medical School, wrote an article in the *New England Journal of Medicine* in which he presented numerous examples of investigators who endangered "the health or the life of their subjects" without informing them of the risk or obtaining their permission. His main thesis was that these cases were not atypical. In almost all the cases the experimental subjects lived in a setting -- prisons, hospitals, mental institutions or military establishments -- that compromised their ability to give consent.[5] Publication of his article stimulated widespread response and further journalistic investigations into abuses in human experimentation.

There were several factors of a moral sort that accounted for these abuses, allowing them to occur as a regular pattern of biomedical activities. Among them were two major factors: the imperative to make medical progress and the unquestioned moral authority of physicians in medical matters. The earliest moral and legal concerns about research subjects in the 1960s were how to control the risks to the subjects, but little attention was given to the research subject's autonomous choice whether to participate in the experiment.

An additional factor that supported abuses in biomedical research in the United States -- social and racial biases -- appeared in a particularly shocking study that was first reported in 1970. The case, named after the town in Alabama where the study originated, is known as the Tuskegee Syphilis Study.[6]

From 1932 to 1972, six hundred black Alabama sharecroppers and day laborers were subjects in a U.S. Public Health Service study designed to determine the effects of the natural course of untreated syphilis. One group consisted of 399 syphilitic men who remained untreated and were not informed of the nature of their illness, while the remaining 201 men, who did not have syphilis, participated in the experiment as a control group.

The subjects knew neither the name nor the nature of their disease; they knew only that they were receiving care for "bad blood". These black subjects were not told that they were participants in a non therapeutic experiment; and they were misinformed when told that research procedures such as spinal taps were "special free treatment" for bad blood. As the American medical historian James Jones has indicated, the blacks' consent was a "manipulated" consent, extracted from subjects who lived in such "social deprivation" that manipulation came effortlessly.[7] During the entire forty years of the experiments, the men were systematically blocked from receiving treatments, even when penicillin became available in the late 1940s.

The study continued uninterrupted and without serious challenge until 1972 when it was reported on the front page of *The New York Times*. It was claimed (as it was at Willowbrook) that researchers were only observing the course of a natural and inevitable disease. A panel appointed by the U.S. Department of health, Education and Welfare to review the study concluded in 1973 that the Tuskegee Study was unethical and recommended that it be terminated at once. The panel stated: "Society can no longer afford to leave the balancing of individual rights against scientific progress to the scientific community alone."

2. Origins of Bioethics: Social Uses of Medicine

The racist dimensions of the Tuskegee Syphilis Study deserve further attention, for they exemplify a second reason for the rise of bioethics in the United States: the morally questionable social uses of medicine, which forced us to examine the cultural setting in which moral problems arise.

When the Tuskegee Study began, syphilis was considered the natural consequence of the innately low character of blacks. Genital and brain development of Negroes were said to vary inversely. Blacks were seen as dirty, shiftless, promiscuous, and with bad personal hygiene. These pre-existing stereotypes of blacks led doctors to take their prejudices as facts. Like American society, American medicine was, especially in the South, racist.[8]

Racism in American medicine was strongly influenced by Social Darwinism that swept America in the late 19th century. Whites predicted that by 1900 the black race would be extinct in the competition for "survival of the fittest." Defects in whites went unreported; but medical journals described defects in blacks in great detail, ostensibly confirming the biological demise of blacks through evolution.

For example, in an 1851 article written by a physician for a medical journal, the author, Samuel Cartwright, asserted that the people of Africa have diseases that render them unable to take care of themselves.[9] Cartwright introduced two new mental diseases of the Negro race. One was drapetomania, which causes the Negro to escape from slavery. The other was dysesthesia aethiopis (roughly translated as Ethiopian rascality), in which lethargy of the intellectual faculties and slothfulness of the body were claimed to be traceable not only to a deficiency of cerebral matter in the cranium, but especially to poor "vitalization of the blood" due to physiological causes in the respiratory system. Dysesthesia aethiopis was thought to be more prevalent among free Negroes (i.e., ex-slaves) because they were not made to work like the slaves who through hard work expanded their lungs and utilized their body and mind.

If medicine was being used to support American attitudes of discrimination against blacks when the Tuskegee study began in 1932, racial attitudes were felt to be entirely out of place in the America in which the Study was exposed in 1972. For in the intervening years the United States had experienced the civil rights movement that had turned public moral attitudes strongly against racial discrimination. Thus, the public moral outrage against the Tuskegee abuse was more than a reaction against the victimization of non-consenting subjects of research; it was an outrage against the social use of medicine to perpetuate racism.

Racist medicine is but one example of the medicalization of social and moral problems -- i.e., of the way in which moral problems in medicine are described and justified in medical terms. There are many other examples, including the ways in which medicine has been an instrument for preserving the subsidiary role of women, for establishing the inferior position of homosexuals, for justifying widespread drug use, and for maintaining the economic superiority of a privileged caste. Bioethics has increasingly been concerned with these social uses of medicine, for the medicalization of ethics serves to conceal important moral problems while distorting the conscience of the society that accepts the deception.[10]

3. Origins of Bioethics: Technologization of Medicine

The third major factor that influenced the rise of bioethics in the United States was a series of events that represented the technologization of medicine. For instance, even prior to 1970 debates about the distribution of scarce life-saving kidney machines sparked an interest in examining the ethical foundations of contemporary biomedicine.

In 1962 in Seattle, Washington, John Myers, a 37-year-old man with end-stage kidney disease, who would have died within hours, was connected to what was called the first true artificial organ in medical history. The Myers case is a celebrated case because the patient was chosen for dialysis by the first selection committee ever to function for this purpose in the United States. The committee -- which consisted of a housewife, banker, lawyer, minister, state official, labor leader, and a surgeon -- had the task of deciding which patients would be selected for treatment with Seattle's life-saving kidney machines and which ones would be denied and thereby die.

A board of physicians first eliminated from consideration those patients who were medically or mentally unsuitable. Children were also ruled out, as were those over the age of 45 and non-residents of the state of Washington. The committee then used the following criteria to choose candidates for dialysis: age and sex of the patient, marital status and number of dependents, income and net worth, emotional stability, education, occupation, past social contribution and future potential, and references.

As cases of this kind in Seattle became more widely discussed because of exposure in the press, the dominant issue became that of justice: is it fair to judge who will live according to such variables as the "social worth" of the individual?[11] By these standards it was clear that, in America, one might have a better chance of being selected to live if one were a boy scout leader, married with children, and a regular church-goer. It is no wonder that science writers began using the term "playing God" to refer to such "god-like" decisions,[12] and theologians began examining the implications of that provocative phrase.[13]   A dominant moral opinion that strongly influenced public policy was that of Ramsey, who argued that we should play God by imitating the God who sends his rain upon the just and the unjust alike: thus, a lottery scheme is the best means of avoiding opprobrious judgements on the personal worth of individuals.[14]

The biomedical technologies that influenced the rise of bioethics also included kidney and heart transplantations. The transplantation of the kidney had begun almost two decades prior to the onset of bioethics; and by 1967 it had achieved considerable success in extending the lives of some five thousand patients with end-stage renal disease. But it was the first transplantation of a human heart that focussed the attention of the public and of scholars on the technique and ethical implications of organ transplantation. The first human heart transplant was performed by Dr. Christiaan Barnard in Capetown, South Africa in 1967. The patient, 55-year-old Louis Washkansky, lived only 18 days; but his next patient, Philip Blaiberg, survived 56 weeks. These events ushered in the Age of Transplantation: in the following year, 101 heart transplants were performed by 64 teams in 22 countries -- a rapid development that was widely regarded in the United States as a massive medical experiment.

These technologies raised questions such as the following: Are some organs so much a part of a person that transplanting them is in some way immoral or unethical in and of itself? Will an unlimited use of artificial body parts change what it means to be human by mechanizing our nature? Should our society do anything about removing unjustified risks from patients who are eligible to receive unproven medical technologies that *might* help them, when the physician is eager to try innovative medical technologies so as to "make a name for himself"?[15]

The use of respirators to prolong human life -- as in the famous case of Karen Ann Quinlan -- provided a major impetus for the rise of bioethics.[16] They represented yet another innovative technology that, like the transplant and implant technologies, raised the question: Are there any moral limits to the use of biomedical technologies in prolonging human life?

Those, then, are the major influences that ushered in the Age of Bioethics in the United States.

4. Bioethics and Social Factors

A "new" field of inquiry has, in the past two decades, come to be designated around the world by a new term. The world bioethics was probably coined by the American oncologist, Van Rensselaer Potter. In his book, *Bioethics: Bridge to the Future*, published in 1971, he said: "A science of survival must be more than a science alone, and I therefore propose the term *Bioethics* in order to emphasize the two most important ingredients in achieving the new wisdom that is so desperately needed: biological knowledge and human values."[17]

The same year (1971), Dr. Andre Hellegers, a Dutch gynecologist and fetal physiologist, made an important decision when he used the term bioethics in naming a new research center -- the Kennedy Center for Bioethics at Georgetown University.[18] He invited me to be a member of that research center at the time of its founding in 1971, and I have been there since. Shortly after my arrival there, I came upon the idea of developing a reference work for this newly emerging area of study. A major question that faced me 19 years ago was this: Should I use the neologism Bioethics in the title of this reference work? I discussed with academic colleagues, particularly the sociologist David Sills and the theologian Paul Ramsey, this question: Do you think the field of bioethics will grow? And if so, will it continue to be known by this new name?

Use of the term bioethics was clearly a risk; but I decided to use the term (Bioethics) in what was to become the *Encyclopedia of Bioethics*. Apparently, the decision was influential, for according to some commentators, the Encyclopedia of Bioethics subsequently became more influential than any previously published encyclopedia in establishing the field on which it reported. By now, the term bioethics is being used throughout the world.

What is the meaning of the term bioethics? "Bioethics is a composite term derived from the Greek words *bios* (life) and *ethike* (ethics). It can be defined as the systematic study of human conduct in the area of the life sciences and health care, insofar as this conduct is examined in the light of moral values and principles."[19] (I use the term "principles" here to refer to any source of normative ethics, not just to rules.)

The scope of the interdisciplinary field of bioethics depends on the number of areas of concern that one includes under the Greek term *bios*. In my understanding, bioethics embraces medical ethics and extends considerably beyond it. Medical ethics deals with value-related problems that arise in the physician-patient relationship or in other settings in the world of medicine. Those problems may be examined in light of normative sources that are either external to medicine -- such as secular and religious ethical principles, societally-defined roles, legal sanction, etc. -- or that are internal to the medical profession -- such as the Hippocratic writings and professional codes of ethics.

The distinctive feature of the scope of bioethics is that it extends to all issues of life, the life sciences, health, and health care. Thus, it extends beyond medical ethics in several ways: It embraces ethical problems and issues that arise in all health professions and among non-professional caregivers such as family members (who give more health care than do professionals); it extends to biomedical and behavioral research, whether or not that research has a direct bearing on therapy; it includes a broad range of social issues, such as allocation of health care nationally and internationally, problems in public and occupational health, and the ethics of population control; and finally, it extends to non-human life: the welfare of animals and plants, the ways in which humans affect the environment and the ways in which the environment, in turn, affects the welfare of all life.[20]

The latter part of the scope of bioethics -- dealing with the environmental sciences and ethical choices -- has not been widely acknowledged as a part of bioethics in the United States; but there are indications that this will change in the near future, for there is increasing interest in approaching questions of health, life, and quality of life in a more comprehensive and "holistic" way. The links among all life forms are becoming more and more apparent. Fortunately, use of the term *bio*ethics permits and even invites us to expand our moral vision in this way.

Bioethics in the United States has been shaped more significantly by assumptions about ethics than it has by the range of issues addressed. The first level of assumptions about ethics is the level where we find a kind of *moralism* in the American outlook. By this I mean that among Americans one commonly finds the outlook that say: If there is a problem, there must be an answer; if we are good citizens, we should join together in trying to find an answer; and if the problem affects the public weal the answer must be formulated in rules that govern behavior. Furthermore, among the American public, rules are fundamentally assumed to be absolute.

Other attitudes that shape American bioethics relate to the *law*. Typical of the American outlook is that if there is a problem, "there's gotta be a law" to solve the problem. Americans are quick to see, in the courts, a remedy for their complaints against doctors by suing them for malpractice; and many of the new societal standards for bioethics have been developed in the courts.

In general, there has been a constant ferment of interchange between ethics and law in issues dealing with bioethics in the United States.[21] For example, the law took over from ethics (actually, from Roman Catholic moral theology) the standard that "extraordinary" (or disproportional) measures need not be taken in sustaining human life. On the other hand, (biomedical) ethics has taken over from the courts the idea that a surrogate decision-maker should, where feasible, be selected to decide what the patient would have decided if he or she could have.

Political factors have also given shape to American bioethics. As soon as bioethical issues appeared in the form of enticing public challenges around 1970, some political leaders identified themselves with the important issues addressed in bioethics. Some have supported various bioethical concerns such as the right to health care. Bioethics as a field of inquiry has been substantially influenced and strengthened by the creation of federal commissions that have studied bioethical problems.[22] In addition, bioethics has been supported by millions of federal dollars contributed for bioethics research and teaching.

Political fears and biases have been major influences shaping popular bioethics. For example, federal officials have continued for many years to ban federally supported research involving human fetal tissue, as well as transplanting of fetal tissue for such therapeutic goals as improving the conditions of people with diabetes, Parkinson disease, etc. Moral influences (such as the fear that the desire to obtain fetal tissue will increasingly become the actual motivation for abortions) join with political influences (such as the political influence of the right-to-life segment of society) in shaping current bioethical policies in this regard in the United States.

The *medical profession* plays a diverse and changing role in bioethics discussions and policy-making. The medical profession is now weaker than it has been in the past, due to growing public mistrust in the power of physicians. This is reflected in the changing code of ethics for American medicine. The 1847 code of Ethics of the American Medical Association (AMA) was a lengthy document that made numerous recommendations on the appropriate virtues of the physician (and of the good patient!).[23] By contrast, the AMA Principles of Ethics of 1980 are so brief that they scarcely say anything that could actually influence behavior.[24] Unlike many European and South American countries, the United States has no tradition of professional medical deontology. Consequently, medical professional influence on bioethics relies on political lobbying by medical associations, papers and policies adopted by such organizations as the American

Medical Association and the American College of Physicians, and the persuasive abilities of physician-writers and physician-philosophers.

5. The Institutionalization of Bioethics

Over the past twenty years bioethics has become extensively institutionalized in the United States, particularly through the establishment of research centers, federal and state commissions, teaching programs, bioethics committees, and bioethics consultation activities. The growth of bioethics has been phenomenal; one can truly speak of a bioethics industry.

Since bioethics did not fit within traditional academic disciplines and consequently was not taught on a systematic basis in colleges and universities, the field gained academic attention in the late 1960s and early 1970s through some important conferences and symposia on themes such as abortion and human research. Some of these conferences resulted in books and even book series; for example, the *Philosophy and Medicine Series* edited by Engelhardt and Spicker began with a conference held in 1974. Today there are no fewer than ten book series produced in the area of bioethics.

The establishment of bioethics research centers has probably been the most significant means of institutionalizing bioethics. The Institute of Religion at the Texas Medical Center in Houston, established in 1954, was the first major center devoted to medical ethics in the United States. The Institute of Society, Ethics and the Life Sciences (The Hastings Center), founded in 1969 by Daniel Callahan and Willard Gaylin, is an independent research center that is not affiliated with any university. It conducts research projects on the social and ethical aspects of the life sciences with a small resident staff and large task force composed of scholars who visit the Center for this purpose; publishes the *Hasting Center Report*, a key journal in the field, and other publications; conducts a program of visiting fellows; and offers (conducts) courses and symposia. The Kennedy Institute of Ethics at Georgetown University was the third major research center for bioethics in the United States and the first to be firmly established as part of a university. Founded by Dr. Andre Hellegers in 1971, the Institute, through its Center for Bioethics, has sponsored research by permanent scholars who are now twelve in number. It sponsored development of basic research tools in the field: the *Encyclopedia of Bioethics*, an annual *Bibliography of Bioethics*, and *Bioethicsline*, an online computerized database; it houses the National Reference Center for Bioethics Literature, a major clearing-house for bioethics literature; it offers an internationally renowned Intensive Bioethics Course annually; its scholars offer bioethics expertise on a regular basis to the deliberations of federal governmental agencies and national commissions; and it sponsors a large Ph.D. program in Philosophy with a concentration in bioethics.

Starting with these three, the number of centers of bioethics in the United States has increased to over two hundred. Major university-affiliated centers now exists at Case Western Reserve University in Cleveland, Baylor College of Medicine in Texas, and the University of Washington, to mention only a few. Graduate Programs in Bioethics are now offered at sixteen institutions, nine of which offer graduate degrees.

The teaching of bioethics has expanded dramatically in the past twenty years.[25] Prior to 1967, virtually the only systematic ethic for medicine was taught in medical schools of Roman Catholic universities, of which there were six in the United States. Systematic Jewish medical ethics and a less systematic Protestant medical ethics also existed, principally in a few teaching hospitals.

In 1967 a new era in the teaching of bioethics and related subjects began. It was in that year that America's first Department for the Medical Humanities was created in the then-new School of Medicine of the Pennsylvania State University at Hershey, Pennsylvania. Its curriculum, which subsequently provided a model for many other universities, included a variety of courses in the philosophical, historical, ethical, literary, religious, and behavioral dimensions of medicine. Students at that University have been obliged to take two such courses during their four years of medical school.

The teaching of what was then called "human values in medicine" grew rapidly in the following years. For example, during one two-year period, from 1972 to 1974, the number of medical institutions reporting special teaching activities in medical ethics more than tripled: the increase was from 17 (of 95 schools) to 56 (of 107 schools).[26] By 1982, by far the majority of medical schools offered courses in medical ethics.[27]

In 1984 a comprehensive report on the quality of medical education insisted that American medical education has been too narrowly focussed on training in scientific information and clinical skills. In addition, the Report said, medical education should impart a thorough knowledge of values and problem-solving skills.[28] It was in 1985 that medical ethics and human values teaching were made mandatory in U.S. medical schools, as well as ethical, behavioral, and socioeconomic subjects pertinent to medicine.[29]

A sign of the growth of bioethics and the medical humanities is that in 1974 there were approximately 31 faculty members for whom teaching and research in medical ethics in medical schools were their primary identification;[30] by the 1982 there were approximately 60 such professorships in ethics and human values.[31] Today I would estimate that there are 125 professors fulfilling these functions in U.S. medical schools.

There is now a national professional society for those who teach bioethics and related humanities, principally in medical schools. Called the Association for Faculty in Medical Humanities, it has some four hundred members. It is a division of the Society for Health and Human Values.[32]

6. Teaching Materials in Bioethics

Bioethics textbooks published in the United States are numerous and are designed to meet a variety of needs. They fall into two categories. First, some bioethics textbooks deal mostly with ethical policies for medicine; they take the approach of applying ethical principles and rights to general medical situations, without including much of a clinical orientation.[33] Another category of bioethics textbooks gives more emphasis to clinical medical problems, either by including descriptive clinical materials or by making extensive use of medical cases and situations.[34] In addition, some general treatises of medical ethics are grounded in the beliefs and principles of some of the major American religious traditions.[35] Casebooks in the legal aspects of medical ethics supply an indispensable component for bioethics teaching.[36] Extensive additional teaching resources are available, including an encyclopedia,[37] curriculum information,[38] printed selected bibliographies,[39] online bibliographical resources,[40] audio-visual aids,[41] journals,[42] and current information services.[43]

Ethics Committees are a recent, unique, and widespread phenomenon in the world of bioethics. First recommended in an article published in 1975,[44] ethics committees were indicated as a necessity by the New Jersey Supreme Court, which stipulated that an ethics committee should have a role in cases like the Karen Quinlan case.[45] A hospital ethics committee is a committee that is concerned with especially difficult ethical questions which arise in the context of making decisions or formulating policy in the domain of clinical practice. It is distinguished from a hospital committee concerned with ethics and biomedical research, known as an "institutional review board."

A major catalyst in increasing the number of hospital ethics committees came from a Report of the President's commission for the Study of Ethical Problems in Medicine and Biomedical and Behavioral Research, which recommended that ethics committees assume a role so as to avoid excessive involvement of the courts in medical decision-making. The President's Commission recommended several functions for these committees, including these: to review treatment decisions made on behalf of incompetent, terminally ill patients; to review medical decisions having ethical implications, with the option to refer cases to a court with proper jurisdiction; to provide social, psychological, spiritual or other counseling for patients, family members, physicians or other hospital staff; to establish guidelines regarding such questions as withdrawing treatment, determination of death, etc.; and to offer educational programs in ethics. Hospital ethics committees usually consist of some combination of physicians, nurses, administrators, attorneys, social workers, psychiatrists, clergy, patient advocates, and trained ethicists.

Ethics committees are one setting in which bioethics consultation occurs. Bioethics consultation is now so widespread that a national group exists for this purpose: the Society for Bioethics Consultation. Its annual meetings are attended by about 125 persons. Journals and newsletters,[46] as well as a number of books[47] are available on the work and methods of hospital ethics committees.

7. The Principle-Based Paradigm for Bioethics

The substantive contents, methods, and orientations of bioethics in the United States are the topic of increasing debate. For the field of bioethics is currently undergoing a major shift of paradigms. One can speak of the dominant paradigm that has governed the field in its first twenty years, as well as a newer paradigm that is now emerging. In my view, the future of bioethics will be determined by the ways in which these two paradigms will be separately pursued and eventually joined.

The dominant paradigm for bioethics -- and of Anglo-American moral philosophy (ethics) more generally -- has been the principle-based paradigm. In this paradigm, dramatic moral quandaries have been given special attention, especially those quandaries that represent the need for a public policy. The question that is asked is this: What ought we to do in cases like this? Thus, it emphasizes an ethic of duty. In this paradigm, ethics depends on a deductive logic and a rationalistic mode of discursive moral reasoning. It determines what principles are important for bioethics; and it then applies those principles to individual cases, with the assumption that a high degree of certitude about moral behavior can be achieved in this way. Often, the first premises of the deductive approach are what has been called ontotheological: the entire enterprise of ethics is driven by a grand theory of humanness, of divinity, of ethics, etc.

When the bioethics movement first began -- and even prior to that, with the renaissance of medical ethics in the late 1960s -- the substantive work of systematic ethics was done predominantly by theologians.[48] In general, the work of the theologians helped to push bioethics in the direction of the principle-based paradigm, yet not without the broader vision associated with theological thought.

The work of Paul Ramsey, the Princeton University Protestant theologian, was very influential. He combined a theology based on love of God with natural law theory to argue strongly against such technological interventions as in vitro fertilization.[49] While Charles Curran's ethical writings rest strongly on themes from revelation, in bioethical matters he often worked to clarify rules and principles that have arisen in the Catholic tradition.[50] Catholic theologian Richard McCormick creatively reworked and applied Cetholic insights and rules to questions such as fetal research and research with children.[51] Karen Lebacqz, a seminary professor, made pioneering contributions to bioethics in her work on national commissions and in her writings on the principle of justice.[52] The one clear exception to the emphasis on an ethic of rules was found in the work of theologian Joseph Fletcher, whose writings on situation ethics reminded us of the complexities and moral implications of the existential situations and particular judgements involved in biomedical ethics.[53] American Jewish theologians working during this period -- including David Feldman, Seymour Siegel, David Bleich, and Fred Rosner -- clarified the implications of Jewish law for development in modern medicine. They did this in a way that spoke to those who were familiar with talmudic scholarship, but also having in mind the moral interests of a secular, general Western public.[54]

In brief, Christian and Jewish theologians turned an important corner starting around 1970: they stopped speaking exclusively to their co-religionists in the moral language of their tradition, and began the challenging task of articulating bioethical standards in a secular, public forum as a contribution to the creation of public policies. This effort not only assisted bioethical policies; the outward turn also affected the priorities and inner workings of moral theology itself.

By the late 1970s it was clear that theologians would no longer dominate bioethics, for philosophers had already begun making extensive contributions to bioethics. Bioethics very much needed the precision, concepts, and intellectual tradition represented by philosophy. Unfortunately, however, philosophers had long regarded practical ethics as falling outside the scope of acceptable philosophical work; instead, in the United States, they had been devoting themselves to what was called mataethics, especially by clarifying the language of morals.

However, philosophers in increasing numbers began turning their attention to the practical moral reasoning required by bioethical questions. Thus, while I could find only three or four American philosophers to serve as Editors and Advisory Board members of the first edition of the *Encyclopedia of Bioethics* in 1972, by 1980 ethics had become acceptable work for philosophers; and by the late 1980s probably the majority of bioethics scholars trained in ethics were philosophers, nor theologians. The results were far-reaching. As the philosopher Stephen Toulmin commented, medicine saved the life of philosophical ethics.[55] Yet, by 1990 Daniel Callahan regretted the secularization of bioethics brought about by the disappearance of theological discourse from bioethics -- a disappearance partly traceable to the emphasis on moral rules.[56]

The philosophers have made several major contributions to bioethics, principally in two areas. They have offered philosophical clarifications of the meaning of such concepts as health and disease;[57] and have offered increasing sophistication to a principle-based approach to bioethics.

The historic cases with which I began this presentation -- the Willowbrook case, the case of the Jewish Chronic Disease Hospital, and the Tuskegee Syphilis study -- represented abuses that called out for publicly acknowledged rules that would correct them in the future. Three philosophical principles arose to serve that function. They were the principle of autonomy (self-determination), beneficence (doing good), and justice (the fair distribution of benefits and burdens in society).[58]

The philosophers most prominently associated with the principle-based paradigm in bioethics have been Robert Veatch,[59] Tom Beauchamp, James Childress,[60] H. Tristram Engelhardt, Jr.,[61] Albert Jonsen,[62] and Ruth Macklin.[63]

They used the principle of autonomy to develop a policy of informed consent, so that patients and subjects of research can control what is done to their bodies and minds. They employed the positive principle of beneficence to assess the goods to be pursued in carrying out the experiments, i.e. the benefits that may be realized by the persons being tested or by other in the future. They made use of the principle of non-maleficence (the principle of avoiding harms, which is part of the principle of beneficence) to develop reasons for controlling the impositions of risks. And they applied the principle of justice to such questions as the fair distribution of burdens to subjects of research (e.g., in not selecting racial minorities in a disproportionate way) and in distributing health-care benefits to the entire population, e.g., in an attempt to avoid objectionable discrimination against the poor.

The foundations of these rules are sources that are diverse and seemingly at odds with one another. The informed consent rule, based on autonomy, was ready-at-hand in the principles of informed consent that arose out of the Nuremberg trials, which had rendered a legal judgement on those who had been responsible for atrocities committed in the name of medical science during Germany's Nazi era.

Intellectually, justifications for the principles of bioethics have been argued in terms of various prominent traditions in Western moral philosophy. One such tradition is utilitarianism, which proposes an overriding principle of utility.[64] Based on the goal of maximizing the overall good or the greatest balance of value over disvalue, the principle of utility is used to construct risk-benefit equations, so as to make it possible to determine whether the benefits of a proposed research protocol or treatment outweigh the risks.

A second philosophical theory, neo-Kantianism, emphasizes rights and duties of persons as its starting-point, rather than consequences of actions. In this moral theory, which is derived from Immanuel Kant, the main ethical principle is individual autonomy, sometimes called the principle of respect for persons. Many of the rights spoken of in North American bioethics -- right to self-determination, to life, to health care, to confidentiality, etc. -- have been argued in a neo-Kantian way.[65] In a *contractual* model for bioethics, developed by Robert M. Veatch, the contractual agreement both assures and limits the rights and duties associated with norms of autonomy, justice, truth-telling, promise-keeping, etc.[66]

Some of the advantages of the principle-based approach in American bioethics are the following. It provides a methodical approach to problems that are inherently complex; it introduces clarity of thought to debates on topics that can be quite diffuse; it offers precision of language in a scientific world that places great value on precise objectivity; and above all, the principles have offered a common language in a pluralistic country that has become an ethical Tower of Babel.

8. The New Paradigm: Experience-Based Approach

In recent years, I have been pointing to a major shift of paradigms in bioethics. I call the "new" paradigm the *experience-based* (principle-based) paradigm.[67] It is arising, in part, because of the inadequacies of the principle-based approach to bioethics.[68]

A principal shortcoming of the principle-based approach is that, by emphasizing the abstract features of a universal ethic (such as universal rights, equality, dignity, etc.) it has excluded much of the particular moral experience of the moral agents involved, such as the experiences of bonding in parenthood, of friendship in professional life, of caring among women, etc. Furthermore, while rights have been an important tool in calling moral attention to the needs of disadvantaged groups, rights language can drive a wedge of adversarialism and alienation between physician and patient and between parent and child when this language is given too much importance. Finally, many people believe that neither physicians nor nurses nor people of any sort actually do much of their moral reasoning by thinking explicitly of principles. Consequently, in the United States, a deep distrust of "the tyranny of principles" in bioethics is becoming more widespread.[69]

In contrast with the principle-based paradigm, which uses deductive reasoning, the experience-based paradigm is more inductive in nature. Its starting point is not the question: What is our duty? but rather: What is going on around me? It looks first to moral perceptions, moral judgements, and moral behaviors; and it regards the task of bioethics as the task of interpreting what they are about. Consequently, it grants an important place to intuition and imagination; for example, it asks what are the images, the metaphors, and the stories that actually guide human decisions.

The inductive, interpretative approach to ethics is not entirely new in Western thought; but since the time of Plato it has always been a "minority view". The intellectual methods employed in it rely on phenomenology, ethical hermeneutics, and American Pragmatism. Because it entails a turn to the subjective, one of its task is to avoid excessive subjectivism. It does this by regarding the task of interpretation as one that relies on conversation in moral dialogue. One part of that dialogue is argument, when principles can be used to help negotiate differences in a pluralistic society. Thus, the new paradigm that takes moral experience more seriously is not that has replaced the previously dominant, principle-based paradigm. Most properly, bioethics involves both approaches.

Authors who were influential in laying the groundwork for the experiential paradigm included the theologians Stanley Hauerwas and William F. May. Stanley Hauerwas, a Protestant theologian, has been instrumental in introducing a new era in Christian ethics as well as in bioethics since the early 1970s.[70] Influenced by American philosopher Alaisdar MacIntyre,[71] Hauerwas strove to reinstate an ethic of character and virtue, which had long been neglected in both theological and philosophical thought. Insisting that we were simply asking the wrong questions in bioethics, Hauerwas proposed that, instead of asking what we ought to be doing (an ethic of duty), we ask what kind of persons we should become (an ethic of character and virtue). In this way, Hauerwas -- and other scholars as well[72] -- advocated a turn to the experience of what it means to be a moral agent in search of the practice of virtue as a basis for bioethics. They worked this out in reference to such questions as care of the mentally retarded, truthful communication, confidentiality, (abortion) and the authority of the physician.

Using an approach that would move bioethics even more decisively away from an orientation based exclusively in rules, theologian Willian F. May has explored the values embedded in our language and experience. He suggests that the task of ethics is, in significant part, to "correct our moral vision," and that our moral reasoning often uses metaphorical images to accomplish this. He works out, in considerable detail, the implications of such images as the physician as fighter, as parent, as teacher, and as one who enters into a covenant with the patient.[73]

Neither Hauerwas nor May were explicitly espousing the experiential paradigm to which they were in fact contributing. Other American bioethics authors who are deliberately pursuing the experience-based paradigm include Eric Cassell, Richard Zaner, Ronald Carson, Larry Churchill, Warren Reich, Caroline Whitbeck, and Mary Mahowald.[74]

Several themes of recent origine in American ethical scholarship are making major contributions to the experiential paradigm in bioethics. One is the rediscovery of the classical tradition of casuistry that flourished in 15th and 16th century Roman Catholic and Anglican moral theology. In an important, recent historical work on casuistry, Jonsen and Toulmin explain casuistry as the art of achieving the practical resolution of particular moral perplexities without reliance on major traditions of moral principles. Rather, casuistry represents a turn to what Aristotle calls *phronesis*, or practical wisdom. It relies on experience drawn from the history of similar cases, the development of maxims arising from and governing these particular judgements, and rethorical reasoning that argues by analogy.[75]

Since medicine is both learned and practiced through cases, a bioethical methodology that relies on paradigmatic cases is very useful in the world of medical ethics. Following the lead of Jonsen and Toulmin, some American authors are now more vigorously pursuing the implications of casuistry for bioethics.[76]

Another major influence on bioethics is the moral voice of women, feminist philosophy, and a philosophy of caring. One of the shortcomings of traditional, principle-based ethics is that it has not taken into account a sufficient number of moral voices. The voice that it has used has been principally the voice of the philosopher -- usually, the male philosopher. Now, conversation on morality in the human community is being carried on by individuals and groups with a variety of voices, many of them new; and among them are women speaking of women's experiences and the moral implications of their experiences.[77]

For example, research on the "moral development" and moral reasoning of women carried out by Carol Gilligan has shown that most women have a notion of morality that is different from most men. Women are more concerned with responsiveness to others, with relationships, and with attitude of caring. By contrast, men are inclined to see themselves in opposition to others; they sense the need to establish rules of fairness that will help adjudicate rights and duties. Briefly, women emphasize a "care perspective" in the context of relationships, whereas men emphasize a "justice perspective" in a world seen as adversarial.[78] More recently, Gilligan and some of her colleagues have indicated that they do not regard care as "belonging" solely to women; increasingly, they point to the importance of the care perspective in men.[79]

There is now interest in the United States in drawing out the implications of the an "ethic of care" for ethical theory generally,[80] and specifically for bioethics, including an ethic of nursing (based on the concept of care).[81]

The implications of an ethics of care in bioethics are nothing less than revolutionary, for they entail correcting the domination of bioethics by an exclusively masculine/rationalist orientation in moral reasoning. Research and reflection on care require that we make room for the moral reasoning that is more feminine in nature and that accord an important place to compassion and the sentiments that lead us into care for one another.

Conclusion

As we move now into a new era of bioethics, we find ourselves encountering a new set of moral problems. In the United States, those problems are: (1) genetics (especially genetic therapies and the mapping of the human genome); (2) health-care allocation (especially the dominance of commercialism in medicine, providing health care for the uninsured, and the prevention and treatment of poor physical and mental health caused by worldwide drug consumption); (3) AIDS as the new epidemic (issues of homophobia, refusing to give medical treatment, quarantine, etc.); and (4) environmental health (the victimization of all life by the negligent and abusive environmental activities of humans).

The major methodological challenges for the future are the following. First, we must enter more intensely into interdisciplinary studies, so that all the disciplines of the life sciences including bioethics can learn from one another. In particular, bioethics must continue to listen to *all* the voices that express genuine moral suffering, genuine moral perceptions, and genuine moral standards in particularized settings.

Both of the major paradigms for bioethics -- the principle-based and the experience-based paradigms -- have validity and usefulness. But the experiential paradigm is primary, for it provides the starting-point for all moral understanding. For it is in experience that we discover what the bioethical questions are; and it is in the human experience of coping with suffering that we can find the meaning that so many are searching for.

Bioethics must foster the pursuit of scholarship in both the interpretation of experience and the elaboration of moral principles. The scholarly work that is needed can be pursued along separate tracks; but bioethics also needs to bring the sensitivity of moral experience together with the rationality of principles. If it does this, it will repeat what it accomplished in the 1970s: it could again make a major contribution in changing the way people understand their moral nature and the moral tasks that face them.

ENDNOTES

1. For historical/sociological surveys of the history of bioethics in the United States, see David J. Rothman, "Human Experimentation and the Origins of Bioethics in the United States," in *Social Sciences Perspectives on Medical Ethics*, ed. George Weisz (Dordrecht, Netherlands: Kluwer, 1990), pp. 185-200; Renee C. Fox, "Ethical and Existential Developments in Contemporaneous American Medicine: Their Implications for Culture and Society" (first published in 1974), in *Essays in Medical Sociology* (New Brunswick, New Jersey: Transaction, 1988), pp. 381-412; Idem, "Advanced Medical Technology -- Social and Ethical Implications" (first published in 1976), in Ibid., pp. 413-461; and Idem, "The Evolution of American Bioethics: A Sociological Perspective," in *Social Science Perspectives on Medical Ethics* (Dordrecht, Netherlands: 1990), pp. 201-217. For a History of North American bioethics from the perspective of ethics scholars, see Albert R. Jonsen, Andrew L. Jameton and Abyann Lynch, "Medical Ethics, History of: North America in the Twentieth Century," in *Encyclopedia of Bioethics*, ed. Warren T. Reich (New York: Free Press, Macmillan, 1978), pp. 992-1004.

2. Robert M. Veatch, *Case Studies in Medical Ethics* (Cambridge, Massachusetts: harvard University, 1977), pp. 274-277.

3. Ruth Faden and Tom Beauchamp, *A History and Theory of Informed Consent* (New York: Oxford University Press, 1986), pp. 274-277.

4. Ruth Macklin, *Mortal Choices* (New York: Pantheon, 1987), p. 190.

5. Henry K. Beecher, "Ethics and Clinical Research," in *New England Journal of Medicine* 274 (1966): 1354-1360.

6. James H. Jones, *Bad Blood* (New York: Free Press, Macmillan 1981).

7. Ibid., pp. 171-187.

8. Ibid., pp. 171-187.

110

9. Samuel A. Cartwright, "Report on the Diseases and Physical Peculiarities of the Negro Race," 1851, quoted in Arthur Caplan, H. Tristram Engelhardt, Jr. and James McCartney, *Concepts of Health and Disease* (Addison-Wesley, 1981), pp. 305-325.

10. For a discussion of medical and biological argument that have been used to rationalize the inferior status of women and the dominance of reproduction in the role of women, see Carroll Smith-Rosenberg and Charles Rosenberg, "The Female Animal: Medical and Biological Views of Woman and their Role in Nineteenth-Century America," in Caplan, Engelhardt and MacCartney, *Concepts of Health and Disease*, pp. 281-303.

11. Paul Ramsey, *The Patient as Person: Explorations in Medical Ethics* (New Haven and London: Yale University, 1970), pp. 239-275.

12. Leroy Augenstein, *Come, Let Us Play God* (New York: Harper and Row, 1969); June Goodfield, *Playing God: Genetic Engineering and the Manipulation of Life* (New York: Random House, 1977).

13. Paul Ramsey, *Patient as Person*, pp. 255-259; idem, *Fabricated Man: The Ethics of Genetic Control* (New Haven and London: Yale University, 1970); and Andrew Varga, "'Playing God': The Ethics of Biotechnical Intervention," in *Thought* 60, (1985): 181-195.

14. Paul Ramsey, *Patient as Person*, pp. 255ff.; see also James F. Childress, "Who shall Live When Not All Can Live?" in *Soundings* 53, (1970): 339-355, reprinted in *Contemporary Issues in Bioethics* (Encino, California: Dickenson, 1978), pp. 389-398.

15. For early bioethical discussions of organ transplants, see "Cardiac Transplantation in Man," Statement Prepared by the Board of Medicine of the National Academy of Sciences, in *Journal of the American Medical Association* 204, 9 (May 27, 1968): 805-806; Guidelines of the American Medical Association, in *Journal of the American Medical Association* 207, 9 (March 3, 1969): 1704-1705; and Paul Ramsey, "A Caveat on Heart Transplants," in *Patient as Person*, pp. 216-238. For a review of the first three decades of the bioethics of organ transplants, see Richard J. Howard and John S. Najarian; Renee C. Fox; and Richard A. McCormick, "Organ Transplantation," in *Encyclopedia of Bioethics*, ed. Warren T. Reich (New York: Free Press, Macmillan, 1978), pp. 1160-1173.

16. New Jersey Supreme Court, "In the Matter of Karen Quinlan, An Alleged Incompetent," 70 *New Jersey Report* 10 (Decided March 31, 1976) reprinted in *Contemporary Issues in Bioethics*, ed. Tom L. Beauchamp and Leroy Walters, pp. 337-346. For the first major survey of these issues, see Sissela Bok,

"Death and Dying: Euthanasia and Sustaining Life: Ethical Views" and Robert M. Veatch, "Death and Dying: Euthanasia and Sustaining Life: Professional and Public Policies," in *Encyclopedia of Bioethics*, ed. Warren T. Reich (New York: Free Press, Macmillan, 1978), pp. 261-286.

17. Van Rensselaer Potter, *Bioethics: Bridge to the Future* (Englewood Cliff, New Jersey: Prentice Hall, 1971), p. 2.

18. The Institute is now called the "Kennedy Institute of Ethics".

19. Warren T. Reich, "Introduction," *Encyclopedia of Bioethics* (New York: Macmillan Free Press, 1978), p. xix.

20. Parts of this explanation of the scope of bioethics are taken from Warren T. Reich, "Introduction," *Encyclopedia of Bioethics* (New York: Macmillan, Free Press, 1978), p. xix.

21. For an explanation of the historical and philosophical aspects of the relationship between law and morality in American bioethics, see Baruch Brody, "Law and Morality," *Encyclopedia of Bioethics*, ed. Warren T. Reich (New York, Free Press, Macmillan, 1978), pp. 817-822.

22. See Ruth Faden and Tom L. Beauchamp, *A History and Theory of Informed Consent*, pp. 96-98, 213-226, for a discussion of the activities of various federal bioethics commissions.

23. American Medical Association, "Code of Ethics" (1847), *Encyclopedia of Bioethics*, ed. Warren T. Reich, pp. 1738-1746.

24. American Medical Association, Council on Ethical and Judicial Affairs, "Principles of Medical Ethics," *Current Opinion* (Chicago: American Medical Association, 1989), p. ix.

25. For further information on the development of medical ethics teaching, see Robert M. Veatch, "Medical Ethics Education," in *Encyclopedia of Bioethics*, ed. Warren T. Reich (New York: Macmillan, Free Press, 1978), pp. 870-876; The Commission on the Teaching of Bioethics, *The Teaching of Bioethics* (Hustings-on-Hudson, New York: Institute of Society, Ethics and the Life Sciences, 1976); Edmund D. Pellegrino and Thomas K. McElhinney, *Teaching Ethics, the Humanities, and Human Values in Medical Schools: A ten-Year Overview* (Washington, D.C.: Society for Health and Human Values, 1982); John Ivey Boufford and Ronald A. Carson, eds., *The Teaching of Humanities and Human Values in Primary Care Residency Training: Resource Book* (McLean, Virginia: Society for Health and Human Values, 1984); Charles M. Culver et al.,

"Basic Curricular Goals in Medical Ethics," in *New England Journal of Medicine* 312, (1985): 253-256.

26. For detailed reports, see: Robert M. Veatch, "National Survey of the Teaching of Medical Ethics in Medical Schools," in *The Teaching of Medical Ethics*, ed. Robert M. Veatch, Willard Gaylin and Councilman Morgan (Hastings-on-Hudson, New York: Hastings Center, 1973), pp. 97-102; and Robert M. Veatch and Sharmon Sollitto, "Medical Ethics Teaching: Report of a National Medical School Survey," in *Journal of the American Medical Association* 235, 10 (March 8, 1976), 1030-1033. See also note 25 above.

27. See Edmund D. Pellegrino and Thomas K. McElhinney, *Teaching Ethics, the Humanities, and Human Values in Medical Schools: A Ten-Year Overview* (Washington, D.C.: Society of Health and Human Values, 1982). See also Thomas K. McElhinney, ed., *Human Values. Teaching Programs for Health Professionals* (Ardmore, Pennsylvania: Whitemore, 1981).

28. Association of American Medical Colleges, *Physicians for the Twenty-First Century.* Report on the General Professional Education of the Physician and College Preparation for Medicine, in *Journal of Medical Education* 59: Part 2, November, 1984.

29. Association of American Medical Colleges, *Functions and Structure of a Medical School.* Standards for Accreditation of Medical Education Programs Leading to the M.D. Degree (Washington, D.C.: Association of American Medical Colleges, 1985).

30. Veatch and Sollitto, "Medical Ethics Teaching", p. 1031.

31. See note 27 above.

32. Society for Health and Human Values, 6728 Old McLean Village Drive, McLean, VA 22101. For a list of additional organizations, centers, and institutes, both in the United States and in other countries, see the *International Directory of Bioethics Organizations*, National Reference Center for Bioethics Literature, Georgetown University, Washington, D.C., 20007.

33. Robert Hunt and John Arras, eds., *Ethical Issues in Modern Medicine* (Palo Alto, California: Mayfield, 1977); Robert M. Veatch, *A Theory of Medical Ethics* (New York: Basic Books, 1981); Tom L. Beauchamp and James F. Childress, *Principles of Biomedical Ethics*, 2nd ed. (New York: Oxford University Press, 1983); Frank Harron, John Burnside and Tom Beauchamp, *Health and Human Values: A Guide to Making Your Own Decisions* (New Haven, Connecticut: Yale University Press, 1983); Tom L. Beauchamp and Laurence B. McCullough, *Medical Ethics: The Moral Responsibility of Physicians* (Englewood

Cliffs, N.J.: Prentice-Hall, 1984); Thomas A. Mappes and Jane S. Zembaty, eds., *Biomedical Ethics*, 2nd ed. (New York: McGraw-Hill, 1986); H. Tristram Engelhardt, Jr., *The Foundations of Bioethics* (New York: Oxford University Press, 1986); Carol Levine, *Taking Sides: Clashing Views on Controversial Bioethics Issues*, 2nd ed. (Guilford, Connecticut: Dushkin, 1987); Ruth Macklin, *Mortal Choices: Bioethics in Today's World* (New York: Pantheon, 1987); Rem B. Edwards and Glenn C. Graber, eds., *Bioethics* (San Diego: Harcourt Brace Jovanovich, 1988); and Tom L. Beauchamp and Leroy Walters, eds., *Contemporary Issues in Bioethics*, 3rd ed. (Belmont, California: Wadsworth, 1989).

34. Howard Brody, *Ethical Decisions in Medicine*, 2nd ed. (Boston: Little, Brown 1981); Edmund D. Pellegrino and David C. Thomasma, *A Philosophical Basis of Medical Practice: Toward a Philosophy and Ethic of the Healing Professions* (New York: Oxford University Press, 1981); Natalie Abrams and Michael D. Buckner, eds., *Medical Ethics: A Clinical Textbook and Reference for the Health Care Professions* (Cambridge, Massachusetts: MIT Press, 1983); Glenn C. Graber, Alfred D. Beasley and John A. Eaddy, *Ethical Analysis of Clinical Medicine: A Guide to Self-Evaluation* (Baltimore, Maryland: Urban & Schwarzenberg, 1985); Albert R. Jonsen, Mark Siegler and William J. Winslade, *Clinical Ethics: A Practical Approach to Ethical Decisions in Clinical Medicine*, 2nd ed. (New York: Macmillan, 1986); Baruch A. Brody and Tristram Engelhardt, Jr., eds., *Bioethics: Readings and Cases* (Englewood Cliffs, N.J.: Prentice-Hall, 1987); and Baruch A. Brody, *Life and Death Decision Making* (New York: Oxford University Press, 1988).

35. Paul Ramsey, *The Patient as Person: Explorations in Medical Ethics* (New Haven, Connecticut: Yale University Press, 1970); Benedict M. Ashley and Kevin D. O'Rourke, *Health Care Ethics: A Theological Analysis*, 2nd ed. (St. Louis, Missouri: Catholic Health Association of the United States, 1982); David M. Feldman and Fred Rosner, eds., *Compendium on Medical Ethics: Jewish Moral, Ethics and Religious Principles in Medical Ethics*, 6th ed. (New York: Federation of Jewish Philanthropies of New York, 1984); Richard A. McCormick, *How Brave a New World?* (Washington, D.C.: Georgetown University Press, 1986); and Earl E. Shelp, ed., *Theology and Bioethics: Exploring the Foundations and Frontiers* (Hingham, Massachusetts: Kluwer Academic, 1985).

36. Judith Areen et al., eds., *Law, Science and Medicine* (Mineola, New York: Foundation Press, 1984; 1987 Supplement also available); Gregory E. Pence, *Classic Cases in Medical Ethics: Accounts of the Cases That Have Shaped Medical Ethics, with Philosophical, Legal, and Historical Backgrounds* (New York: McGraw-Hill, 1990).

37. Warren T. Reich, ed., *Encyclopedia of Bioethics*, 4 vols. (New York: Free Press, Macmillan, 1978).

38. *Syllabus Exchange Catalog*, obtainable from the Bioethics Literature, Georgetown University, Washington, D.C. 20007. The Catalog is an international collection of syllabi from universities and health centers.

39. Up-to-date resources include: *Basic Resources in Bioethics* (National Reference Center for Bioethics Literature, Kennedy Institute of Ethics, Georgetown University, Washington, D.C. 20007). Most recently published in 1988, it is updated periodically. See also: Leroy Walters and Tamar Joy Kahn, eds., *Bibliography of Bioethics* (Washington, D.C.: Kennedy Institute of Ethics, Georgetown University; issued annually since 1975).

40. *Bioethicsline*. Produced by the Kennedy Institute of Ethics for the National Library of Medicine; searchable through the MEDLARS system.

41. Nadya Shmavonian, compil., *Human Values in Medicine and Health Care: Audio-Visual Resources* (Philadelphia: United Ministries in Education, 1983); and Pat Milmoe McCarrick, compil. and ed., *Bioethics Audiovisuals: 1982 to Present* (Washington, D.C.: National Reference Center for Bioethics Literature, Kennedy Institute of Ethics, Georgetown University, 1988).

42. Numerous journals in a variety of disciplines publish important articles dealing with bioethics. The following are some of the more important journals dealing specially with the field of bioethics: *American Journal of Law and Medicine*; *Bioethics*; *Hastings Center Report*; *IRB: Review of Human Subjects Research*; *Issues in Law and Medicine*; *Journal of Health Politics, Policy and Law*; *Journal of Medical Ethics*; *Journal of Medical Humanities and Bioethics*; *Journal of Medicine and Philosophy*; *Law, Medicine and Health Care*; *Medical Humanities Review*; *Second Opinion*; and *Theoretical Medicine*.

43. *BioLaw* (Frederick, Md.: University Publications of America, 1983 to present; annual with bimonthly updates offering legal documents and articles; previous title: *Bioethics Reporter*); and two series published by the National Reference Center for Bioethics Literature, Kennedy Institute of Ethics, Georgetown University, Washington, D.C.: *New Titles in Bioethics* (list of library acquisitions published monthly since 1975); and *Scope Notes Series* (an occasional series of abstracts and annotated bibliographies on popular bioethical topics).

44. Karen Teel, "The Physician's Dilemma: A Doctor's View: What the Law Should Be," in *Baylor Law Review* 27, (1975): 6-9.

45. See note 16 above.

46. *Ethical Currents*, a newsletter, and *Health Progress*, a journal, cover topics of interest to hospital ethics committees in Catholic hospitals. The *Hastings Center Report* biannually publishes a special section on ethics committees. *Hospital Ethics* reports on court decisions and ethical literature pertinent to hospital committees. Another journal is *Hospital Ethics Committees (HEC) Forum: An Interdisciplinary Journal on Hospitals' Ethical and Legal Issues*.

47. Ronald E. Cranford and A. Edward Doudera, *Institutional Ethics Committees and Health Care Decision Making* (Ann Arbor, MI: Health Administration Press, 1984; Margaret Kelly and Donald McCarthy, *Ethics Committees: A Challenge for Catholic Health Care* (St. Louis, MO: Catholic Health Association of the United States, 1984); etc.

48. Leroy Walters, "Religion and the Renaissance of Medical Ethics in the United States: 1965-1975," in *Theology and Bioethics*, ed. Earl E. Shelp (Dordrecht: Reidel, 1985), pp. 3-16.

49. See the works cited above.

50. Charles E. Curran, *Contemporary Problems in Moral Theology* (Notre Dame, Indiana: Fides, 1970); *Transition and Tradition in Moral Theology* (Notre Dame, Indiana: University of Notre Dame, 1979); *Critical Concerns in Moral Theology* (Notre Dame, Indiana: University of Notre Dame, 1984).

51. Richard A. McCormick, *How Brave A New World? Dilemmas in Bioethics* (Washington, D.C.: Georgetown University Press, 1981).

52. Karen Lebacqz, ed., *Genetics, Ethics and Parenthood* (New York: Pilgrim, 1983); *Professional Ethics: Power and Paradox* (Neshville: Abingdon, 1985); *Six Theories of Justice: Perspectives from Philosophical and Theological Ethics* (Minneapolis: Augsburg, 1986).

53. Joseph Fletcher, *Morals and Medicine* (Princeton, New Jersey: Princeton University, 1954); *Situation Ethics* (Philadelphia: Westminster, 1966); *The Ethics of Genetic Control* (Garden City, New York: Anchor, 1974).

54. The three most significant presenters of the halakhic tradition were Immanuel Jakobovits, *Jewish Medical Ethics: A Comparative and Historical Study of the Jewish Religious Attitude to Medicine and its Practice* (New York: Bloch, 1959; rev. ed., 1975); Fred Rosner, *Modern Medicine and Jewish Law* (New York: Yeshiva, 1972); and David M. Feldman, *Birth Control in Jewish Law* (New York: New York University), 1968.

116

55. Stephen Toulmin, "How Medicine Saved the Life of ethics," in *Perspectives in Biology and Medicine* 25, 4, (1982): 48-62.

56. Daniel Callahan, "Religion and the Secularization of Bioethics," in *Hastings Center Report*, A special Supplement (July/August, 1990): 2-4.

57. Christopher Boorse, "On the Distinction Between Disease and Illness," in *Philosophy and Public Affairs* 5, (1975): 49-68; and Arthur Caplan, H. Tristram Engelhardt, Jr. and James J. McCartney, *Concepts of Health and Disease*, cited above. See also the series, *Philosophy and Medicine*, ed. H. Tristram Engelhardt and Stuart Spicker (Dordrecht and Boston: Reidel [now Kluwer] 1975 to present).

58. The National Commission for the Protection of Human Subjects of Biomedical and Behavioral Research, *The Belmont Report: Ethical Guidelines for the Protection of Human Subjects of Research*, DHEW Publication No. (OS) 78-0012 (1978).

59. Robert M. Veatch, *A Theory of Medical Ethics*.

60. Tom L. Beauchamp and James F. Childress, *Principles of Biomedical Ethics*, 3rd ed., cited above.

61. H. Tristram Engelhardt, Jr., *The Foundations of Bioethics* (New York: Oxford University, 1986).

62. Albert R. Jonsen, Mark Siegler, and William J. Winslade, *Clinical Ethics: A Practical Approach to Ethical Decisions in Clinical Medicine*, 2nd ed. (New York: Macmillan, 1986).

63. Ruth Macklin, *Mortal Choices: Bioethics in Today's World*.

64. See R. M. Hare, "Ethics: Utilitarianism," in *Encyclopedia of Bioethics*, ed. Warren T. Reich (New York: Free Press, Macmillan, 1978), pp. 424-429.

65. See H. Tristram Engelhardt, Jr., *Foundations of Bioethics*.

66. See Robert M. Veatch, *A Theory of Medical Ethics*.

67. Warren T. Reich, "Experiential Ethics as a Foundation for Dialogue Between Health Communication and Health-Care Ethics," in *Journal of Applied Communication Research* 16, (1988): 16-28.

68. For a recent critique of the traditional intellectual underpinnings of bioethics, see "Philosophical critique of Bioethics," K. Danner Clouser and Loretta M. Kopelman, eds., *The Journal of Medicine and Philosophy* 15, (1990).

69. Stephen Toulmin, "The Tyranny of Principles," in *Hastings Center Report*, (December, 1981): 31-39.

70. Stanley Hauerwas, *Vision and Virtue* (Notre Dame, Indiana: Fides, 1974); *Truthfulness and Tragedy: Further Investigations into Christian Ethics*, with Richard Bondi and David B. Burrell (Notre Dame, Indiana: University of Notre Dame, 1977); *A Community of Character: Toward a Constructive Christian Social Ethics* (Notre Dame, Indiana: University of Notre Dame, 1981); and *Suffering Presence: Theological Reflections on Medicine, the Mentally Handicapped and the Church* (Notre Dame, Indiana: Notre Dame University, 1986).

71. Alaisdar C. MacIntyre, *After Virtue: A Study in Moral Theory* (Notre Dame, Indiana: University of Notre Dame, 1984).

72. Gilbert C. Meilaender, *The Theory and Practice of Virtue* (Notre Dame, Indiana: University of Notre Dame, 1984); Earl E. Shelp, ed., *Virtue and Medicine* (Boston: D. Reidel, 1985); and James F. Drane, *Becoming a Good Doctor: The Place of Virtue and Character in Medical Ethics* (Kansas City, Missouri: Sheed & Ward, 1988).

73. William F. May, *The Physician's Covenant: Images of the Healer in Medical Ethics* (Philadelphia: Westminster, 1983).

74. See Warren T. Reich, ed., *Experience as Source of Bioethics* (forthcoming).

75. Albert R. Jonsen and Stephen Toulmin, *The Abuse of Casuistry: A History of Casuistry* (Berkeley, California: University of California, 1988).

76. Barry Hoffmaster, Benjamin Freedman and Gwen Fraser, eds., *Clinical Ethics: Theory and Practice* (Clifton, New Jersey: Humana, 1989).

77. See, for examples, Susan Sherwin, "Feminist and Medical Ethics: Two Different Approaches to Contextual Ethics," *Hypatia* 4, (1989): 57-72.

78. Carol Gilligan, *In a Different Voice: Psychological Theory and Women's Development* (Cambridge, MA: Harvard University, 1982).

79. Linda Kerber et al., "On *In a Different Voice*: An Interdisciplinary

Forum," in *Signs: Journal of Woman in Culture and Society* 11, 2, (1986): 304-333.

80. Eva Feder Kittay and Diana T. Meyers, eds., *Women and Moral Theory* (Totowa, New Jersey: Rowman and Littlefield, 1987).

81. It is interesting that a small but significant literature on an ethic of care in health care preceded the important Gilligan studies. Anne H. Bishop and John R. Scudder, Jr., eds., *Caring, Curing, Coping: Nurse, Physician, Patient Relationships* (University, Alabama: University of Alabama, 1985); Barbara A. Carper, "The Ethics of Caring," in *Advances in Nursing Science* 1, 3, (1979): 11-19; Anne P. Griffin, "A Philosophical Analysis of Caring in Nursing," in *Journal of Advanced Nursing* 8, 4, (1983): 289-295; and Sara T. Fry, "The Role of Caring in a Theory of Nursing Ethics," in *Hypatia* 4, 2, (1989): 88-103.

Chapter 3

ORIENTATIONS AND TENDENCIES OF BIOETHICS
IN THE FRENCH-SPEAKING WORLD

Jean-Francois Malherbe

To my knowledge, the French term "Bioéthique" appeared for the first time in 1973, when *Revue théologique de Louvain* published an article by Edouard Boné entitled "La Préoccupation bioétique dans les pays anglo-saxons." [1] Yet, thanks to David Roy, the first French-speaking Bioethics Center [2] was created in Montréal during the second half of the seventies. The center, and its publication of *Cahiers de bioéthique*, [3] made a remarkable contribution to spread the concept of bioethics in French-speaking countries.

In 1983, the Catholic University of Louvain formed a Center of Bioethical Studies in Bruxelles which was the first center of French language in Europe. [4] By the end of the eighties, those centers had multiplied in Lille, Lyon, Paris, Bruxelles, Québec, Genève, and Strasbourg. [5] Such a list is the sign that "French- speaking bioethics" goes well beyond the limits of France. Moreover, it cannot be reduced to a Parisian phenomenon, even if the most important centers are located there. From Québec to Switzerland, going through Belgium's French community and the French regions of the Ile-de-France, Nord-Pas-de-Calais, Lyonnais and Alsace, all the French-speaking countries north of the Mediterranean are interested in the bioethical phenomenon. Neither the medical ethics guidelines of the Swiss Academy of Medical Sciences, [6] nor the beautiful volume of Marie-Hélène Parizeau[7] recently published by Laval University of Québec, will contradict the above statement.

A unity of place, time, and language characterizes French-speaking bioethics. Is it possible to identify other common characteristics? I think it is, especially for two specific reasons: *i.e.*, a particular model of relating to the legal system on one hand, and to the medical profession on the other. "Anglosaxon bioethics" has been developing in a context defined by a system of "common law" which is structured on the basis of an inductive method. Here, ethical and legal considerations are intermingled in the solution of issues raised at the level of medical suits. Our legal system, on the other hand, is structured on the model of the "Roman Law" which is deductive. Although relating to one another, ethics and law don't get confused. Roman (or French) law is bound, on one hand, to protect the ethical values of citizens, and on the other, to preside over the application of the law through the tribunals. Therefore, the ethical concern precedes and follows the law, but it does not contaminate it. In the "Roman Law" system, ethics and law are articulated through the mediation of the legislative process. But, in the "Common Law" system much more defined by jurisprudence, tribunals are less dependent upon the decisions of the central power.

Such a distinction could appear only formal, yet it carries out a particular sociological distinction within bioethics operators. In fact, while in the "Common Law" system those involved in the field of bioethics are essentially lawyers and physicians, in the "Roman Law" system the proportion is inverted in favor of philosophers and theologians. In the English linguistic region, bioethics is more legal than ethical, whereas in the French region, it is more ethical than legal. For this reason, bioethics cannot be developed in the future without close relation to the practice of philosophy. All these remarks will become more understandable through the development of this paper which I conceive in three parts: the first two are more encyclopedic -- yet rendered lighter thanks to the endnotes -- and the third more reflective, where I try to define different styles in "doing bioethics".

It would be foolish to describe the field covered by fifteen years of French bioethical literature even with the support of electronic means. Such a bibliography is, in any case, available.[8] I thought it would be more interesting to try to structure the field of inquiry with some points of reference, and to convey my intentions through examples. Although these points of reference and examples are carefully chosen, I cannot pretend an absolute objectivity. My own position inevitably interferes with the reconstruction of the field. Indeed, some sort of arbitrariness is difficult to avoid, and it could be negated only at the cost of academic mystification.

Having said this, it seems important to distinguish between *problems*, *topics*, and *styles*.

By *problems*, I mean the web of interferences of the field of bioethics with other scientific sectors. Through the presentation of the problems involved, French bioethics will emerge in its typical interdisciplinary character defined by natural and human sciences, as well as theological, philosophical, and political disciplines.

Topics refer to the different issues with which French-speaking bioethicists have been dealing and which still fuel their discussions. These topics are genetics, artificial procreation techniques, organ transplant, neurologic and psychiatric sciences, AIDS, experimentation with human subjects, ethics committees, and, finally, death, futile care, aggressive treatment, and euthanasia.

By *styles*, I mean different ways of "doing bioethics," the different styles of reflection which take up the name bioethics. It is necessary to make a choice among them in order to be coherent with the scientific goals of bioethics. In the final part of my lecture, I will attempt to make such a discernment.

1. Problems

French bioethics is difficult to understand without taking into consideration some major works which, at first sight, appear to belong to other disciplines.

1.1. Natural Sciences

In order to understand the positivistic mentality of French medicine, it is necessary to study seriously the work of the physiologist Claude Bernard, *Introduction à l'étude de la Médecine expérimentale*.[9] Since 1865, this book has been defining the great methodological principles -- still in effect thanks to Karl Popper, who rejuvenated them -- within French scientific and medical research.

On the other hand, more recent works of eminent researchers such as François Jacob, Jacques Monod, Henri Laborit, Albert Jacquard, Jean-Pierre Changeaux, Henri Atlan, André Pichot, and Jacques Testart[10] aim -- each in its own way -- at providing a different kind of epistemological foundation for medical and scientific research; that is to say, one which is less positivist and more open to interdisciplinary work confronting the history of science and mythological as well as religious and philosophical thought. Indeed, today, the field of bioethics is structured upon the tension between an "old" and a "modern" approach. According to some physicians, medical deontology and even legal medicine can provide sufficient resources for coping with new emerging issues. Others, however, feel the need for a completely new revision of the relation between the human being and his/her body, the natural environment, and cultural environment. The latter calls for a revision of those relations where a new approach of medicine to health is involved.

1.2. Human Sciences

Natural sciences are not the only sciences to interfere with bioethical problems. Indeed, the debate in bioethics has been defined by the contribution of human sciences as well. I am referring in particular to law, psychoanalisis, and sociology. With the exception of the human and citizens' rights,[11] the work of legal scholars on bioethical issues are not numerous, yet they are of very high quality. I am referring, in particular, to the remarkable work of Jean-Louis Baudoin and Caterine Labrusse-Riou, *Produire l'homme, de quel droit?*[12] This legal study on artificial procreation shows the necessity for biomedical progress and juridical tradition to interrogate each other in order to garantee the institutional character of the relation between parents and child within society. The human being has to remain, primarily, the subject of rights, even when he/she becomes the object of technological manipulation.

In the field of psychoanalysis, the clinical studies of Genevieve Delaisi de Parceval on sperm donors and artificial insemination should be mentioned.[13] These studies clearly prove that the sperm does not constitute -- as reductive biology claims -- the essential aspect of paternity, but rather a system of social relations whose concrete features vary according to culture. Yet, it has not been the suffering[14] connected with the reality of sterility alone which has drawn the attention of the disciples of Freud and Lacan. Denis Vasse, for instance, has tried to illustrate -- on the basis of a rigorous clinical practice -- the complexity of conscious-unconscious relations between physicians and patients as part of the negation of suffering. Indeed, one of the contributions of psychoanalysis to bioethics is the fact that since the body is human only in virtue of suffering, the communication of such suffering implies -- in the healer as well as in the healed -- the transition from an alteration of the body to an alteration of the relation.

In sociology, the contributions of François Isambert and his team[15] have drawn attention -- together with the already classic works of Edgar Morin[16] -- to death and life. They have greatly contributed to the opposition to the "posivistic trend" toward those realities.[17] The essential merit of sociology of ethics -- which remains at the level of a factual description of social values and which, therefore, should not be confused with ethics itself -- has been to make clear the classical distinction in philosophy between morals and morality. The former deals with what people think is the right thing to do, whereas the latter with what a particular cultural tradition prescribes. The historical and social reality of this distinction underscores the urgency of a thoroughly critical reflection on the relation between social facts and moral norms. Indeed, only a sheer positivism would deem useless any ethical reflection which does not reduce moral criteria to a pure compliance with current standards.

1.3. Religious Doctrines

French-speaking bioethics -- with the exception of Quebec -- is profoundly influenced by the Magisterium of the Catholic Church.

Everyone's position is, therefore, defined by its relation to the Catholic Magisterium. As a matter of fact, some of the positivistic convinctions are meant to be anticlerical in essence. The result of such a situation is the following: the partial polarization of the field of bioethics because of the religious question risks overlooking the core of the problem at stake -- that is to say, the debate on the human being and the society.

Three different currents of thought can be distinguished among French-speaking theologians involved in the field of bioethics field. First are those committed to the Catholic doctrine, and who are "more Catholic than the Pope". Second are those ready to compromise and to provide means of a more subtle or nuanced interpretation. Third is that group involved in pastoral work, whose concern is to be with and guide believers in their problems and hesitations.

The first group is taken seriously only within restricted circles. However, some journalists inclined to scandalism and division rather than truth, have given this group a lot of publicity. As a result, they have triggered an aggressive and yet unjustified anticlericalism within the scientific community. The third group is formed by people whose voice is not heard in scientific discussions. Nontheless, their patient and tenacious work deeply contributes to the moral education of our fellow citizens. The second group is, finally, the most interesting from the point of view of scientific bioethics. The purpose of these theologians is to promote -- by means of a critical and systematic reflection -- a sensitivity toward those anthropological and ethical values which have shaped the great western spiritual tradition.

Apart from our own personal creed, it is impossible to be indifferent toward the treasure of humanity and ethical experience enshrined in this tradition. To this current of thought belong Catholics such as Guy Durand in Québec,[18] Xavier Thévenot, Paul Valadier, and Patrick Verspieren in France,[19] as well as the Calvinist Eric Fuchs in Switzerland.[20]

1.4. Philosophies

There are not many philosophers involved in the field of bioethics. Still, bioethics is considered to be a minor genus of applied ethics. However, some of the contemporary French philosophers have brilliantly contributed to the field by identifying it as an eminent context for philosophical speculation. Michel Foucault, in particular, has shown the historical dimension of medical outlook in *Naissance de la clinique*.[21] Paul Ricoeur has deeply marked the question of the foundation of bioethics with his research on the relation of anthropology and ethics as well as with his meditation on the relation between technology and politics.[22] His work on the life of language and hermeneutics are also noteworthy.[23] Emanuel Lévinas' philosophy of alterity -- particularly in his incomparable *Totalité et infini* -- defines, once and for all, the impassable limit to the subjugation of others.[24] Jean Ladrière has structured with rigor the relation between modern science, critical philosophy, and Christian faith on the basis of a philosophy of language and interpretation.[25] In 1975, Ivan Illich denounced the fact that individuals were severed from their health by those institutions which were supposed to cultivate it.[26] With *Istitution immaginaire de la sociétè*, Corneille Castoriadis has shown -- thanks to the definition of the autonomy of human subjects -- the relevance of psychic, social, and political dimensions in the interpretation of great historical phenomena of our technological society.[27] François Laplantine's research on the different aspects of sickness and health has renewed the philosophical approach to the normal and the pathological as it was framed by Georges Canghuilhelm in 1966.[28] With his philosophy of technology, Gerbert Hottois continues to question the signs with which our technological society conceals or manifests itself.[29]

Such a list is certainly not exhaustive. Indeed, it was not meant to be. Its purpose is simply to elucidate the importance which the philosophical foundation has for French bioethics. Perhaps philosophy underlines my education and my interests as well. Indeed, philosophy is precisely the rigorous discipline which calls us to give an account of our options and opinions. Without philosophy, there is no bioethics worthy of its name, *i.e.*, worthy of the human beings bioethics has to serve.

1.5. Political Sciences

Finally, in political science, Luc Ferry, Jean-Marie Ferry, and Alain Renaut have fostered discussions on the "communicative ethics" of Jürgen Habermas.[30] In French bioethics field, they have provoked the awareness -- which I deem essential -- that bioethics can do its job in a pluralistic society only on the basis of a method for the discussion of problems. The function of such a method is to regulate the imperatives of democracy, professional activities, and the research on the human qualities of life in society. I think the "communicative ethics" of Jürgen Habermas can offer a decisive contribution to the field of bioethics as it is witnessed by the work of the French national committee of ethics on life and health sciences. Lucien Séve has explained in detail the proceeding of the committee in a remarkable booklet,[31] to which I will turn in the third part of my paper.

2. Topics

French bioethics is defined by the polarizations mentioned above and by a certain number of issues which I shall enumerate without any pretension of being exhaustive.

As for other languages, French bioethics is fractured in different areas of which it is possible to delineate only some salient features.

2.1. Genetic Manipulation

The issue of "genetic manipulation" is at same time very old and fairly recent. The expression "genetic manipulation" can be understood in two different ways: in general terms, it designates the manipulation of the process of procreation; more stricly, it designates the recombination of desossiribonucleic acyd (DNA) aiming at modifying the genetic code of a cell and, eventually, its derivatives. In his *Carnets d'un biologiste*,[32] Jean Rostand had already foreseen that genetics would offer the greatest opportunities to manipulate and transform the human being. Yet, the question of whether such practices are acceptable is not new. It is precisely with a seminar on "Ethics and Genetics"[33] that the Center of Bioethical Studies got started in 1982-83, before its formal institutionalization. The seminar ended with a reflection on the "autopoiesis" of the human being. The human being cannot be self-made from every point of view, *i.e.*, scientific, moral, and social. Yet, the fact that the human being -- according to the famous expression of Vercors -- is an "un-natural animal"[34] triggers the question of the end of his/her creativity. It seems reasonable to admit the capacity of the human being to transform him/herself, provided that this transformation is prevented from making the human being doubly "un-natural" and, thus, incapable of making itself.

The question of how to set limits within the practical context of new technologies had been left pending at every monthly meeting only to be retrieved in numerous occasions later on, as was the case with the colloquim "Genetics, Procreation, and Law," organized in Paris in January 1985.[35] From that moment on, the issue of genetic manipulation has been the object of many in-depth studies and discussions, and even more with the emergence of another related issue, *i.e.*, genetic screening. Recently, François Gros has been successful in making an inventory of the techniques available as well as of the problems raised by their application.[36] Regardless of the ultimate outcome, the issue of genetic manipulation will be the object of numerous and lively discussions. This issue will simultaneously force the question of the human "nature" to the forefront. This last theme is related to the ecological problem and with the question of the economic consequences of the production of these methods of transformation on industrial scale.

2.2. Artificial Procreation Techniques

The whole concern of bioethics is often reduced by those who are ill-informed to the problem of artificial procreative techniques. Most of the couples in Western countries today -- once they are ready to pay the financial and psychological price involved -- can avoid having children when they don't want them; or they can have them when they want; or, finally, they can have the kind of children they want. There are many diverging opinions on this issue, more so than on the issue of genetic manipulation. For those who think of conjugal bonds as sacred, it is inconceivable for a baby to be born but *from* and *within* marriage.[37] For others, medicine cannot substitute for the moral judgments of clients; instead, it has to use all available means to answer to their desires for procreation.[38] The variety of opinions between these two extremes is remarkable: there are those Catholics, faithful to the positions of the Magisterium, who try at the same time to be as open as possible;[39] there are those Catholics who disagree, and yet remain Catholic;[40] there is the so called "pluralistic" approach of the French national committee on ethics;[41] there is a moratorium for some researchers,[42] *etc*. Independent of the evaluation of these positions, the debate has drawn attention to the ineluctable character of some radical questions, for instance: Is there something like a "right to have a child"? And, is there a right of the child to be born in a family? The other question which emerges from both ethics and law, together with the aforementioned two fundamental questions, concerns the meaning given to the presence of a child in the life of individuals, couples, and society as a whole.

Do we consider the child as a subject in itself, *i.e.*, as the other, whose presence is something to wish and in which to rejoice? Or, is the child like an object, *i.e.*, a consumer product which is disposable in some way, to be accepted or refused. Finally, is a child to be welcomed in his/her own terms, or are we to select that child according to our wishes?

2.3. Prenatal Diagnosis and Abortion

The abortion issue, together with prenatal diagnosis, depend on the question of the anthropological status of human embryo. Nobody thinks it legitimate to oppress a human being, yet not every one agrees on when the life of the human being begins. Without entering into detail, two sharply divided points of view can be schematically distinguished. The first point of view -- which I would qualify as "phenomenological" -- maintains that the human embryo is biologically, but not morally, human, unless it is envisaged by other human beings as a possible life-project.[43] On the other hand, according to the point of view which I would define "ontological," the human embryo is similar to us, even when it does not express all its potentialities.[44] For this reason, all other human beings are bound to accept and protect the embryo regardless of their attitude toward it.

In contradistinction to what happens in the case of euthanasia, the dialogue between the two points of view mentioned above seems very difficult. One of the factors which, in my opinion, motivates the rigidity of the antagonism is the intolerance of some religious positions (canon law prescribes excommunication for anyone who commits an abortion or cooperates with it in some ways). Scientific attitudes are also condemned which hold that an early embryo is just biological material that can be manipulated, not unlike the product of a biopsy. Thanks to the media, such extreme positions often receive all the attention, thus leaving in the dark the slow and patient work of those who try to accompany and sustain the moral choice of people passing through truly difficult situations.[45]

Nevertheless, the issue of the anthropological status of the embryo takes us back to the same question underlying the issue of assisted procreation, *i.e.*, what is the child to us, subject or object? It seems that the technological and commercial advances in our society increasingly lead us to consider the Other more as an object than a subject. This is a sociological fact. It is important to note, however, that a publicly shared opinion does not immediately constitute an ethical justification. At this level, a deeper critical reflection seems necessary.

2.4. Organ Transplantation

The third important issue is defined by the cluster of ethical questions related with the practice of organ transplantion. Publications on this issue are still few in the French literature. The volume entitled *L'homme greffé*, edited by Jean Hamburger, should be called to mind.[46]

Such scarcity seems to be motivated by different reasons. First is the fact that most of the surgeons consider this practice not particularly problematic in the absence of "technical" contra-indications. Second is the difficulty -- given the hopefully temporary absence of a plausible clinical alternative -- of discussing in depth the thorny question of brain death as a death criterium *tout court*. Third is the incompatibility of our desire to survive at any cost and the repugnance we feel toward the idea of giving away our organs. The principle governing the decision to remove and transplant organs is the so called "opting out" principle, *i.e.*, the citizens not in favor must express their position. Consequently, the difficult issue, whether the citizen's corpse belongs to the family or to society, is never faced. Moreover, the promulgation of laws has not alleviated the scarcity of donors; insteac, it has called into question the democratic character of these laws. Indeed, a social problem cannot be resolved by playing on citizens' ignorance. Here, we have a ground of bioethical research difficult to delineate, and yet, in the long run, very interesting.

2.5. Neurosciences

Neurosciences and psychiatry are not the same thing, yet they are related by the same very question which André Pichot has tried to disentangle with remarkable analytical rigor,[47] *i.e.*, could behaviour, emotional life, and mind in the human being be reduced to the functioning of its nervous system and its brain? Jean-Pierre Changeaux's *L'homme neuronale*[48] frames the problem in its acuteness. The author's positions have not convinced everyone. However, it is difficult to question his success in readdressing the classical, yet never entirely resolved, philosophical problem of the relation between soul and body, between mind and nervous system.

2.6. Psychiatry

Different types of psychotherapy and behavioral therapy constitute a problem. Yet, while some question their scientific character,[49] others declare their existential effectiveness.[50] Moreover, the methods involved in psychiatric research are the object of a deep discussion. See, for instance, Anne Fagot-Largeault's rigorous and well documented study, *L'homme bioethique.*[51]

2.7. AIDS Epidemic

Bioethical reflection has produced different types of literature on the issue of AIDS. The most numerous of them are certainly works which explain the nature of the disease and stress the importance of global preventive measures.[52] It is more difficult to find essays dealing with psychological, sociological, and political implications of the disease. Among those essays, two publications should be mentioned: Emmanuel Hirsch's *Le SIDA: Rumeurs et faits*[53] and Eric Conan's *Le SIDA dans l'espace public.*[54] The latter, published by the periodical *Esprit*, is a remarkable analysis on the public and/or private character of the disease. The ethical reflection is almost nonexistent. The rare studies in this field simply mention some fundamental principles of medical deontology or analize briefly juridical and institutional consequences of the epidemic. The AIDS issue does not fail to raise some ethical questions in the strict sense, *i.e.*, screening and consent, information and confidentiality, therapy and aggressive treatment, *etc.* The solution to these problems is relegated -- in the absence of a deep critical reflection -- to the internal policy of the hospitals and other health care institutions. I will return on the ethical and anthropological dimensions of AIDS in the third part of the paper. Indeed, beyond the paradoxical character of warning commercials -- with their message of prevention, on one hand, and the highly erotic character of our affluent society, on the other -- what remains to be considered is the anthropological dimension of the epidemic, thee mortal virus of which can be trasmitted through those very acts intended to express and to celebrate life.

2.8. Experimentation with Human Subjects

Medical Academies began reflecting upon ethically acceptable conditions for experimentation with human subjects long before the 1947 Nuremberg trials of Nazi criminals. Claire Ambroselli has traced the history of this process of reflection.[55] Yet, the Nuremberg trials played a special role in sensitizing public opinion on the issue of experimentation with human subjects. Why is such an issue so difficult? Jean Bernard, President of the "French National Committee for the Ethics of Life and Health Sciences," has answered this question with a statement which is both brilliant and pertinent. Experimentation involving human subjects, he says, is "morally necessary while being at the same time necessarily immoral!" What does all this mean?

Scientific experimentation is morally necessary in a society which entrusts public health to scientific medicine. The alternative would be the restoration of magic and witchcraft. On the other hand, experimentation is immoral because it treats being, defined essentially as the subject of a personal destiny, as an object of research. Is such a "bracketing of the human element"[56] morally acceptable when the end of the procedure is precisely to serve humanity? Is there not here a particularly perverse contradiction between means and ends?

Before the Nuremberg trial, specialists had tried to define a middle way. They insisted that the human subject who clearly accepted to be part of a research protocol consented to an operation which would make him, for a moment, an object. The request was taken up again by the Nuremberg Code[57] as well as the Helsinki Declaration of the World Medical Association in 1964, revised in Tokyo in 1975.[58]

French literature on the issue of informed consent is essentially made by specialists in medical deontology, medical law,[59] or by official institutions in charge of defining ethical guidelines for scientific research in the medical field.[60]

General studies on the topic are still few. Among them: the fouth number of *Cahiers de Bioéthique* published by the Bioethics Center of David Roy in 1982,[61] *L'homme bioéthique* of Anne Fagot-Largeault,[62] and the article of Michel Lacroix in the January 1987 issue of *Esprit*.[63] Indeed, only a global point of view could justify, at the same time, the necessity of informed consent and some limitations imposed upon it when the advantages of experimentation are proportionally balanced.[64] On the other hand, it is precisely one of the functions of ethics committees to verify the proportion between risks and benefits in experimentation with human subjects, the quality of their consent, and the scientific validity of the protocol which provides for their involvement.[65]

2.9. Ethics Committees

The issue of ethical committees is the object of a wide literature.[66] In order to clarify the debate on ethics committees, it is indispensable to distinguish their different functions. Ethics committees have four functions whose institutional character varies from one region to the other. It seems appropriate to enumerate and define these four functions without entering into a sociological analysis. First, ethical committees have a *consulting* role, *i.e.*, they provide projects of bills and professional regulations in the area of bioethics. For example, the Counsel for Medical Research in Canada[67] accomplishes this function. Yet, not only it is necessary to provide guidelines, but also to make them operative. Therefore, the second function of ethics committees is *to ascertain* that the Helsinki-Tokyo Declarations on scientific and medical research with human subjects are respected. Most ethics committees in university hospitals accomplish this surveillance function. In other situations, it has been deemed necessary to extend the competence of ethics committees so as *to make* the hospital *more humane*. Indeed, many aspects of the hospital's life -- and not only in the case of experimentation -- run the risk of treating patients as objects rather than as subjects. Therefore, it is necessary to watch over the risks involved in the hospital's organization. Finally, the case of physicians who wish *to consult* a restricted committee before making particular difficult choices with their patients is increasingly frequent. In this case, ethics committees have the function of "helping to make a clinical decision." In sum, the four forms of ethics committees are: study groups financed by public powers or professional institutions, committees of surveillance on the matter of experimentation and humanization of the hospital, and assistance groups for making clinical decisions. In some cases, ethics committees have two, threee, or even four of these functions together. My job here is not to express my judgement on concrete institutional configurations, but simply to mention their existence.

2.10. Aggressive Treatment and Euthanasia

The last among the major issues in French bioethics is, in my opinion, the issue of death together with all the questions related to it, *i.e.*, aggressive treatment, euthanasia, palliative care, *etc.* All the authors involved in debates on this issue agree in repudiating aggressive treatment, yet it has not disappeared from our hospitals. Some, in agreement with Léon Schwartzenberg, see euthanasia as the only possible alternative to aggressive treatment.[68] Others, together with Elisabeth Kubler-Ross and her disciples in Québec and Europe,[69] maintain that assistance to dying patients constitutes an alternative to aggressive treatment.

The dialogue on euthanasia and assisted death, unlike the dialogue on the anthropological status of the human embryo, is a fruitful confrontation between points of view only apparently alternative to each other. Three remarkable factors contribute to this situation. First, a quality assistance to dying patients is in many cases inconceivable without pain therapy. Although the medical community seems to still discourage such a non-healing therapy, the importance of providing medical assistance to dying patients is deemed important by a growing number of physicians dealing with the problem. Second, the position of Catholic religious authorities on the issue of the end of life seems more nuanced and applicable than in the case of issues concerning the beginning of life.[70] Finally, contrary to the what the founders of the Association for the Right to Die with Dignity have hoped, the idea of a living will -- although, in itself, generous -- has met many difficulties of application.[71]

In moral terms, the situation could be portrayed in the following way: active and direct euthanasia is refused by all the authors with the exception of those who consider this form of euthanasia like a *minus malum* in extremely dramatic cases. Passive euthanasia is also refused by all the authors when there is the possibility of acting with respect toward the human dignity of the dying person. Everybody agrees on active but indirect euthanasia, even those who refuse the distinction between direct and indirect euthanasia. Therefore in the end, the practice of palliative care, including pain therapy and assistance to dying patients can reconcile the different points of view in the debate. Yet, great changes in the mind set of the community still have to be made in order to make this type of care common. Nontheless, at a theoretical level, the issue of euthanasia seems to have found a philosophically sound answer with the consensus of a large majority.

3. Styles

French bioethics constitutes an interdisciplinary field structured according to different polarities, *i.e.*, natural sciences, human sciences, religion, philosophy, and political sciences. At the same time, the field is defined by the discussion on the issues we have been considering above. The approach to these is characterized by different styles which I will attempt to describe in a critical manner.

My point of view -- although not shared by everyone -- is that the term bioethics covers different approaches which -- by ignoring its conditions of possibility -- do not properly fit the definition of bioethics. I will rapidly list these different styles before proceding to the description of their character.

3.1. Doing Bioethics

"To do bioethics" means trying to clarify the issues at stake in problematic situations raised by biomedical advances, and to offer -- on the basis of such clarifications -- to the decision making process solutions which are as human as possible.

If this is the case, then the practice of bioethics has to integrate three essential dimensions of moral judgement, *i.e.*, the *situations* which constitute the problem, the *principles* to be respected, and above all the moral *conscience* of the persons involved in these difficult situations. When one of these three element is neglected the very root of bioethical questions is left out of consideration. Indeed, the so called bioethical production presents this negligence. Here are some examples.

3.2. Three Perversions of Bioethics

The *first* perversion of bioethics consists in neglecting the character of problematic situations. In other words, failing to recognize that the legitimate claim to universality of moral choices -- indeed, the singular decision of each human being somehow engages the whole humanity -- has particular features each time. It is possible to mistreat the human being (concrete) in the name of respect for Humanity (generic). This kind of perversion in bioethics can be found especially in the writings of so called "traditionalist" authors. Recently I had the chance to thoroughly criticize one of these writings. In *Union et procréation*, Alain Mattheeuws states that, presently, the teaching of Catholic Magisterium on artificial procreation relies upon a constant and unchanged tradition.[72] Yet, even if such a theological thesis can be proved, we have not made any progress in discerning what are the issues at stake in particular situations. The repetition of traditional principles is never enough in bioethics.

The *second* perversion of bioethics does not consist in neglecting the singular character of problematic situations, but rather in stressing this character to the point of ignoring the claim to universality which is a constitutive element of ethical research. The fact that a certain aspect of humanity is at stake in every human decision is given up in the name of respect for the singularity of concrete situations. This kind of perversion of bioethics can be found in authors whom I believe definitely qualify as "situationists." Unfortunately, this literature, which easily gives up the constitutive claim of ethics to universality, is rather frequent in bioethics. For example, the *gray literature* favored by Nicole Léry[73] deals exclusively with cases without ever attempting to give an account of opinions, scale of values, and presuppositions underlying the solutions proposed. Another feature of the same perversion -- and one which is also very diffuse -- is the reduction of bioethics to a pure list of data provided by human sciences. No mention is given, for example, of the reasons why a particular statistic about a particular behaviour is elevated to the rank of a moral norm.

The *third* perversion of bioethics consists in the use of a double language, that is to say, repeating in public traditional principles while yielding in private to the exceptions of a compassionate heart. Such an attitude -- typical of both clerical and medical paternalism -- is even more perverse because it denies the interlocutor an informed and enlightened moral conscience which can be taken

138

into account. In these cases, one's judgment is imposed upon another, together with the consequences of the suggested decision. Fortunately, such an attitude today is almost always unmasked by the majority of bioethics' disciples.

Having enumerated these "perversions," there remains to be considered the different forms of bioethical work which contribute to the global purpose. The analysis of three examples will allow me to clarify my position.

3.3. The Political Style

As I mentioned briefly in the first part of the article while talking about the political aspect of bioethics, it is essential to identify the feautures of a real "consensus", and the conditions for creating it.

Two opposite positions can be found. The first tries to create an agreement on a particular formulation which conceals some imprecisions, and therefore can be interpreted in different ways. I would characterize this position as "the politics of a least common denominator." The agreement reached in these cases is purely fictitious. Such empty rhetoric will be completely useless as soon as formulae are confronted with concrete reality. Take, as an example, recent debates on abortion in Belgium: in the absence of a real philosophical debate, a law has been promulgated the formulation of which the majority of senators and deputies agree. Yet, it is feared that interpretations will be various and contradictory.[74]

The second position consists in looking for a consensus "at the top", rather than "at the bottom", i.e., looking for the greatest, rather than the least common denominator. This is a more difficult task. It presupposes a dedication to dialogue and reflection. Yet, the "French National Committe for the Ethics of Life and Health Sciences" had the courage to adopt such a method.

An interesting booklet written by Lucien Séve, and published by the Committe with the title *Biomedical research and respect for human person*, testifies that the fruits of this work are worthy of the difficulties it has met.[75] Let me quote entirely a particularly significant passage of this document entitled

"Ascendent lines concerning the respect for the human being": "There are two possible attitudes toward insoluble contradictions, that is, two conceptions of the lesser evil, and two ways of conceiving the "case by case". The one consists in despairing of good, cursing progress, damning science, thus reducing the ambitions of biomedical ethics to the proportions of a pragmatic and disenchanted deontology. That is not our attitude. We prefer to trust in the duty toward humanity, in the benefits of knowledge, and in the possibility of harmonizing them in a better way."

Certainly, it would be pure utopia to hope that, one day, science, technology, society, and human being will be free from contradictions. On this very point, all our philosophies provide the same reason even if they start from different perspectives. Yet, searching attentively for something which could be modified in each of these contradictions, and perhaps, overcome is not yearning for utopia. This is what biomedical research does when it tries to freeze human ova, for example. This process cannot be achieved without sacrificing some embryos thus creating an ethical problem which some of us totally deplore. Therefore, a completely new situation is sought where artificial procreation can avoid freezing and storing embryos. Not all the doubts raised by artificial techniques of procreation will be thereby solved, yet it would be possible at least, to put an end to some deplorable facts.

While recognizing the right to a differt opinion, our committee has largely agreed in allowing this kind of research. In this case, the lesser evil is not a remedy without perspective, but rather, a significant step toward something better. Here the end does not justify the means. We don't agree with the maxim of an act without principle where the means disqualify the end. Rather, we deny the right to produce an embryo *in vitro* for the sake of research in the same way in which we deny the right to mistreat a person "for the good of future humanity." Indeed, which humanity could be grounded on the contempt for the individual?

However, respect for the person implies the appreciation of the possible benefits of research for the good of all. The example mentioned above illustrates the following question: is not our solution an attempt to solve tomorrow the insoluble contradiction of today? Our way of proceding traces as much as possible, and in every field the ascendent lines of respect for the human being without exception. Indeed, it is not enough to conscientiously denounce what offends the human being. It is necessary to do everything possible so that the human being won't be offended any more. More than an instance of moral consultation behind the scenes of biomedicine, bioethics can become an active center of public morality in the life of society.[76]

The search for a consensus in a pluralistic society honors not only those involved in it, but also humanity itself because such a process envisions and anticipates a different society. This style of bioethical work is authentic without necessarily being the only valid one. It is not the French Committee alone which works in this way. In Canada, for example, the Commission for the reform of law and the Counsel of medical research have published guidelines and recommendations in line with the same methodology.[77]

3.4. The Philosophical Style

Philosophers, in my opinion, have a particular responsibility in the field of bioethics. Indeed, citizens with different *Weltanschauungen* can promote a dialogue in view of a better consensus only by giving an account of their philosophical options. Yet, explaining one's options to others, proposing sound justifications, and distinguishing the essential from the accidental elements of one's philosophy presupposes a deep knowledge of cultural heritage and historical tradition. On this very point "professional" philosophers are requested more than on any other issue of bioethical reflection.

As a consequence of an interdisciplinary seminar of the staff of our center for bioethical research, Sergio Zorrilla and I have confronted each other on the issue of AIDS. Our work together -- still unfinished -- has produced a volume with the title *Le citoyen, le médecine et la SIDA*.[78] What are the avenues which this work has uncovered?

At first sight, it may seem that an epidemic does not imply many philosophical questions, yet this is not true. In the case of an epidemic whose virus is deadly -- at least at present -- and which is transmitted especially through acts meant to give, or at least, to celebrate life, death and life have become tragically intertwined. Thus, the human being has to face one of the most difficult questions of his/her existence, *i.e.*, what is the meaning of relational life? What is the meaning of sexual expression in relational life? What is the meaning of sexual desire? Faced with these radical and old questions, we turn to our predecessors in order to confront our own experience with theirs. Yet, even within one homogeneous cultural tradition, predecessors are legion. The role of philosophers, therefore, is to mediate the questions of their fellows with that of the tradition to which they belong. One task of philosophers will be to try to grasp the essence of human relations as the source and ground of ethical claims, and to establish this foundation as the reference point for any discussion on the issue of AIDS.

Such a task is not the only one awaiting philosophers. The need is to order all the phenomena characterizing our historical situation, beginning with those elements which the AIDS crisis has highlighted, in order to relate them, once again, to the ethics handed down by our tradition.

The situation is in many aspects paradoxical. The paradox can be seen in the contradiction between the anti-panic logic underlying public discourse on AIDS on one hand, and the great fear among those who have had a direct experience of people with the disease on the other. Ultimately, our ability to cope with chaos is here in question. Indeed, every institution within society is defined by its relation to chaos, *i.e.*, by means of a particular mechanism which the socially integrated individual assimilates -- more or less well -- and usually in an unconscious way. Our society today tries to overcome chaos by trusting technical rationality. Thus, science and technology promote an effective activity which confronts the power of chaos. Seduced by the effectiveness of technical rationality, our society has come to the point of practicing a "metaphysics without regression" -- that is to say, securing control over chaos through scientific "discursive universe".

But, far from being removed, chaos is simply displaced. By advancing within the horizon of technology, society gradually loses any perception of the meaning of technology, and it rejects present chaos by denying it. Through scientific research, the future is endowed with the ability to solve problems whose actuality remains unrecognized. In this way, science and technology contribute to disguising chaos. Therefore, even if terrorized by the spread of the epidemic, our society is not inclined to understand the reality of people with the HIV virus.

Another feature of the same paradox is the medical discourse which pretends to ground AIDS prevention on the use of the condom. Yet, in a concrete relation, this type of prevention does not seem to work that easily. Any discourse on prevention cannot really be heard when contrasted by another anti-panic discourse which strenghtens our resistances toward questioning the way we relate to sexuality. Indeed, prevention presupposes the ability of individuals to understand sexual behaviour and to consciously modify it in light of a rational perception of risks and threats.

Publicity, in turn, contributes to encourage the kind of behavior which a correct analysis of AIDS would rather modify. It should be noted also, that television leaves the individual in an indecisive situation by means of contradictory messages. If, on one hand, condom advertisements say "you are threatened," erotic publicity, on the other, reassures the individual to "have fun without fear".

Ultimately, the emphasis on prevention is not really perceived because it questions something untouchable, *i.e.*, our image as owners of our body, managers of our private life, lords of our intimacy. The AIDS epidemic is seen as a menace to the progress of individual freedom, and yet, it paradoxically favors a complete detachment of organic sexuality from any existential intentionality.

These are some of the paradoxical traits of a situation which calls us to retrieve some elements of our traditional ethics of relation. How to proceed in that? In spite of the interest it creates, the question cannot be taken up in this context. My goal is simply to explain the validity and the need of a philosophical "style" of doing bioethics, and its different components are not always clear to all "bioethicists."

3.5. The Religious Style

The need for citizens to engage in dialogue in view of a public consensus, or for philosophers to confront the situation of today's society with its ethical tradition, seems clear enough. On the other hand, the inflation of religious discourse on ethics poses the question of its legitimacy in the field of bioethics. The analysis of a third "style" of bioethical work will give us the opportunity to specify the exact position of religious arguments in bioethics.

When, in a public debate, somebody says "life is God's gift; therefore, it has to be protected against abortion and euthanasia," he says something true, yet he does not add anything to the debate. A religious argument based on God's revelation is, indeed, very important for the believer. However, it is not valid in a pluralistic debate where others may not share the same conviction that humanity's life derives its meaning from its relationship with God.

We may say to someone who does not believe in God that human life has to be respected from the beginning, that from that moment on there is a being who is in relation with God, that God loves him/her.... The non-believer may answer, "So what?"

In my opinion, the context of an argument based on religious faith is communication among believers. These arguments help believers in framing their vision of God, the world, the other, and themselves. The right context for a religious argument is also an open dialogue between believers of different religions, or between believers and non-believers. In these cases the end sought is to understand each other, and the presupposition is that everyone explains his/her beliefs in the best possible way. It may be useful to society that believers explain to those who do not share their beliefs how faith represents a coherent vision of human destiny, a deep promotion of humanity, and how it could contribute to bioethical debate.

The periodicals *Laennec*[79] and *Études*[80] -- many articles on bioethics, and especially those by Patrick Verspieren -- are two remarkable examples of this style of bioethical discourse. It will be noted that a well formulated religious argument not only helps the believer to understand better the reasons of his/her faith, but also contributes to make others understand the validity of a believers' point of view.

Such a critical attitude shared by many Christian theologians and philosophers is rooted in an act of faith. Yet, it is justified not only by philosophical method, but also by Christian faith which deems even the most critical exercise of philosophy a necessity. According to the Christian belief God creator of the universe is also creator of the critical and technical intelligence of human being. "Critical" etimologically means "related to choice". Critics separate what cannot be mixed. Being critical means, therefore, trying to have clear ideas. "Technical," on the other hand, means "art," "manner," concerning what is "manual," that is, the *savoir faire*. Christians consider both critical and technical intelligence as gifts of God the Creator. God gives intelligence to human beings. Christians believe also that God reveals Himself in Jesus Christ. Moreover, since God is the One who cannot deceive nor be deceived, what God communicates of Himself in His revelation does not contradict what He allows human beings to discover with the authentic exercise of critical intelligence. The problem consists in defining the "authentic" use of intelligence. But this is also the work of human intelligence, *i.e.*, to discover in the human being what is more human.

Who, among the Christians, could pretend to have understood completely the whole revelation in a transparent, clear, and definitive way? Even granted that the revelation is completed with the death of the last apostle, could we maintain that its meaning has been completely exhausted? On the other hand, who could claim an absolute authenticity in the use of critical intelligence? Said in another way, any discrepancy -- which could be seen, and is frequently seen -- between what Christians understand of the revelation and what they understand through the human exercise of their critical intelligence shows that something has not been understood correctly. Yet, this fact does not mean *a priori* that the revelation has to take over critical intelligence. It may well signify a misinterpretation of this or that element of revelation as well as the lack of authentic critical sense in the process of understanding.

Faith in God the Creator goes to the point of saying -- at least at an eschatological level -- that there is no possible contradiction between what can be understood with the exercise of intelligence only, and what can be understood through revelation. I deem these methodological observations on the religious "style" of bioethical work necessary, because it is not always easy to understand under which conditions this particular style can have a place in bioethics.

In conclusion, French-speaking literature is characterized by an interdisciplinary approach which includes the natural sciences, human sciences, religious doctrines, philosophy, and political sciences.

It is also characterized by an interest in some particular issues, ten of which I have mentioned.

Finally, it is characterized by a variety of styles of bioethical work. I deemed necessary to make a choice among the arguments on the basis of the interests which can be found in bioethics. The variety of styles is not exclusive of French language. Yet, it is so significant that I had to dedicate to it at least a third of my paper.

To sum up, I would like to return on the basic contributions of my survey. What underlines the "political" style is the will to create a possible consensus within a given society. Characteristic of the "philosophical" style is the attempt to retrieve -- in a particular situation which is critically analyzed -- the tradition of which the philosopher is part. What characterizes the "religious" style is the conviction that faith -- when expressed in a way which allows communication -- can bring into the debate an enlightening and enriching perspective.

The political question consists in knowing the agreement upon which we can live together. The philosophical question consists in knowing what progress brings to us and how such progress challenges human beings. The religious question consists in knowing how to live one's faith in a society which does not share it any longer.

Different prices have to be paid. The political price is to opt for a maximum, rather than for a minimum, consensus. The philosophical price is to distinguish between the essential and the accidental elements of cultural tradition. The religious price is to recognize that what is prescribed in the name of God can be proved as such also in the name of man.

Ultimately, these are the conditions for a constructive dialogue in bioethics.

ENDNOTES

1. E. Boné, "La préoccupation bioétique dans les pays anglo-saxons," *Revue Théologique de Louvain* (1973): 340-356.

2. Centre de Bioéthique de l'Institut de Researches Cliniques de Montréal, 110 Avenue des Pins, ouest, Montréal, Québec, H2W 1R7, Canada.

3. "La bioéthique," Cahiers de Bioéthique 1 (Québec: Les Presses de L'Université Laval, 1979); "Le diagnostic prénatale," *Cahiers de Bioéthique* 2 (Québec: Les Presses de l'Université Laval, 1979); "Médecine et adolescence," *Cahiers de Bioéthique* 3 (Quebec: Les Presses de l'Université Laval, 1980); "Médecine et expérimentation," *Cahiers de Bioéthique* 4 (Québec: Les Presses de l'Université Laval, 1982).

4. The first center in Europe was created in Spain: Centro Borja de Bioética, Llaseres 30, Sant Cugat (Barcellona), E.

5. Together with the Center of Bioethical studies of Bruxelles which I direct: Laboratoire de Médecine Légale, Département Éthique et Santé, Faculté de Médecine, 8 avenue Rockefeller, 69008 Lyon, F; Inserm - Centre de Documentation et d'information d'éthique des sciences de la vie et de la santé, 101 rue de Tolbiac, 76564 Paris Cedex 13, F; Centre d'Éthique Médicale, Facultés Catholique de Lille, 60 boulevard Vauban, 59046 Lille Cedex, F; Département d'Éthique Biomédicale du Centre Sévres, 12 rue d'Assas, 75006 Paris, F; Comité d'Éthique des Facultés et du Centre Hospitalier Régional de Strasbourg, 4 rue Kirschleger, 67085 Strasbourg Cedex, F; Commission d'Éthique de l'Académie suisse des Sciences Médicales, Peterplatz 13, 4051 Basel, CH; Centre de Bioéthique, Université Catholique de Lyon, 25 rue du Plat, 69288 Lyon Cedex 02, F; Centre de Recherches Interdisciplinaire en Bioéthique, Institut de Philosophie ULB, avenue Adolphe Buyl 143, 1050 Bruxelles, B.

6. Directives médico-éthique de l'Académie Suisse des Sciences Médicale, in particular: "La personne âgée dans un foyer", in *Directives médico-*

éthique pour le traitement de la stérilité par fécondation in Vitro et transfer d'embryons, Peterplatz 13, 4051 Bâle, CH.

7. M. H. Parizeau, "Bilan et prospective de la recherche en Bioéthique au Quebec," in *Bioéthique, méthodes et fondaments* [Les Cahiers Scientifiques de l'Association canadienne-francaise pour l'avancement des sciences] 66, (1989): 245-251. Very interesting is also the beautiful synthesis on origins, currents, and method of today reflection on transmission and respect for life G. Durand, *La bioéthique* (Paris: Cerf-Fides, 1989).

8. Service de Documentation du Centre d'Études Bioéthique, Promenade de l'Alma 51/4534, 1200 Bruxelles, B.

9. C. Bernard, *Introduction à l'étude de la médicine experimentale* (Paris: Flammarion, 1984).

10. H. Atlan, L'organisation biologique et la théorie de l'information (Paris: Herman, 1972); H. Atlan, *A tort et à raison: intercritique de la science et du mythe* (Paris: Ed. du Seuil, 1986); P. Changeaux, *L'homme neuronal* (Paris: Fayard, 1986); A. Jacquard, *Inventer l'homme* (Bruxelles: Ed. Complexe, 1984); H. Laborit, *L'inhibition de l'action* (Paris: Masson, 1981); J. Monod, *Le hasard et la nécessité. Essai sur la philosophie naturelle de la biologie moderne* (Paria: Ed. du Seuil, 1970); A. Pichot, *Eleménts pour une théorie de la biologie* (Paris: Maloine, 1980); J. Testart, *L'oeuf transparent* (Paris: Flammarion, 1986).

11. J. Morange, La déclaration des droits de l'homme et du citoyen (Paris: PUF, 1988); *Ethique médicale et droits de l'homme* (Paris: Actes Sud et Inserm, 1988); Centre Universitaire de recherches administratives et politiques de Picardie, *Bioéthique et droit* (Paris: PUF, 1988).

12. L. L. Baudoin and R. C. Labrusse, Produire l'homme: de quel droit? (Paris: PUF, 1987). See also Notes et études documentaires, *De l'éthique au droit* (Paris: La documentation française, 1988); P. Verspieren, "L'expérimentation sur l'homme: analyse d'une loi," *Etudes*, no. 6 (1989): 763-775.

13. G. Delaise de Parceval, *La part du pére* (Paris: Ed. du Seuil, 1981).

14. D. Vasse, *Le poids du réel, la souffrance* (Paris: Ed. du Seuil, 1984).

15. Centre de Sociologie de l'Éthique, École de Hautes Études en Sciences Sociales, 54 boulevard Raspail, 75006 Paris, F.

16. E. Morin, *L'homme et la mort* (Paris: Ed. du Seuil, 1970); *La vie de la vie* (Paris: Ed du Seuil, 1980).

17. Among the most important contributions are: F.A. Isambert and G. Terrenoire, *Éthique de sciences de la vie et de la santé* (Paris: La Documentation française, 1987); "L'amniocentése et les medecins: le diagnostic prénatal des malformations congénitales," *Éthique et pratiques symboliques* 1, (1980), at 171; F.A. Isambert, "La bioéthique à travers ses éscrits," *Revue de métaphysique et de morale* 3, (1987); "Le consentement: le point de vue d'une éthique rationelle," *Médecine et hygiéne* 44, (1986): 2021-2023; "Naissance de la bioéthique aux Etat-Unis," *Prospective et santé* 31, (1984): 63-70.

18. G. Durand, *Sexualité et foi* (Québec: La Corporation des Editions Fides, 1977).

19. X. Thévenot, *Repéres éthiques* (Mulhouse: Ed. Salvator, 1982); *La Bioéthique* (Paris: Le Centurion, 1989); P. Valadier, *L'Eglise en procés* (Paris: Calmann-Lévy, 1987); P. Verspieren, *Face à celui qui meurt* (Paris: Desclée de Brouwer, 1985).

20. E. Fuchs, *Le desir et la tendresse* (Genéve: Labor et Fides, 1984).

21. M. Foucault, *Naissance de la clinique* (Paris: PUF, 1963).

22. P. Ricoer, *Du texte à l'action: essais d'hermeneutique* (Paris: Ed. du Seuil, 1986).

23. P. Ricoeur, *La métaphore vive* (Paris: Ed. du Seuil, 1975); *Temps et récits*, 2 vols. (Paris: Ed. du Seuil, 1985).

24. E. Lévinas, *Totalité et infini. Essai sur l'esteriorité* (La Haye: Martinus Nijhoff, 1968).

25. J. Ladriére, *Les enjeux de la rationalité* (Paris: Aubier/Unesco, 1977); *L'articulation du sens: discours scientifique de la foi* vol. 1 (Paris: Ed. du Cerf, 1984); *L'articulation du sens: les languages de la foi* vol. 2 (Paris: Ed. du Cerf, 1984).

26. I. Illich, *Némésis médicale: l'expropriation de la santé* (Paris: Ed. du Seuil, 1975).

27. C. Castoriadis, *L'Institution imaginaire de la societé* (Paris: Ed du Seuil, 1975).

28. F. Laplantine, *Anthropologie de la maladie* (Paris: Payot, 1986); G. Canguilhem, *Le normal et le pathologique* (Paris: PUF, 1966).

29. G. Hottois, *Le signe et la technique* (Paris: Aubier, 1984).

150

30. J. Habermas, *Théorie de l'agir communicationnel: rationalité de l'agir et rationalisation de la societé* vol. 1 (Paris: Fayard, 1987); *Théorie de l'agire communicationnel: pour une critique de la raison fonctionnaliste* vol. 2 (Paris: Fayard, 1987); J. M. Ferry, *Habermas: l'éthique de la communication* (Paris: PUF, 1987); L. Ferry, *Philosophie politique. Le droit: la nouvelle querelle des anciens et de modernes* vol. 1 (Paris: PUF, 1984); *Philosophie politique. Le systéme des philosophies de l'histoire* vol. 2 (Paris: PUF, 1984); L. Ferry and A. Renaut, *Philosophie politique. Des droit de l'homme à l'idée républicaine* vol. 3 (Paris: PUF, 1985).

31. Comité consultatif national d'éthique pour les sciences dela vie et de la santé, *Recherche biomédicale et respect de la personne humaine* (Paris: La documentation française, 1988).

32. J. Rostand, *Carnets d'un biologiste* (Paris: Stock, 1959).

33. *Ethique et génétique* (texts collected by J. F. Malherbe) (Louvain-la-Neuve: Cabay, 1983).

34. Vercos, "Les animaux dénaturés," in *Le livre de poche* (Paris: Éditions diverses), pp. 210-211.

35. *Génétique, procréation et droit* (Paris: Actes Sud, 1985).

36. F. Gros, *L'ingénierie du vivante* (Paris: Ed. Odile Jacob, 1990).

37. Congregation pour la doctrine de la foi, *Le don de la vie humaine naissante et la dignité de la procreation* (Paris: Ed. du Cerf, 1987); J. M. Hennaux, "L'Instruction Donum Vitae," *Vie consacrée* 3, (1987): 1-4.

38. See Dr. F. Leroy's paper presented at the symposium *La bioéthique dans les années '90*. The symposium took place at Anvers on May 21-22, 1987: *La bioéthique dans les années 90* (Gand: Omega editions, 1988).

39. Institut Catholique de Lyon, *Le statut de l'embryon humaine* (Lyon, May 15-16, 1987, Coll. de Recherche en bioéthique).

40. E. Boné and J. F. Malherbe, *Engendrés par la science* (Paris: Ed. du Cerf, 1985); E. Loumaye and J. F. Malherbe, "Éthique et clinique de la fécondation in vitro" *Louvain Médicale*, (1988); C. Lefevre, *Maître de la vie* (Paris: Le Centurion, 1987); H. Wattiaux, *Génétique et fécondité humaines* (Louvain-la-Neuve: Publications de la Faculté de théologie catholique, 1986).

41. Comité consultatif national d'éthique pour les sciences de la vie et la santé, *Éhique et recherche biomédicale* (Paris: La documentation française, 1987).

42. J. Testart, "La fécondation," *La Recherche* 213, (1989): 1008-1019.

43. See Dr. F. Leroy's paper in note 38.

44. Fédération Internationale des Universités Catholiques, *Débuts biologiques de la vie humaine. Des chercheurs chrétiens s'interrogent* [Coll. Catalyses] (Louvain-la-Neuve: Ciaco, 1988), in particular the paper of J. F. Malherbe, "Le statut personnel de l'embryon humain. Essai philosophique", pp. 103-119; Comité consultatif national d'éthique, *Avis de recherches sur l'embryon* (Paris: Actes de sud/Inserm, 1987).

45. C. Bruaire, *Une éthique pour la médecine* (Paris: Fayard, 1978); J. F. Malherbe, *Pour une éthique de la médecine* (Paris: Larousse, 1987).

46. J. Crosnier and H. Kreis, *L'Homme greffé. D'une chimére à l'autre* (Paris: Larousse, 1986); R. C. Fox, *L'incertitude médicale* (Louvain-la-Neuve: Ciaco, 1988).

47. A. Pichot, *Étude théorique des rapports du biologique et du psychologique chez l'animal et chez l'homme* (Louvain-la-Neuve: Cabay, 1983).

48. Quoted in note n. 10.

49. J. Van Rillaer, *Les illusions de la psychanalyse* (Bruxelles: Ed. Pierre Margada, 1980).

50. L. Cassiers, *Nos illusion de psychanalystes* (Wavre: Presses Universitaires de Louvain-la-Neuve, 1983).

51. A. Fagot-Largeault, *L'homme bioéthique. Pour une déontologie de la recherche sur le vivant* (Paris: Maloine S.A., 1985).

52. See, for example, the bibliography at the end of the work quoted in note 78.

53. E. Hirsch, ed., *Le Sida, rumeurs et faits* (Paris: Ed. du Cerf, 1987).

54. E. Conan, "La Sida dans l'espace public," *Ésprit*, n. 3-4 (1988): 63-70.

55. C. Ambroselli, *L'éthique médicale* (Paris: PUF, 1988).

56. H. Jonas, "Réflexion philosophiques sur l'expérimentation humaine," in *Médecine et expérimentation* (Québec: Presses de l'Université Laval, 1982), pp. 303-340.

57. "Code de Nuremberg 1947-1987," in *Éthique médicale et droit de l'homme* [Actes du Sud Inserm] (Paris: Arles, 1988), pp. 41-42; "Déclaration d'Helsinki," in *Éhique médicale et droit de l'homme*, pp. 171-172.

58. "Déclaration d'Helsinki," in *Handbook of Declarations*, ed., The World Medical Association (England: 1985), pp. 38-40; "Déclaration de Tokyo," in *Handbook of Declarations*, pp. 47-48.

59. Groupe d'Étude du droit médical, *Expérimentation chez l'homme du nouveau médicament* (Paris: Masson, 1986).

60. Conseil de Recherches médicales du Canada, *Lignes directives concernant la recherche sur des sujects humains* (Ottawa: 1987); *Pour une éthique internationale de la recherche sur des sujects humains* [Proceedings of the International Conference of Bioethics, Ottawa, Canada, april 5-10, 1987] (Ottawa: 1987); J. L. Baudoin, "L'expérimentation sur les humain: un conflit de valeur," *Mc Gill Law Journal* 26.

61. See *Cahiers de biéthique* 4 quoted in note 4.

62. See note 51

63. M. Lacroix, "La bioéthique et l'expérimentation sur l'humain," *Esprit*, n. 11 (1985): 51-71.

64. I tried to develop such point of view in the course which I held at the University of Montréal in 1990. Currently, I am working on the Introduction to an ethics of medical experimentation.

65. See *L'homme biéthique* quoted in note 51.

66. A. Langlois, "Les comités d'éthique locaux et la recherche biomédicale en France," *Études*, n.2 (1988): 177-188; B. Matray, "Le comité consultatif national d'éthique: depuis tres ans une recherche original et désintéressée," *Laennec*, n. 1 (1986): 1-5; C. Ambroselli, *Comités d'éthique à travers le monde: recherches en course 1986* (Paris: Ed. Tierce, 1987); G. Sokal, "Commission d'éthique médicale," *Louvain Médicale* 107, n. 9 (1988): 513-518; A. André, "Les comités d'éthique en Belgique," *Bulletin du Conseil national de l'Ordre des Médecins* 40, n. 6 (1988): 59-69; M. H. Parizeau, "Canada: les comités d'éthique," *Lettre d'information du Comité consultative national d'éthique pour les sciences de la vie et de la santé*, n. 10 (1987): 3; J. F. Malherbe, "La bioéthique à l'hôspital," *Louvain Médical* 107, n. 9 (1988): 497-502.

67. See the first three references in note 60.

68. L. Schwartzenberg, *Requiem pour la vie* (Noé: Préaux Clercs, 1985).

69. E. Kubler-Ross, *La mort* (Ottawa: Ed. Québec/Amerique Inc., 1981). See also Centre d'Études Bioethiques, *Quand l'autre meurt* (Louvain-la-Neuve: Ciaco, 1983).

70. "Déclaration sur l'euthanasie, par la Congrégation pour la doctrine de la foi (1980)," in *Biologie, médecine et éthique* [Textes du Magistère catholique], ed. P. Verspieren (Paris: Le Centurion, 1987), pp. 414-425.

71. Many people who had signed a living will refused it in the imminence of death.

72. A. Mattheeuws, *Union et procréation* (Paris: Ed. du Cerf, 1989). See also J. F. Malherbe, "La persistance de la réference à la nature dans les discours personnalistes sur les fins de mariage chrétien," *Le Supplément* 171, n. 12 (1989): 181-195.

73. The expression "gray literature" designates unpublished texts produced by research centers. This type of literature circulates mostly outside the official information's channels. See, for example, *La mort médicalisée*, Pessac, 4th day of ethics, january 29-31, 1987. Also *Éthique médicale et droits de l'homme: la violence et les soins* (Vol. II and III), Lyon, january 20-22, 1983; *Éthique, consentement et santé*, Lyon, january 26-28, 1984.

74. See, for instance, the dossier *La libre Belgique* of april 10, 1990.

75. See note 31.

76. See *Recherche biomédicale et respect de la personne humaine*, pp. 41-42.

77. See the first three references in note 60.

78. J. F. Malherbe and S. Zorrilla, *Le citoyen, le médecine et la Sida* (Louvain-la-Neuve: Ciaco, 1988); J. F. Malherbe and S. Zorrilla, "Le Sida, révélateur de la crise du sujet," *Le Supplement* 170, n. 9 (1989): 81-90.

79. See the following issues of *Laennec*: "Parole d'Eglise et conscience chrétienne," n. 6 (1989); "Biologie moderne et procréation humaine," n. 6 (1984); "La contraception, vingt ans aprés," n. 12 (1981); "Face à la demande d'avortment," n. 12 (1978); "Respect de la vie, respect de la mort," n. 6 (1974).

80. See the following articles published by *Études* between 1966 and 1989: P. Valadier, "Petite apologie de la conscience," n. 3 (1989); G Delaise de Parceval, "Procréation artificielles et intéréts de l'enfant," n. 2 (1989); P.

154

Verspieren, "Une apologie de suicide," n. 2 (1988); P. Verspieren "Entre vie et morte: l'affaire Damien," n. 4 (1988); P. Valadier, "Une morale dans une société pluraliste," n. 2 (1988); A. Gomez-Muller, "Le droit à la vie, droit politique," n. 11 (1988); P. Verspieren, "Les fécondations artificielles, à propos de l'Instruction romaine," n.5 (1987); P. Verspieren, "Sida la nécessaire vigilance," n. 4 (1987).

Chapter 4

EUTHANASIA IN THE NETHERLANDS

Maurice A. M. De Wachter

In the field of bioethics, the Netherlands has drawn attention on many occasions regarding topics such as artificial procreation[1] and AIDS[2]. It is, however, the practice of euthanasia that appears more frequently in the international popular and scientific press. We have therefore decided to illustrate with this bioethical problem, a debate that has been going on for almost two decades in Holland. Despite this long experience, one should note that the term euthanasia is used for different forms of assistance that is offered to dying patients and that the Dutch doctor is not always certain which of these conventions deserves the name euthanasia. The outlines of a consensus, however, can be discerned. More and more, what we mean by euthanasia is the act of a doctor that, upon a patient's request, end the latter's life. Sometimes the doctor's act is confined to the assistance of a patient that wants to end his life. In this case we do not speak of euthanasia, but rather of assisted suicide. These two practices, euthanasia and assisted suicide, make up the center of the debate in Holland. Little attention has been given to the intentional death of unconscious patients, such as persons in a coma, newborns with severe birth defects, the mentally deranged and some psychiatric patients.

On the international level, the information regarding euthanasia in Holland is often confusing because there are no clear definitions, and therefore it is unclear what it is all about. Moreover, people are not well informed of the legal situation.

There is a dual purpose for these observations on the particular debate concerning euthanasia in Holland: on one hand, to illustrate the clinical cases to which the term euthanasia applies, and on the other to explain the cases of assisted suicide. The State Commission's generally recognized definition of euthanasia states that "euthanasia is the intentional conclusion of someone's life by another, upon the request of the former."[3] Conversely, the term "assisted suicide" means giving the patient who asks the means to end his own life. As one can tell, the distinction between these two practices rests on the agent, which for euthanasia is another person (often the doctor) and for assisted suicide is the patient himself. To complete the commentary on such medical practices in Holland, dying patients who are not in possession of their faculties must be mentioned. At this point, it will be useful to take stock of the situation by pondering how Holland could have embarked on this practice. Finally, there is good reason to wonder what the possible consequences are of an ethical debate that places so much importance on definitions.

1. Euthanasia

As already stated above, euthanasia in Holland is understood to be active intervention through which a doctor ends a patient's life upon the latter's request. This definition applies under three conditions:

1) a voluntary action: this implies a persistent, conscious and willing request on the part of the patient;

2) a situation of discomfort; *i.e.*, the state of an illness that both the doctor and patient consider beyond any possible improvement or recovery;

3) the advice of a colleague: in this way, the confirmation of a third party is sought on the doctor's and patient's decision regarding the appropriateness of the request.

If these three conditions are taken into consideration, one realizes how, in critical situations, many medical practices can no longer be referred to by the term euthanasia, especially in the following cases:

1) when a doctor respects the patient's refusal to be treated, either before or after the start of therapy;

2) when any treatment that is futile or is senseless is foregone;

3) when medicines necessary for pain relief are administered.

In fact, these three situations demonstrate morally correct medical practices and do not deserve the label of euthanasia.

Let us examine the case of Mr. H., who at 40 years of age was stricken with poliomyelitis during a vacation in Tunisia. After seven months of intensive treatment, he was informed that there could be no improvement in his state of almost total paralysis. He was then transferred to a specialized center far from his home. Only his wife visited him and he received a permanent respiratory aid. He fought but gave up hope and wanted to die, yet no one around him wanted to discuss his death. He turned to the Association for Voluntary Euthanasia, who were willing to help, but required that he first discuss the idea with his wife. She listened, but responded that as faithful Catholic, they should not take life. However, more than five years after the start of the illness, Mrs. H. accepted her husband's request. The Association organized a final trip for the couple. Mr H. was resolute in his decision which was the result of two years of deliberation.

Together they agreed that death would bring an end to his unbearable suffering. Before fixing the moment of death, Mr. H. had a final meeting with a psychiatrist. He determined that Mr. H. was not clinically depressed but was perfectly aware of what he was about to do. Since every alternate solution was tried without the least success, the psychiatrist judged that Mr. H.'s request was justified. The euthanasia was carried out by helping the patient drink a lethal dose of a soporific, followed by a massive dose of valium in order to render the patient unconscious. The respirator was then disconnected and curine was injected. The patient died fifteen minutes later after which the doctor wrote "active euthanasia" on the patient's file.

Three brief observations: first, this was the very first case in which mental suffering was recognized as a primary motive for not prosecuting the doctor under the law. Second, this case brings euthanasia and assisted suicide together; in this, it seems particularly representative of practice on the level of family doctors. Third, it seems, in fact that the implementation of euthanasia could have been avoided altogether by complying with the patient's request, that is, by giving him valium and removing the artificial respirator.

It is rumored that in the near future requests for euthanasia will rise. These requests will come not only from older, disabled people, but also from patients who suffer from acute, chronic illnesses, such as sclerosis.

2. Unconscious Patients

A strict interpretation of the definition of euthanasia and its conditions does not permit its use to describe either the situation of persons in a coma, or that of newborns with severe birth defects. These cases are nevertheless helpful in our discussion, in order to better specify what euthanasia is, or rather, what it is not.

Recently, the case of a female patient who was in a coma for more than sixteen years aroused the attention of the entire country. Since she had been reduced to an irreversible vegetative state for the past two years, her husband asked permission from a judge to actively terminate his spouse's life. The numerous refusals of different judges were neutralized by a verdict of October 1989 which declared that the artificial nourishment of the woman was a medical treatment. This verdict opened up the possibility that this treatment could be considered senseless, and therefore could be halted. The death of Mrs. S. followed eleven days later.

The case of newborns is closer to the practice of euthanasia. The classic case is well-known: a trisomy 21 with cardiac as well as duodenal atresia complications. To the extent that it is necessary that the patient makes a conscious request, these babies will never fall under the rules of euthanasia. Yet this is precisely what some pediatricians in the Netherlands are requesting.

The problem of ending the life of newborns with serious birth defects is limited to a narrow group of babies who survive as a direct result of intervention aimed at prolonging their lives. The quality of their lives, however, will remain below what parents and doctors find acceptable. In their 1988 report, the Perinatal Section of the Netherlands Association of Pediatricians intervened in the euthanasia debate, so that, in view of the newborn's impending death, any assistance in maintaining life can be blocked.[4] Moreover, some even ask that the child's life be actively terminated if the child should continue to live without this vital assistance. Here is their reasoning: often in neonatology, treatment must begin before there is sufficient information. In uncertain cases it is often better not to forego treatment. Rather, one should fully and thoroughly render aid, obtain the necessary information, and then decide whether to continue treatment or whether there is sufficient reason to end the child's life. The law currently in effect does not permit this choice. But, the report states, the baby is thus doubly a victim either because in such conditions the doctors tend to forego treatment from the start, or because they prolong treatment even when it has been proven useless. Parents are victims as well since they are not given the necessary information and this prevents them from taking part in a sensible decision. The pediatrician's dilemma is thus a choice between two evils: either to harm the parents by not involving them in the choice, which is just like not furnishing the greatest aid to the child right from the start, or to lie regarding the true cause of death. According to the above-mentioned report the solution should come out of the introduction into law of a morally clear distinction between the end of treatment that prolongs life, but is useless, and the intentional termination of life once it is clear that preserving that life is senseless.

3. The Path to the Practice of Euthanasia

The legal question of euthanasia has been heard in many courts of law since 1973.[5] It even reached the Supreme Court in 1984 and 1986. The interaction between the courts and the Medical Association must be accorded some importance; in fact, between 1973 and 1988, the Medical Association complained many times about the lack of legal protection for its members and came out in favor of a change in the law that would permit doctors to perform euthanasia. Let us take a closer look at each one of the following three factors; the law, the state commission's report, and the development of internal guidelines in hospitals that practice it.

From the legal point of view, we can see that in all cases between 1973 and 1983 two conditions are always mentioned. First of all, the patient must have freely and voluntarily made a request; it is not enough that the patient wishes to die or agrees with the idea of ending his life. Rather, it is the patient himself that must take the initiative. It is not even permissible for the doctor to encourage the patient to make the request. Nevertheless, the doctor could feel the need and the duty to inform the patient on various options, and in so doing could give the impression of having encouraged the patient to make the request. In this situation the judges state there are many dangers that must be avoided. But here, one must judge on a case by case basis. A voluntary request will only be made in the absence of any familial pressure. Finally, the patient's request must be conscious as well as persistent. To conclude, we can say that the courts place such importance on this first condition that, in the few known cases in which euthanasia was performed without the patient's request the doctors were convicted.

The second condition mentioned in all proceedings on euthanasia concerns the situation of unbearable suffering. The courts want an objective evaluation of the medical situation to avoid falling into the subjectivity of the requests. In this way, when real treatment solutions exist, the patient's fear does not become a sufficient reason for refusing treatment. If one is attentive to the patient's needs and if one offers an adequate regimen for treating pain, then these anxieties can be prevented. In other words, euthanasia can never be permitted to be the response to the lack of a cure, to fear or to solitude. Thus, euthanasia is acceptable only if it is the keystone of a good program of care for the terminally ill. In short, a situation judged 'unbearable' must be open to alternative treatments; the patient, of course, will make his own choice between which treatment to follow.

There is a third condition that has gained validity over the years, and that is consultation with another colleague. Through consultation, one can confirm the accuracy of the patient's diagnosis and prognosis. It is also possible through consultation, to verify and confirm that euthanasia is practiced correctly and to make sure all the (legal) conditions are observed.

We have previously stated that *the state commission's report* had its own role in the path that the Netherlands followed. Indeed, the commission promoted rapid progress down this path. Set up in 1982, this Commission had the task of informing the government on euthanasia. It was composed of fifteen members: seven jurists, three doctors, two psychiatrists, one nurse and two theologians. A large majority accepted the proposition that euthanasia would no longer be considered a crime under the following conditions: first, if it is performed by a doctor; second, if it is practiced in a painstaking and precise manner, i.e., that the patient is informed of the gravity of his condition, the patient makes the request and a colleague is consulted; and third, if the patient finds himself in a situation without any hope of improvement.

Moreover, the state commission advised the government to make a decision quickly for two reasons. The first was that there was a danger euthanasia would become a political affair, thus forcing the parliamentarians to vote according to the party line rather than allowing them the possibility to vote their conscience. The second reason was that continuing the development of jurisprudence on the question of euthanasia would require too much time.

162

In any case, the commission recommended the insertion of a "conscience clause" in any new law which would state that no health worker could ever be forced to participate in the active ending of a life.

The hospital guidelines constitute the third determining factor in the progress of euthanasia in the Netherlands. While euthanasia remains a crime punishable by up to twelve years in prison, doctors, hospitals and other health care institutions will try to protect themselves through policies that prevent the Attorney General from prosecution. Thus, since 1985 numerous university clinics have had their own directives. This also goes for public health institutions in large cities, such as Amsterdam (1987) and Rotterdam (1988).

It is naive and simplistic to say that euthanasia is accepted in Holland. Without doubt, both theory and practice are more advanced and open than other Western countries. A certain tolerance on the part of the public and the professionals has been established, but the debate continues. Dutch society realizes that many serious problems have yet to be resolved. There is no comprehensive ethical or legal framework and more than a few citizens feel uncomfortable with this new tolerance.

The most recent event was the institution in February 1990 of a commission presided over by Remellink. This commission was responsible for shedding light on doctors' practices of omission or commission which lead to patients' deaths and making sure this was done on the patients' request.

4. The Metamorphosis of a Definition

The definition of euthanasia as "an active intervention, upon a patient's request, executed by a doctor after consultation with a colleague with a view towards ending the life of that patient who is in extreme discomfort" without doubt constitutes a great step forward. This definition, however, brings with it less advantageous consequences that cannot be hidden.

Among the advantages of this definition is that it clarifies the facts and establishes the necessary conditions. Such clarification, first of all, allows a clear distinction to be drawn between euthanasia and various other practices, such as the treatment of pain, the cessation of treatment either because the patient requests it or because the treatment is proven useless, or the cessation of any vital aid to persons in a coma or other unconscious patients. Secondly, this definition enunciates the criteria that must be respected in order to speak of euthanasia, such as whether or not it is really a situation of discomfort, without which we are speaking of the terminal phase of the illness or the patient's last death struggle.

Thus, one can say that the definition that is gaining ground in the Netherlands offers these two advantages: first, it clarifies and establishes the criteria employed. Second, it reflects empirical conditions of the medical act, and provides an analytic description of it. As such, the definition has its own coherence and consistent logic.

Nevertheless, we must not forget that the definition is the result of many years of legal and ethical debate. Because of this, the definition has become enriched with a certain moral authority. That is, the definition expresses "the public acceptance of a rule of behavior that is taken to be superior and is accepted as legitimate."[6] In this manner, the definition acquires a normative quality and becomes the advocate and defender of a particular moral position. Thus, the definition of euthanasia clears a path for its implementation. It is important for the public debate that this added moral dimension be identified and distinguished from the logical result of the definition. Indeed, a definition's primary goal is to eliminate confusion, not to end the debate. Thus good definitions facilitate good discussions. In our case, it is a question of keeping up with the moral connotations that surpass logical clarifications. It is thus not a critique of the definition as a logical description of the facts, nor it is necessarily a refutation of the normative quality that the definition contains, at least while its moral authority does not prevent the continuing of the ethical debate in terms of approval or disapproval. In other words, while the ethical debate is still possible the definition will be neither the final point nor the conclusion of the debate. On the contrary, the definition represents an instrument of clarification just as much as a moral stand that stimulates debate.

A second consequence of euthanasia's definition is the danger that, little by little, the necessary conditions for factual description will become sufficient conditions. This would once again render almost impossible any moral dispute on euthanasia's practice in conformity with its definition. Moreover, the transformation from necessary to sufficient conditions contains in itself the risk of the establishment of a set of procedural rules and directives that might substitute the debate itself. On the other hand, we must note that in the Netherlands euthanasia's definition and its three conditions (*i.e.*, voluntary request, situation of discomfort, and consultation) are in a large part legal in their nature and origins. Despite the fact that bioethics and medical law are often intertwined, it is *de rigueur* to deny any extrapolations. One must therefore wonder if the arguments that hold well for law, hold equally well for ethics and vice versa.

Conclusion

Underlying the moral and legal debate on euthanasia is the conception that a person has the right of free choice. As a legal norm, freedom of choice regarding euthanasia is recognized in many countries and it is surprising to note that in Holland, such a right does not exist. In fact, a Supreme Court decision of 1984 denied the existence of a right of euthanasia as a right of free choice. The Court told the doctor, who defended himself by invoking his duty to respect the right of the patient to decide alone on such a matter, that in this case it was a question of an opinion that society did not consider sufficiently correct so as to constitute, on its own, legal permission to perform euthanasia.[7] Thus for the Dutch Supreme Court, euthanasia is not part of a person's right of free choice. This judgement contrasts with the position of those who presume, often without discussion, that human responsibility for one's own life is based on the freedom to end that life, if it is under conditions of incurable illness. Therefore, we must note that Dutch society in 1990s still has not reached a consensus on the moral right to free choice concerning matters of life and death.

The goal of this presentation was to demonstrate that definitions are not neutral; they are not innocent instruments that serve to describe factual reality. Rather, the definitions determine our perception of reality; they select, accentuate and embody an aspect of it and for this reason, definitions require constant revision and re-definition.

ENDNOTES

1. M. De Wachter and G. De Wert, "The Netherlands: Tolerance and Debate," in *The Hastings Center Report* 17 (1987): 15-16.

2. M. De Wachter, "Una strategia per il controllo dell'infezione da HIV: il bisogno di molti interventi," in *La sorveglianza della siero-positivita' e la notifica di AIDS come malattia infettiva e contagiosa in Italia*, ed. P. Cattorini (Milano: 1990).

3. Commission d'État, *Rapport Euthanasie* (La Haye: 1985). A summary in English can be found in J. K. M. Gevers, "Final Report of the Nehterlands State Comission on Euthanasia," in *Bioethics* 1 (1987): 163-174.

4. Nederlandse Vereiniging voor Kindergeneeskunde, *Doen of laten?* (Utrecht: 1989).

5. See M. De Wachter, "Active Euthanasia in The Netherlands," in *The Journal of the American Medical Association* 262 (1989): 3316-3319.

6. I. Ladd, *Structure of a Moral Code* (Cambridge: Harvard University Press, 1957), p. 85.

7. *Nerderlandse Jurisprudentie* 106 (1985): 459, sub. 7.2.

Chapter 5

BIOETHICS IN THE SPANISH-SPEAKING WORLD

Diego Gracia Guillen

Introduction

The term "bioethics" was used for the first time by Potter in 1970 and has completed its first twenty years of existence. This term is coming of age, which explains why it is beginning to have a sufficiently mature and systematic doctrine behind it.

Bioethics is a typical product of North American culture. This culture has surpassed its geographic boundaries and spread to all other nations, especially those that make up the so-called First World. Bioethics, therefore, is not an exception to the commonly admitted fact of the United States' unquestioned supremacy in the biological and medical sciences. My thesis is that this comparison is not entirely exact since in their purely scientific and technical aspects, the innovations from the other side of the Atlantic can be compared through simple translation. On the other hand, a mere translation is not enough when it comes to the social and human aspects implied by these innovations; an entire process of "recreation" is needed. In my opinion, this is the challenge of current European bioethics: to see if it is capable of recreating bioethical issues, in light of its traditions and its own culture. North American scholars are aware of this issue and that is why they have launched important projects in the field of transcultural ethics over the past few years.

Western Europe's own medicine is extremely similar to its North American counterpart. Nevertheless, there are many rather important social and cultural differences between them. This is extremely clear especially if the comparison is made between North American and Mediterranean countries, like Spain for example. This explains why in my country an assimilation process of North American bioethics had to be initiated; the assimilation was then followed by a process of "recreation." The "recreation" process, without any doubt, is not complete, although I believe some of the results that have been obtained are important. In what follows, I will try to demonstrate what the bioethical issues are in the Spanish-speaking world and what exactly is the process of recreation that Anglo-Saxon thinking on bioethics is undergoing.

Ethical Issues of Medicine in the Spanish-Speaking World

The scientific and technological development of current medicine is very similar in the entire so-called First World. European medicine is not distinct from North AmericaN medicine. However, it is somewhat behind in applying new therapeutic and diagnostic technologies. Spain is a Western European country and currently has a yearly per capita income above $10,000 dollars per inhabitant. Spending on health services is about six percent of THE GNP. With some small variations, its problems are the same as any in other developed or typical First World medical system. The same, however, is not true for Spanish-speaking countries in the Americas. Therefore it is appropriate to first describe the issues and their occurrence in the different countries of the Spanish-speaking world. In this first section we will describe the issues in Western medicine that caused the current conflicts in bioethics; in the second part we will describe the characteristics that bioethics must have if it is to be modern and if it is to aid in finding solutions to bioethical issues; in the third part we will describe the occurrence of these problems and issues in different Spanish-speaking countries.

1. Current Ethical Issues in Western Medicine

The practice of medicine has always raised ethical issues and required that the doctor possess high moral standards. The uninterrupted series of deontological documents that dot the history of Western medicine from the hippocratic oath to today demonstrate this point. Without question, no other epoch in medicine has faced such moral issues as does ours today. Now more than ever, health professionals require adequate ethical training. This explains why publications on medical and clinical ethics have grown exponentially in recent years. Such growth has given rise to the elaboration of a large body of doctrines which today are indispensable to the training of good doctors. There are three types of reasons for this change.

1.1. The Emancipation of The Patient

The first reasons have to do with the changes that have occurred in recent years in the physician-patient relationship. Classical medical ethics was based on the principle that disease not only altered the individual's physical equilibrium, it altered mental and moral equilibrium as well. Pain alters a man's capacity of judgement to such a point, as Aristotle has already said, that it prevents him from making wise decisions.[1] For this reason, the primary virtue (and almost the only one required) of the patient is obedience. The physician-patient relationship is by its very nature asymmetric and vertical since a physician's functions is to command, and a patient's function is to obey. According to the classical stereotype, a good patient was always passive, neither asked questions nor protested, and established a relationship with the physician that was extremely similar to that of a boy and his father. Classical medical relationships were thus paternalistic. In the physician-patient relationship, the physician assumed the role of a father seeking what was best for the patient, without, however, taking the patient's own will and desires into account. This explains why for a long while in the history of medicine it was possible to find a vast output of ethical codes for physicians, but none for patients.[2] Ethical codes for patients came into existence not more than twenty years ago. It was only at the beginning of the 1970's that the physician-patient relationship began to be interpreted as a process of relations between adults, each one autonomous and responsible. In this manner, the patient ceased being treated like an infant, as was previously the norm in the classical model. Today it is said that the more medical relations are conducted as adults the more mature they will become. To achieve this goal, it was necessary to stop treating the patient as a child. The patients themselves -- who wanted this type of relation -- demanded also that a body of rights be respected (which gave rise starting from 1972 to codes of patient's rights). The most important of these rights was that of informed consent. In the physician-patient relationship, the physician has the technical information and the patient has the capacity to consent or decide; neither can operate without the other and each is necessary. Every medical act is a negotiation and explanation process between the two parties, just as occurs in other aspects of human life, such as in marriage, in the family, in social and political life, *etc*. In all these areas of human life, relations went from vertical and compulsory to horizontal and participatory. Medicine was no exception to this trend.

This process made relations more mature, but also increased conflict within them. It is however a phenomenon that has occurred in all other areas of human relations. Such relations were made more unstable, but at the same time they gained in maturity. Indeed, it is not even necessary that these relations be stable in order to be human or ethical. On the contrary, what very often occurs is that the human equilibrium is always unstable and requires a continuous process of adjustment.[3]

1.2. The Coming of New Biotechnologies

Another factor that caused a multitude of problems and ethical conflicts is the enormous progress of medical technology in the last thirty years. Starting from the 1970's, the development of various substitution procedures for organic functions considered vital (dialysis and kidney transplant in the case of kidney function, artificial respiration, resuscitation techniques, defibrillation, *etc.*) has allowed the medicalization of the last phase of human life (unthinkable until a short time ago) and even a revision of the definition of death. The concept of brain death today allows people whose heart still beats and who, according to classical definition, are alive, to be diagnosed as dead. On the other hand, the concentration of new, life-saving technologies in some hospital services (known since the 1970's as Intensive Care Units) raises a new group of ethical issues: who will and who will not be allowed this intensive care? When can the respirator be disconnected? Which patients should be revived and which should not? In all of these issues, should medical criteria alone be taken into account, or should the patients' desires be taken into account as well? What role in decision-making do the following actors have: the relatives, the insurance companies, and the state?

Even more extraordinary than technologies at the end of life are those that permit the manipulation of the beginning of life. These technologies include as genetic engineering, artificial insemination, in vitro fertilization, embryo transfer, prenatal diagnosis, and so on. What ethical principles should guide medical practice in these areas? How can we determine what is moral and what is immoral in a pluralist society such as ours in which it is not easy for people to agree on concepts of good and evil? The list of questions could easily go on.[4]

1.3. Medicine as Social Organization

The third area of ethical issues regards equal access to health services and equitable distribution of limited and scarce economic resources. In our era, and for the first time in history, every citizen's access to health care has been promoted. It seems that the very idea of justice demands that all individuals satisfy necessities that are as fundamental as medical care. Well, what are medical necessities? How can we differentiate in health matters between the necessary and the superfluous? Economists assure us that in the health field, offer creates its own demand and thus the consumption of health goods is practically unlimited. Is there a moral obligation to satisfy these growing needs in light of the principle of justice? How can rational limits be established? Given that in the realm of health the needs will always be greater than the available resources, what criteria should be utilized for the distribution of scarce resources?

The convergence of these three types of factors has meant that current medicine is completely distinct from that of any previous period. It can be confirmed without question that the physician-patient relationship has changed more in the past twenty five years than in the past twenty five centuries, that is, from the beginnings of Western medicine up to the 1970's. This has meant that medical ethics is now more important than it has been at any other time. A new discipline had to be created that no longer identifies with traditional professional deontology. For this reason, the previous name was discarded and the term bioethics was substituted.[5]

2. Medical Bioethics and Its Characteristics

Deontological medical codes, like those of any other profession, are declarations of principles that health professionals pledge to respect from the moment of their entrance into such a group. Declarations of principles are necessary, but today they have become insufficient. Ethical issues have acquired such breadth and magnitude that new procedures of analysis are needed. Bioethics is attempting to respond to these needs through procedures of analysis and methods of resolving ethical issues that respond to some fundamental requirements. These requirements, without which medical bioethics are impossible, are the following.

2.1. Bioethics as Civil Ethics

In the first place, medical bioethics must be civil or secular, not directly religious. Until a very short time ago, medical ethics had a openly sectarian and religious character. Today this is impossible perhaps only because Western countries have lost uniformity in religious beliefs. In fact, in a modern hospital one finds believers, agnostics, atheists, and within all these groups very different moral codes coexist. On the other hand, these societies have elevated the respect for everyone's moral beliefs (right of freedom of conscience) to the category of a fundamental human right.

This does not mean that moral agreement is impossible on the acceptable minimums which everyone can demand. Indeed, this constitutes the nucleus of civil ethics of the community. What I mean is that this agreement must be rational and not directly linked to religious beliefs. In bioethics, this means that, with all persons directed towards the scrupulous respect of the freedom of conscience, health institutions are obliged to establish some minimum moral standards that everyone has a right to enjoy. These minimum moral standards must not be set according to religious morals. Rather, they must be established according to strictly rational criteria. Medical bioethics must therefore be secular bioethics.

2.2. Bioethics as Pluralistic Ethics

Moreover, bioethics must be pluralist ethics which means accepting diverse focuses and approaches and attempting to bring them together in a greater whole.

This process, which in the political order gave rise to democratic and parliamentary customs, has its own specificity in the area of ethics. On principle, it is stated that an action is immoral when it is not able to be universalized which means that a benefit to some is achieved through harm to others. This indicates that the decision was not sufficiently pluralistic and universal. If in making a moral decision we take into account the interests of all humanity, then there can be no doubt that the particular interests of specific individuals would be canceled out and only the common interest, *i.e.*, the common good, would remain. It follows that pluralism must not be considered an *obstacle* to the construction of ethics, but rather the *condition* that makes it possible. Only universal pluralism can give rise to truly humane ethics.

2.3. Bioethics as Autonomous Ethics

The third characteristic that current bioethics must have is autonomy, and not heteronomy. Moral systems are heteronomous when the norms are imposed on the individual from the outside while opposite systems are considered autonomous. Heteronomous ethics comes in different types: *i.e.*, naturalistic (the criteria of goodness is constituted by the adhesion to the natural order), sociological (the criteria of morality are the norms and conventions specific to each society), theological (the criteria are those present in revealed texts), and so on. For autonomous ethics, the criteria of morality can only be that of the human being. Human reason is what constitutes morality and is the highest court; for this reason it is called conscience and the "voice of the conscience."

2.4. Bioethics as Rational Ethics

From all this we deduce that medical ethics must be rational. Rational is not synonymous with rationalist. Rationalism was an interpretation of rationality that survived in Western culture for many centuries, but that nowadays is totally unacceptable. Rationalism's thesis is that the mind can know *a priori* all reality. Moreover, rationalism states that it is possible to construct a system of ethical principles from which one can deduce, with mathematical precision, all possible consequences. This was Baruch Spinoza's dream in his *Ethica more geometrico demonstrata*. At least since Gödel's time we know that not even the same mathematical reasoning has the capacity to establish complete and self-sufficient systems. This demonstrates that human rationality always has an open nature and is in continual expansion with an *a priori* or principalist moment and an *a posteriori* or consequentialist moment. Ethical reasoning is no exception to this rule and must be developed on this dual level.

2.5. Beyond Conventionalism

To conclude, modern medical ethics aspires to universalism and goes beyond pure moral conventionalism. It is one thing if human reason is not absolute, it is another if it cannot establish universal criteria and if it remains in pure conventionalism. Ethical reasoning, like scientific reasoning, aspires to universal laws, while always being open to a process of continual revision.[6]

3. Bioethical Issues in Spanish-Speaking Countries

It is likely that the medical and bioethical issues that we have described up to this point become clearer as the level of development of the country being analyzed increased. It is important to keep this in mind when studying such a large area -- like that of the Spanish-speaking world -- that includes developed countries like Spain, and many other developing countries like those in Latin America. It is clear that these situations are different and must be examined separately.

3.1. The Situation of Spain

The current Spanish situation fits rather well in the general picture presented in the preceding sections[7]. With the start of democracy in 1975, the already-begun secularization process in Spanish society accelerated enormously and today is equal to that of its neighbors. Thus Spain's civil and political ethics no longer have the sectarian character of the past. In the field of medical ethics, this makes the institutionalization of bioethics that responds to the five aforementioned requirements necessary (*i.e.*, secular, pluralistic, rational in character, *etc.*). On the other hand, the consumers in the Spanish health system are increasingly aware of their autonomy and are demanding a larger share of information and decisions. This is proving to be a great source of problems. Other problems derive from the principle of justice and the principle of equal access to health services for everyone. At the beginning it was thought that the 1986 approval of the new health law extending services to the entire population put an end to this type of problem. Reality, however, has shown otherwise. In fact, it is possible that in the next few years certain types of medical services will be restricted. This is due to the high costs of new technologies.

As one can see, ethical conflicts in the Spanish health system are not very different from those in other Western European countries. Perhaps for this reason everyone sees the essential need for developing bioethics that help resolve these issues. We will return to this topic later.

3.2. The Situation in Latin American Countries

The situation of Latin American countries is different. This is the result of a confluence of different factors, some economic, others political and cultural. In general, Latin American countries are developing countries in economic terms. This means that they possess a poorly financed health system and that most of the population receives inadequate health care.

The typical characteristic of developing countries' health systems is that in the large cities there are very well equipped medical centers that welcome the part of the population that can pay for such services. The rest of the people, however, have very precarious medical care. Moreover, in these countries the most important bioethical issues are those regarding justice and the distribution of scarce resources. Many sectors of the population have neither seen the arrival of advanced medical technology nor the process of the emancipation of patients. These are not the most important problems, even if there are rich sectors that enjoy advanced medical services in the large cities. In developing countries, society is divided into two very distinct groups: the comfortable bourgeoisie on one hand, and the great mass of the population on the other. This means that two completely different types of health systems exist, one with the typical problems of Western medicine, and the other with very different problems.

I would like to add a final observation on Spanish-speaking countries and that is their typical profound Catholic religiosity. It is well-known that Latin America today has the largest number of Catholics in the world. On the other hand, in these countries the secularization process that occurred in Europe in the eighteenth century, did not take place uniformly. So, while the cultured bourgeoisie is secularized the great mass of the people is not. This allows us to understand why morals in these societies continue to be fundamentally confessional, Catholic. These societies have neither known the religious pluralism specific to the North American colonization, nor have they undergone the European secularization process. Consequently, the observations that we defined as specific to Western bioethics are not well understood, except in cultured circles. This allows us to see why the development of bioethics, as it is conceived of today, has only just begun in these countries, and only in very restricted circles. If there is a notable delay between the development of North American bioethics and its repercussions in Europe, then the delay is even greater in the case of Latin America; the difficulties of adapting the movement are greater since the differences are much greater.

From what has been said, we can deduce that bioethics has just begun in Latin America and that it may be premature to speak of acquisitions and solutions. For this reason, the second part of my work which is dedicated to solutions to problems in bioethics, I will only deal with the case of Spain which for me is close and is one I know better.

In Search of Solutions: Bioethics in Spain

Spain, like Italy, is a country that has two extremely important cultural characteristics: on one hand, it is a European country, on the other, it is a Mediterranean country. I believe that each of these observations is very distinctive so I will dedicate the first to sections of this second part to it. I will then analyze how some Spanish groups have attempted to resolve problems in procedure and work methods. To conclude, I will describe the development of ethics committees.

4. European Bioethics: in Search of "Minimal Ethics"

Previously we stated that a mere translation of North American bioethics is not possible in Europe. This is because our ethical and philosophical traditions are very different. At least until the seventeenth century, Anglo-Saxon philosophy had an empiristic approach, while that of continental Europe was much more rationalistic. This had important consequences on morals. Usually empiricist philosophies were emotionalistic (the importance that they give to the principle of autonomy) and consequentialistic (their preferential attention to the principle of beneficence). On the other hand, philosophies of continental Europe tended to be rationalist. They believed it was possible to establish absolute principles that are obliging both morally independently of the empirical will of their subjects, and deontologically (the importance that justice has in these traditions as an absolute principle, before any other moral consideration). As a result, Anglo-Saxon ethics are utilitarian, while continental ethics are not. It is not possible to understand the recreation process of North American bioethics in continental Europe, specifically in Spain, without these presuppositions.

Moral utilitarianism is a typically Anglo-Saxon creation, that began in the era from Bentham to Stuart Mill. This form of utilitarianism, that had the goal of the greatest good for the greatest number of individuals, gave way to another form. This different form, under Continental influence -- Kant above all -- held that ethical norms must always answer to the principle of universality. These norms would respond to these principles in such a way that the criterion would not be the greatest good for the greatest number, but rather the greatest good for all. However, even this version of utilitarianism is Anglo-Saxon. The most representative example is probably in the prescriptivism of Richard Hare. His fundamental ethical criterion was based on "the attribution of equal importance to the equal interests of all parties."[8] A disciple of Hare's, Peter Singer, who is very influential today in Anglo-Saxon bioethics, formulated this principle in a more precise manner: the fundamental principle of ethics is that of the "equal consideration of the interests" of all the subjects involved.[9] The influence of these approaches on North American bioethics was enormous, perhaps even decisive.

To verify this, one only needs to skim through the well-known book *Principles of Biomedical Ethics* by Tom L. Beauchamp and James F. Childress.[10] These authors start from the utilitarian criterion that the basic moral obligation is the achievement of the greatest good possible for all, or at least for the majority. It is a clearly beneficentist principle that Beauchamp and Childress denominate as principle of beneficence: avoid evil when possible (principle of non maleficence) and promote the good. However, the good is not independent from individual autonomy and what some consider good, others consider bad. Everyone agrees with the affirmation that the realization of the good must be based on the consent of the one being acted upon. Moreover, the principle of beneficence is inseparable from the principle of autonomy: there is no beneficence without autonomy. To conclude, it is necessary to establish the so-called principle of justice, in order to reduce the inequalities that the two previous principles generate (or that they do not avoid). Justice, therefore, has only a compensatory character.

This canonical model of North American bioethics had a great influence on later development. As we will we pay closer attention to later, absolute priority is given in this model -- logically enough in a teleological ethics -- to the dual concept of autonomy-beneficence. The ends must always be the most beneficial ones and the interested parties are the very persons who must recognize the ends as beneficial.

I do not believe I am mistaken when I state that continental European tradition is very different. In the first place, it clearly is a deontological tradition.

182

European philosophy has always believed it to be possible to speak of absolute principles on which morals can be founded. The clearest example can be found in the Kantian categorical imperative. It requires us to treat human beings as ends, not means, and humanity as the kingdom of ends. If this is so, then there are also absolute obligations before the empirical autonomy of the individual. These absolute obligations derive from the categorical imperative and can be summarized in two principles, *i.e.*, non maleficence (which in this light is an absolute principle and not the negative part of the principle of beneficence) and justice (which does not have the function of compensating in some way empirical errors, but to fulfill the obligation of treating everyone in the same manner).

In current ethical literature, the problem of the existence of absolute ethical principles before the empirical autonomy of the individual is known under the controversy on "minimal ethics." The question was raised in Germany during the Third Reich. What happened was that a resounding majority of Germans opted for a model of society that to others seemed simply immoral. According to the dual concept of autonomy-beneficence, it seems that they could not object.[11] Without doubt, Theodor W. Adorno could write a book called *Minima Moralia*[12] in which he called for a minimum level of morality below which immorality reigned, even if everyone accepted this lower level. This is a typically European topic, perhaps because the history of our last one hundred years. As I see it, the principles of non maleficence and justice constitute moral minimums; they do not exhaust moral life. Beyond the minimum ethics, there is another that is not the ethics of duty but that of happiness composed of the dual idea of autonomy-beneficence. This is "maximum ethics." Minimum ethics establishes itself as absolute while maximum ethics is aware of its relativity. The idea of happiness is determined in large part by cultures and by idiosyncratic peculiarities of each people. The dual idea of autonomy-beneficence is much more culturally conditioned than that of non maleficence-justice. Well, I believe that current Spanish bioethics understands the concept of non maleficence-justice in a way which is distinct from central European and Nordic cultures. I will venture to call this way "Mediterranean." This is the topic of the next section.

5. Mediterranean Bioethics: in Search of "Maximum Ethics"

It is an undisputable fact that the already described movement of the eighteenth century dealt a tremendous blow to ethics based on virtue-vice, and substituted it with ethics based on rights and duties. Although they are not opposing, but complementary concepts, they have since then been considered rivals. The basis of the ethics of virtue was born in Greece and such ethics has continued to survive until today in Mediterranean and Catholic cultures, while the morals of duty arose in Nordic area and developed in Anglo-Saxon and Protestant countries.

This is the thesis maintained by Alasdair McIntyre in his book *After Virtue*.[13] What McIntyre calls "the classical tradition" is based on the idea of virtue, while modern and post-modern ethics attempted to be formed, not around virtue, but around rules and principles. McIntyre believes the result was disastrous because, for him, such an endeavor is impossible. The modern pretense of going "from virtue to virtue and beyond virtue" was *a priori* condemned to failure. "We must concern ourselves with virtue, first of all, with the goal of understanding the function and authority of rules; moreover, we must begin to investigate a completely different path than that started on by Hume, Diderot, Kant, or Mill." These thinkers are the great representatives of Northern European culture and clearly this culture has its roots in Protestantism. McIntyre believes that the greatest figures in the Enlightenment were not French, but German: Kant and Mozart. French culture lacked various features, including foundations in secularized Protestantism and a new type of university such as those in Könisberg, Edinburgh, or Glasgow. The French Revolution expressed, at least in its first phase, the intention of assuming these Northern European customs. It was not an accident that Kant saw in the French Revolution the expression of his own way of thinking.

184

From the eighteenth century Germanic and Anglo-Saxon countries lived "after virtue;" this was not so for Mediterranean countries. According to McIntyre, this is the case of, among others, the Spanish and Italian cultures. In these countries, a morality very close to the classical tradition was preserved, a morality of virtue. Before morality of principles and rules, there exists morality of virtue. According to McIntyre, it is time to make the most of this model by returning to the classical tradition: ethics must not be understood as mere solutions to intellectual problems, but as the acquisition of habits and qualities of character. For that reason, McIntyre's book ends with these words:

> What matters at this stage is the construction of local forms of community within which civility and the intellectual and moral life can be sustained through the new dark ages which are already upon us. And if the tradition of the virtues was able to survive the horrors of the last dark ages, then we are not entirely without grounds for hope. This time however the barbarians are not waiting beyond the frontiers; they have already been governing us for quite some time. And it is our lack of consciousness of this that constitutes part of our predicament. We are waiting not for a Godot, but for another -- doubtless very different -- Saint Benedict.[14]

Leaving his conclusions aside, I believe that McIntyre's analysis begins with a mistake which is probably due to his distance from the current Mediterranean world. Even here modern culture has arrived in such a way that we are all living "after virtue." This is why it is equally urgent for all of us to go "beyond" it. However, having stated all this, we must concede that popular morals in our countries continue to be based on the idea of virtue, perhaps more than in other latitudes. One can see this very clearly in the medical health field. Our patients are not as worried as Anglo-Saxon patients about respect for their autonomy and scrupulous information regarding their illness; they are more interested in finding a doctor they can trust. The virtue of trust for them is more important than the right to information. For this reason, I believe that our bioethics must not marginalize this very important aspect of the moral life of our countries.

I would like to refer particularly to the virtue of friendship because this is the virtue in which the Spanish contribution has been most significant. In the world of Sophocles, as McIntyre reminded us, morality, political life, and friendship were identified with one another. For this reason, Aristotle said, "when men are friends there is not need for justice." In this tradition, friendship is moral virtue *par excellence* and consequently, is the ethical basis of virtue. We can conclude by saying that a virtuous doctor must always be a friend as well.

A doctor and Spanish humanist, Pedro Laín Entralgo, has written fundamental books on the topic of medical friendship, especially one called *La Relacion Medico-enfermo*.[15] This relationship must be based on what Lain calls "medical friendship." This medical friendship is made up of benevolence, beneficence and trust. The primary importance of Lain's study was recognized by some of the most noted scholars in bioethics today including Mark Siegler,[16] Edmund Pellegrino,[17] Eric Cassell[18] and James Francis Drane.[19] Because of the influence of such scholars, the idea of friendship as standard in the doctor-patient relationship was circulated in bioethics. Even the *President's Commission*, following Mark Siegler, pointed out the necessity of going beyond pure paternalism and pure autonomy by grounding health relations in trust and confidence, *i.e.*, friendship: "The elasticity of the relationship (doctor-patient) depends very much on the trust and confidence between the patient and the health worker."[20]

In defining the type of relationship that the doctor and health worker must generally establish with the patient, it is usually affirmed that such a relationship must be based on service. The doctor must be at the service of the patient. I think that this is a grave error. The old social and legal form of servility cannot be the ideal of human relations. These relations must not be based on service, but on friendship. Friendship is the virtue *par excellence* of human relations.

Perhaps for this reason Aristotle said that it was "the most necessary thing in life," and added that "without friends no one would want to live, even if they had all other goods; even the rich and those who have high offices and powers seem to need friends above all... in poverty and other misfortunes, friends are considered the last refuge."[21] Undoubtedly in these situations friends are few in number. This is what occurs in the case of illness. The patient does not ask for pity, but for confidence, love, and friendship. "Those who suffer," said Aristotle, "feel their suffering eased when friends share in their pain."[22]

Philia is love, but it is a trusting, confident love. Friendship is characterized by confidence and love. This is why friends are "intimate." The sphere of friendship is exactly that of confidence. Three theological virtues exist between friends: faith, hope, and love. The center of friendship is hope, understood as confidence. Since one confides in a friend, one gives a friend one's trust: it is called "trusting trust". Also, one confides in a friend because one loves him: it is "trusting love." Friendship is more that ethics, it is a religion. Agape and charity are usually considered Christian virtues, *par excellence*. However, as Lain Entralgo states, agape only reaches the surface while benevolence and beneficence join in the confidence and trust specific to friendship. As Edmund Pellegrino[23] and Warren Reich[24] have explained, the result is that com-passion is understood as the act of putting one's self in another's place, identifying with the other's experience. Compassion is not pity, rather it is a human relationship based on devotion, perseverance, respect for the person, and responsibility. As Reich states, com-passion is a relationship with another based on love, benevolence, comprehension, and friendship. Here, Mediterranean bioethics has a good field of expression. In this, the Spanish contribution has been and continues to be important.[25]

6. Problems in Procedure

Other than some evident objectives relating both to "maximums" and "minimums," bioethics must resolve the concrete problems of clear procedures. Modern medical bioethics is characterized by its markedly procedural nature, through which concrete norms for conflict resolution form. In its more simplified version, this procedure must consist of two moments, one a priori or principalist, the other a posteriori or consequentialist.[26] This means that to judge ethically any concrete act, two types of analyses must be made: one "retrograde," comparing it with ethical principles, and another "anterograde," evaluating the possible consequences. The principles are always universal and the consequences are always specific. For this reason, we speak of a double contrast in the concrete act in relation to two criteria: the "U" or universal criterion and the "P" or particular criterion. These criteria can be expressed as follows: Criterion "U" - *if an action is to be considered moral or correct, it must be able to be universalized in such a way as not to go against the respect owed to all and to every individual.* Criterion "P" - *if concrete decisions are to be considered responsible and good, they must take into account the particular condition of the facts and the consequences that could derive from them.*

Criterion "U" is always the "norm," the *prima facie* duty while criterion "P" allows us to justify, in specific cases, exceptions to the norm. Exceptions are made when acts that on principle are correct, cannot be considered good in certain concrete circumstances, perhaps only because the consequences of other possible courses of action are better or at least not as bad. The paradigmatic example is that of the so-called "compassionate lie," frequently a part of medicine. Criterion "U" obliges one to tell the truth. There are, however, situations in which the consequences that would follow are so negative that it is considered prudent to lie. The "P" principle is a criterion of "prudence" and without prudence no moral life is possible. When we judge it prudent to lie, we do not do so because it is a good thing, but rather because we know that telling the truth would have worse effects. We justify exceptions by appealing to the consequences that compared to other possible consequences appear not good, but at least less damaging. In reality, when we make exceptions to the norm, we are never opting for a good, but rather for what is called a "lesser evil." What we translate into action is bad, but it is the least possible evil in such a concrete situation; in such a case, it is the only decision that can be considered good.

It would seem that the procedural aspect could be considered exhausted, but this is not the case. It is obvious that there must be as few exceptions as possible and that moral life demands that we establish "when" ("C") we can appeal to "P."

Criterion "C" - *this collaborates in the realization of the application conditions of "U," taking into account the contingent situation.*[27]

From these criteria, a method for analyzing moral problems can be constructed that consists of at least three moments:

Moment I	*The "Prima Facie" Duty*
	* The moral norm
	* Criterion "U"

Moment II	*Prudence*
	* Exceptions to the norm
	* Criterion "P"

Moment III	*Moral Obligation*
	* The making of a decision
	* Criterion "C"

Once the procedure is established, a specific method of analysis of ethical questions in clinical practice can be elaborated.[28] Naturally, this method will have to begin from concrete cases and clinical histories. From here, we see the importance of a model of clinical history which is broad enough to take into account moral problems. A very commendable model is that of Weed, the "clinical history according to problems." This model allows the identification of a patient's distinct problems, whether they are biological, human, or ethical, and allows the tracking of the evolution of each of these problems. Experience shows that one cannot invest in the analysis of the ethical problems in a clinical history without having first closely studied the biological problems. Thus, for example, one cannot confront the question of removing organs from a patient for transplant unless what is called brain death is certain. Neither is it possible to discuss the ethical problems of a persistent vegetative state if one has not first carefully diagnosed the case. The result is that the first part of any method in clinical bioethics must consist of patients' clinical histories. Without a good clinical history in which the biological problems are analyzed (their etiology and possible evolution), no further ethical analysis is possible. In the clinical history, not only must the biological problems be identified, but the ethical problems must be distinguished as well. It is necessary to identify all of them in order to analyze them separately, one by one. It is a fact tested by those who work in clinical ethics that the most frequently committed error by those who begin to use these procedural models consists in mixing other problems into the discussion of ethical problems to such an extent that one is no longer sure what problem is really being discussed.

Every moral problem must be subjected to the same analytical process. Just as biological problems are studied with the same rule specific to clinical biological history, the study of moral problems must be studied with an identical procedure. This procedure is essentially the one described above. The only notable difference is that in clinical bioethics, the "U" and "P" criteria constitute a system of principles that in the first case are the principles of non maleficence and justice, and in the second case are the principles of autonomy and beneficence. As I have already indicated, the difference is that in the first case these principles have an "absolute" nature and in the second case they have a "relative" nature. This is easily understood by comparing the principle of non maleficence to the principle of beneficence. We can never harm others even if they ask. But undoubtedly we cannot do good to others against their will since in that same moment the presumed good changes to harm (except, clearly in cases of loss of capacities or competencies, *e.g.* children, mentally infirm, *etc.*). Beneficence is always relative to autonomy, while non maleficence leaves aside the will of the subject that receives the action. The same occurs with justice which obliges us to treat everyone with equal consideration and respect and not to discriminate among human beings if it is not to the benefit of those less fortunate.[29]

Non maleficence and justice are the expression of criteria "U" and constitute the general characteristic of the physician-patient relationship. Moreover, they must be considered "prior conditions" and cannot be renounced if the relationship is to be ethical. On another level, we find what can be called "internal conditions" to the relationship which satisfy criterion "P." These conditions are autonomy on the part of the patient and beneficence on the part of the physician. The goal of the physician-patient relationship is not only "to do no harm" (non maleficence) and is not only to avoid discrimination (justice), but it consists also in doing as much good as possible; for this reason the relationship is initiated. The relationship in one way or another always consists of a negotiation between the patient's autonomy and the physician's beneficence who is in search of the best that is possible in every concrete situation. Therefore, the method of clinical ethics can be represented with the following outline:

First Part: Clinical History of the Problems

I. *Basic Data*

   * Identification dates
   * Precedents among relatives
   * Personal precedents

* Current Illness

* Exploration

* Analysis and laboratory tests

II. *Identification of the Problems*

* Biological problems

* Human problems (economic, social, cultural)

* Ethical problems

III. *Evolution of Biological Problems*

* Symptoms

* Signals

* Interpretation

* Treatment

* Complementary explorations

IV. *Details of the Data*

* Problems of admission

* Investigation and treatment of the problems

* Final state of the problems at the time of discharge from the hospital

* Final diagnosis

Second Part: Analysis of Moral Problems

I.   *Comparison of the problem with the ethical presuppositions of the physician-patient relationship*

* Principle of justice

* Principle of non maleficence

II. *Comparison of the problem with the ethical elements that constitute the physician-patient relationship*

* Principle of autonomy

* Principle of beneficence

III. *Moral Obligation*

* The making of the decision

7. Ethics Committees

It is highly probable that medical and health services today are better than any other time in the history of medicine not only from a technical point of view, but also from a moral point of view. As we have already stated these services have undoubtedly much more conflict. In and of itself, conflict is neither harmful nor negative since it is an inherent characteristic of the human condition. However, conflict should be reduced as much as possible. In the framework of the physician-patient relationship it sometimes happens that the conflict is so acute that there is no way to resolve it within the relationship. For this reason, it is necessary that health institutions have specific places to resolve moral conflicts and moreover that the cases do not leave the health sector and arrive in court. With such goals, the Institutional Ethics Committees (IEC) were created; they are composed of representatives from different health sectors and some community members.

The function of these committees is generally of a consultative, not decisional nature. They attempt to mediate ethical disputes and aid in making decisions in cases in which they are consulted. The Institutional Ethics Committees are neither solely composed of physicians, nor of health workers; they include representatives of health care consumers as well. This is because, according to what has been stated, ethical decisions are correct only if everyone's point of view is taken into account, not just that of some persons.

Undoubtedly, on principle, open and pluralistic committees are better suited to making ethical decisions than those that are not. Thus, the problem of the IECs is not that they are pluralist, but that they are not sufficiently pluralist. However broad they may be, they will only be composed of a small group of people. What follows is the danger that these committees will operate taking into account only the interests of the few (the groups directly represented) and not the interests of everyone (according to the principle of justice and non maleficence). To avoid this, the IECs must always proceed with method in analyzing their cases; such a method might be the one we proposed earlier. Doubtless if the IECs operate in this manner, their decisions will be right and correct, *i.e.*, ethical.

This will be useful in many ways. In the first place, by teaching health personnel to make moral decisions. In the second place, by avoiding conflicts that continue to grow and finally end up in court. In the third place, by protecting physicians should they end up in court. When an IEC, after having taken into account the different perspectives on the facts, makes a decision it is difficult for a judge not to accept that decision. Thus, the specific methods of clinical ethics and the IECs aid in developing the quality of health services both subjectively and objectively. The IECs contribute to the advancement of better medicine.

In the Spanish-speaking world, IECs have just come into being. The experiences that we have had are all in private institutions, generally religious hospitals. In the case of Spain, the fact is that the public health system undoubtedly delayed the establishment of such committees. There is no doubt, however, that the current situation is particularly promising. In fact, the Minister of Health is about to initiate an agreement with the Complutense University of Madrid; this agreement has the goal of training one doctor in bioethics for every hospital in the country. The objective is that this person will become part of the hospital by dedicating part of his time to the management of both the hospital's IEC and the Ethics Committee on Research and Clinical Experimentation. Moreover, the Minister of Health is currently working to establish a National Bioethics Committee that will be charged with elaborating the general policy that the hospital committees will apply.

As far as I know, there is no experience of this extent in Latin America. Some IECs exist in private hospitals and certain countries, such as Argentina, are attempting to establish a National Ethics Committee. As for the rest, Committees on Research and Clinical Experimentation have not been established in any Latin American country. They have been functioning in Spain since 1978.

Conclusion

We have offered an outlook on Spanish and Latin American bioethics. Undoubtedly, it is very little compared to what still must be done. But this small amount is quite a bit relative to what existed just a few years ago. Personally, I believe that the most difficult part has already been done and that experts in bioethics in my country will soon know how to respond to the challenges; they will substantially contribute to the quality improvement health care, making it better and more humane. Fundamentally, this is the goal of our bioethics.

ENDNOTES

1. Aristotle, *Et. Nic.* 1140 b 17-21

2. See D. Gracia, *Fundamentos de Bioética* (Madrid: Eudema, 1989), pp. 23-120.

3. See D. Gracia, *Fundamentos*, pp. 121-198.

4. See C. Viafora, *Fondamenti di Bioetica* (Milano: Ambrosiana, 1989), pp. 7-10.

5. See, D. Gracia, "La relacion medico-enfermo en España: Balance de los ultimos veinticinco años," *Todo Hospital* 62, no. 12 (1989): 23-26.

6. See C. Viafora, *Fondamenti*, pp. 26-37; D. Gracia, "Principios de la practica medica: Aspectos bioeticos," in P. Farreras and C. Rozman, *Medicina Interna* (Barcelona: Doyma), vol. 1 (forthcoming).

7. See D. Gracia, "Spain. From the Decree to the Proposal," *Hastings Center Report* 17, no. 3 (1987): 29-32.

8. R. M. Hare, *The language of Morals* (Oxford: Clarendon Press, 1952); "Ethical Theory and Utilitarianism," in *Contemporary British Philosophy*, ed. H. D. Lewis (London: Allen and Unwin, 1976), pp. 116-117.

9. P. Singer, *Etica Practica* (Barcelona: Ariel, 1984), p. 33.

10. T. L. Beauchamp and J. F. Childress, *Principles of Biomedical Ethics* (New York: Oxford University Press, 1979).

11. See A. Cortina, *Etica Minima* (Madrid: Tecnos, 1989); D. Gracia, "Bioetica Minima," in *Fundamentos*, pp. 527-596.

12. See T. W. Adorno, *Minima Moralia. Reflexiones desde la vida dañada* (Madrid: Taurus, 1987).

13. A. McIntyre, *After Virtue* (Notre Dame, Indiana: University of Notre Dame Press, 1984).

14. Ibid., p. 245.

15. See P. Lain Entralgo, *La relacion medico-enfermo: Historia y Teoria* (Madrid: Alianza, 1983).

16. See M. Siegler, "Searching for Moral Certainty in Medicine," *Bull N.Y. Acad. Mod.* 67, (1981): 56-69.

17. See E. Pellegrino and D. C. Thomasma, *A Philosophical Basis of Medical Practice* (New York: Oxford University Press, 1981), pp. 198 and 216-219. See also *For the Patient's Good. The Restoration of Beneficence in Health Care* (New York: Oxford University Press, 1988).

18. See E. J. Cassel and M. Siegler, eds., *Changing Values in Medicine* (Frederick: Md. University Publications of America, 1979); E. J. Cassel, *The Place of the Humanities in Medicine* (New York: The Hastings Center, 1984); E. J. Cassel, *The Healer's Art* (Cambridge: The Mit Press, 1985).

19. See J. F. Drane, "La bioetica en una sociedad pluralista. La experiencia americana y su influjo en España," in *Fundamentacion de la bioetica y manipulacion genetica*, ed. J. Gafo (Madrid: Publicaciones de la Universidad Pontificia Comillas, 1988), pp. 87-105. In the very first page Drane states his conviction that American authors have much to learn from Southern European ethics. Two aspects of Spanish ethical tradition which many American thinkers increasingly recognized as necessary are a more realistic metaphysics and a special emphasis on the person and on virtues. See also J. F. Drane, *Becoming a Good Doctor: The Place of Virtue and Character in Medical Ethics* (Kansas City: Sheed and Ward, 1988).

20. President's Commission for the Study of Ethical Problems in Medicine and Biomedical and Behavioral Research, *Making Health Care Decisions: Volume I* (Washington, D.C.: U.S. Government Printing Office, 1983), p. 37.

21. Aristotle, *Et. Nic.*, VIII, 1:1155 a 5-12.

22. Idib., IX, 11: 1171 a 29-30.

23. See E. Pellegrino, "Health care: A Vocation to Justice and Love," in *The Professions in Ethical Context*, ed. F. A. Eigo (Villanova University: Proceedings of the Theology Institute of Villanova University, 1986), pp. 97-126. See also by the same author "Cada enfermo es mi Hermano," in *Dolentium*

Hominum 3, (1988): 58-62, and "Agape and Ethics: Some Reflections on medical Morals from a Catholic Perspective," in *Catholic Perspectives in Medical Morals*, ed. E. Pellegrino, J. Langan and J. C. Harvey (Dordrecht: Kluwer Academic Publisher, 1989), pp. 277-300..

24. See W. Reich, "Un'etica della vita centrata sulla famiglia," in *Famiglia oggi* 34, luglio-agosto (1988): 64-74.

25. See D. Gracia, *Fundamentos*, pp. 597-602.

26. On this point see the excellent book of A. Da Re, *L'etica tra felicita' e dovere* (Bologna: Dehoniane, 1987).

27. K. O. Apel, "Limites de la etica discursiva?" in *Razon comunicativa y responsabilidad solidaria*, ed. A Cortina (Salamanca: Sigueme, 1985), p. 261.

28. An interesting alternative to the method here proposed can be found in C. Viafora, *Fondamenti*, pp. XVII-XIX.

29. See D. Gracia, *"Primum non nocere"*. *El principio de no-maleficencia como fundamento de la etica medica* (Madrid: Real Academia Nacional de Medicina, 1990).

Chapter 6

ORIENTATIONS AND TENDENCIES OF BIOETHICS IN GERMAN-SPEAKING WORLD

Alberto Bondolfi

1. Cultural and Institutional Background

In order to be able to adequately evaluate the German production in medical ethics and bioethics, it is necessary to consider it in a wider context; that is to say, the renewed interest in ethical phenomena in general, and the growing awareness of new knowledge and techniques related with genetic technology.[1] Since the early seventies, the first of these phenomena characterizes both German philosophy and theology, and it is known by its programmatic name *rehabilitation of practical philosophy* (Rehabilitierung der praktischen Philosophie).[2]

2. The "Rebirth of Practical Philosophy" in Germany and Its Orientation

Since the second half of the sixties, the philosophical and sociological literature shows an increasing interest in normative questions in general, and particularly in ethical questions. Hermeneutic philosophy, as well as social philosophy related to the "School of Frankfurt", began giving special attention to ethical problems. On the other hand, interest in existential philosophy, which had so strongly monopolized moral reflection during the sixties, diminishes.[3]

Up until the eighties and nineties only a restricted group of scholars drew from analytic tradition, but this small, little known group focuses entirely on the clarification of the epistemological status of moral language. No attention is given to practical applications of some relevance.[4]

Already in 1964 K. H. Ilting[5] spoke about the necessity of rehabilitating *practical philosophy*, *i.e.*, as a reflection on the ethical praxis of individuals as well as social and political institutions. In a programmatic essay published in a well known anthology in 1972/74, Manfred Riedel outlines this program of research and cultural intervention in the field of human sciences.[6] The expression "rehabilitation of practical philosophy", designates the renewal, rebirth and actualization of interest in moral, social and political problems. The goal underlying this interest is more or less explicitly declared: the philosophical re-proposition of different questions, *e.g.*, the conditions for acting in a morally correct way, the public aspect of a good life, and the definition of a good political order in a democratic society.

2.1. The Neo-Aristotelian Approach

The first doctrinal trend -- which does not mean yet another version of scholasticism -- goes back to the Aristotelian tradition. This approach triggered a renewal of ethical and social research. Indeed, it is not surprising that interest in the ethical and political doctrine of Aristotle has taken place, once again, on German soil.[7] Unlike France and the Anglosaxon world, the German curriculum of philosophy and law, up to the eighteen century, included the so called *philosophia practica universalis*, which in turn was divided into *philosophia moralis sive Ethica*, *philosophia oeconomica*, and *philosophia civilis sive Politica*. The reasons for the renewal of practical philosophy however can be traced back to the theoretical and practical crisis of the universe of late-industrial society.[8] German neo-aristotelianism doesn't come into direct contact, at least in its first moments, with an analogous movement in America.[9] Only recently have German scholars become aware of American reflection on *Communitarianism*.[10]

2.2. The Hermeneutical Approach

Upon examination of other ethical orientations, it is noteworthy that the so called Critical Rationalism -- although very active in the sixties as a critique of moral language -- has not significantly contributed in recent years to the field of ethics. It has marked, however, a kind of basic attitude toward ethical propositions viewing them as "empty utterances".[11]

Other approaches, such as philosophical hermeneutics,[12] seem more active. Although deeply rooted in German speaking culture, hermeneutics had been hitherto more significantly present in other realms of philosophical reflection. Its relevance for normative ethics remained obscure. Hermeneutics has finally shown the inadequacy of a purely empirical or behavioristic method in approaching the phenomenon of moral act. Hermeneutics can articulate the relation between living ethos and ethical reflection without falling into the so called naturalistic fallacy because it understands the subject as being "in action" not only *per accidens*, but in virtue of its inmost structure.

Perhaps this philosophical approach has been more successful outside philosophy, particularly within the field of moral theology in both Catholic and Protestant confessional traditions.[13]

2.3. The Analytic Approach in Ethics

Unlike Scandinavian countries and the Netherlands -- which had seen since much earlier the formation of prestigious schools (see for instance the philosophers of law Ross and Olivecrona) -- in Germany analytic ethics had been hardly known and appreciated until the Seventies. However, during these last years the situation has profoundly changed. The most important works of Anglosaxon moral philosophy of this century have been translated. Moreover, various anthologies provide a direct access to articles originally published in American journals.[14] Nowadays synthesis are available which make possible the approach to ethics in light of analytic methodology.[15]

202

2.4. Marxist Ethics

The tradition inspired by marxist thought has not developed a strong ethical reflection. Exceptions, such as the ethics of austro-marxism or the analytical re-interpretation of traditional marxist positions, do not invalidate, but rather confirm this diagnosis.[16]

On the whole, ethical research in German speaking countries may appear to be a phenomenon which belongs essentially to academia. This is not always the case considering the large production of monographies which lack a clear-cut philosophical tone.[17] These evidence a global sensitivity permeating at different levels multifarious sectors of German cultural life.

2.5. Theological Ethics

The contribution of theology to ethical reflection and bioethics needs some preliminary remarks, for one must recall the strong academic tradition of theology in the German world. Furthermore theology is relatively independent from the churches, and enjoys the same juridical status that all other disciplines have. It is not by chance, therefore, that interesting forms of interdisciplinary dialogue between theologians, philosophers and scientists can take place in a context of institutional equality. Possible conflicts are resolved within the frame of the academic institution itself on the basis of rules universally recognized by all parties.[18]

Relevant for German speaking world is also the *Societas Ethica*, an interconfessional and interdisciplinary organization of philosophers and theologians, who are interested in ethical research and discussion in German world as well as in nearby countries (*i.e.*, Netherlands, Scandinavian and Eastern countries). Since the early Seventies the *Societas Ethica* pleaded for new forms of interdisciplinary dialogue within German universities both in ethics in general and in bioethics in particular. The first results of this work, *i.e.*, the creation of permanent positions in medical ethics, were to be seen in Netherlands and in Scandinavian countries, but not in Germany.[19]

The renewed interest in fundamental ethical questions portrayed above cannot be considered the only reason for the flourishing of studies in biomedical ethics, but constitutes one of the factors which motivates this new concern. Ultimately such a renewal can be seen as an academic attempt to articulate questions which emerge from everyday praxis, and from other sectors of scientific research.[20] At this level, as the early bioethical literature witnesses, researchers have taken their first steps on ground fundamentally alien to philosophical and theological speculation.[21] Scientific and speculative avenues eventually merged, and gave birth to a new discipline. Bioethics defines a space where data and quandaries emerging from laboratories and clinics encounter reflections on principles elaborated in philosophical and moral theological seminars.[22]

3. Models of Moral Argumentation and Ethical Theories in German Speaking Biomedical Ethics

An original element in German literature is the absence of a mechanical distinction between bioethics on one hand and medical ethics on the other. While this distinction is underscored in English literature, German scholars prefer to adopt a model of continuity.[23] Medical ethics has been present within German universities for a few decades although not institutionally defined as a course apart, provided with appointed positions and a clear curriculum.[24] These institutional structures have facilitated the formation of research teams whose contribution distinguishes the peculiar theoretical mark of german production.

3.1. A Particular Historical Sensibility

The approach to bioethics is characterized, first of all, by an historic perspective. German medical faculties have always cultivated the study of history of medicine through the creation of specific institutes devoted to this kind of investigation. Research within these institutes has been increasingly understood as having a preparatory function to specific moral reflection.[25] Emphasis is laid in the literature upon denouncing a reductive self-understanding of medicine in terms of natural science. Indeed, a critical analysis of medicine in its historical development, seems to convey a different view. Medicine would be more like a science-bridge; it would make possible the application of a body of knowledge borrowed from natural sciences to its particular object. That is, to the human subject, with respect to his natural and cultural aspects alike. This particular interpretation of medicine has given much attention to the study of medical anthropology whose task consists in the philosophical clarification of fundamental medical categories such as pathology, illness, healing etc.[26] A pioneer in this kind of reflection, D. von Engelhardt, has tried to coherently articulate the relation between historical data (interpreted according to Thomas Kuhn's paradigm of scientific revolutions) and normative conclusions for solving specific moral conflicts.[27]

The anthropological reflection of the scientist and physician Viktor von Weizsäcker,[28] has had great impact upon this group of historians of medicine.[29] His influence is marked by the attempt to put, once again, the ill subject at the center of medical knowledge. He claims that it is the ill patient himself who provides the key to understand the genesis and the development of any disease. Within this perspective every pathology is seen as a complex interconnection of external factors and predispositions internal to the subject himself, and not as a fact purely extrinsic to the ill patient. The recent shift in interest from classical medical ethics to bioethics, has probably resulted in obscuring the centrality of this anthropological reflection for medicine, at least in German scholarship.[30] It remains to be seen how it is possible to preserve this attitude toward medicine in light of new situational contexts.

3.2. Different Attitudes toward Technological Civilization

German literature is certainly not lacking in global diagnosis. Their goal is to face and interpret recent progress in molecular biology, and to evaluate its direct consequences for clinical applications. Both young scholars, involved in ecological movements, as well as older experts more sensitive to "traditional" values have made such attempts.[31]

Among other authors who have contributed to the field of medical ethics and bioethics with their critique of civilization, Hans Jonas must be named.[32] This German-American philosopher whose fame reaches well beyond the German world, begins his reflection with a global diagnosis on the devastating consequences of recent developments in genetic biology. According to Jonas, it is absolutely necessary to become aware of the effects of man's intervention upon nature. Such intervention has not only quantitatively increased. It has also reached a level whose destructiveness human beings are not aware of any longer. Deceived by neo-liberal and neo-marxian utopias alike, modernity has far too optimistically relied upon a radiant future to come. Both attitudes emerged from the confidence in a *Prinzip Hoffnung* (hope principle) whose power could no longer be constrained and mastered.[33] A new principle therefore, *Prinzip Verantwortung* (responsibility principle), was progressively invoked as a corrective counterforce capable of polarizing the sort of ethical discomfort which penetrates our civilization.

Jonas is skeptical toward the possibility of revising Western anthropocentrism considered to be, by some contemporary theologians, the indirect product of Christian influence. Contrary to the opinion of those who still regard such an anthropocentrism as an indispensable element in framing contemporary ethics,[34] Jonas suggests instead to overcome it by means of a so called "heuristic of fear and respect".[35]

Human beings have to learn a kind of methodical suspicion toward themselves and their position in nature, as well as toward their utopic dreams.

Jonas' diagnosis is not limited to analyzing the shortcomings related with anthropocentric and utopic mindset. He also adopts a position regarding concrete issues[36] such as procreative techniques, diagnostic possibilities created by new genetic discoveries *etc*. Moreover, his conception of responsibility takes into account, not only immediate consequences of scientific research, but interests and rights of future generations as well.[37]

Hans Martin Sass, a Professor at the University of Bochum and at Georgetown University in Washington D.C., represents a clearly optimistic attitude, within the German world, toward new biotechnological applications both to human beings and to the animal and vegetal environment.[38] This author makes a distinction between two different attitudes present within the wide bioethical literature: a so called *defensive* and an *offensive* ethics. The former is dominant in the German speaking world, and seems to rely more on fear and irrational premises than on sound arguments.[39]

Moral conflicts in bioethics do not arise at the level of a specific discipline, but simply witness the difficulty of readjusting the relation between the world of one's personal values and technology. In interpreting these conflicts against the backdrop of premises extrinsic to technological progress, "defensive" ethics ends up by arbitrarily restricting citizens' power toward opportunities which new discoveries unfold. In this sense "defensive" ethics has to be considered politically dangerous because of its claim to stronger statal control possibly limiting freedom.

Sass invoked the so called *Risikomündigkeit* which is a mature disposition in assuming and controlling risks. Offensive ethics is intrinsically defined by the category of risk. By using this category the philosopher of Bochum takes part in a wider discussion characterizing German social philosophy, and in which the category of risk is understood as a fundamental feature of contemporary modern societies.[40]

A primary concern in the so called offensive ethics is the distinction between value propositions not directly conducive to actions, and statements which directly give rise to decisions and actions. Value propositions deserve complete tolerance since they cannot be definitely proven, and so, cannot be imposed upon anyone. But a different degree of tolerance has to be used toward statements which will directly affect society.

Sass' typology cannot resolve, in my judgment, the complex problem of ethical pluralism, yet it may provide a key for interpreting the diffent positions in the bioethical discourse.

3.3. The Debate on Normative Ethics

In virtue of the very nature of scientific disciplines, biological discoveries, genetic and medical alike, can hardly avoid its empirical results from having immediate normative meaning. Within biological phenomena and organic life a form of teleology can be found, that is a finality intrinsic to them.

The tendency of German biological reflection until recently has been to give an anthropomorphic account of these phenomena by attributing to them not only factual objectivity, but also immediate moral meaning. The results of research done by K. Lorenz and his school have influenced this tendency.[41] Indeed, German ethical reflection has never been too mindful of the naturalistic bias.[42]

Lately however, a sort of anti-naturalistic attitude has prevailed especially in biology. The reason for this re-adjustment is due in part to the weakness of naturalistic arguments whn used in public debates, particularly those concerning emotionally laden issues like abortion or the status of the embryo.[43] In both cases, referring to biological information in order to justify a particular action as moral or immoral has not led to a better consensus on the issue at stake. On the contrary, it has generated accusations of ideological prejudice on both sides.[44]

On the question of the foundation of moral norms, the debate is defined by the opposition *deontology* vs. *teleology*.[45] The opposition is also expressed with the terms sanctity of life vs. quality of life, as employed in the Anglosaxon world. It is important to note, that unlike the Anglosaxon tradition, the two

208

argumentation models do not exclude each other sharply. As a matter of fact, some German publications aim at pointing out their possible co-existence.[46] In my opinion the two models contradict themselves only at the level of formal definitions. Yet they may find points in common when it comes to practical applications. *General norms*, characterized by their formality, require a deontological foundation. This could be the case of norms such as the golden rule or the categorical imperative. On the other hand, *concrete norms* of action rely upon a teleological model of argumentation.

In the specific field of bioethics, a deontological foundation is required for norms such as "primum non nocere" or for defending the right to life. Yet, more nuanced considerations of a teleological nature are necessary for solving concrete conflictual cases such as prenatal diagnosis, transplantation *etc.*

4. First Scientific Institutions

German speaking world has without any doubt been sensitive and fast in recognizing moral issues raised by the introduction of new techniques and practices both in medicine and in genetics. On the other hand, the effort to create institutions dealing with this new sensibility has taken time. German university are almost exclusively "statal", and function through the structure of autonomous Länder.

Research coordination at a national and international level among different German speaking countries (Germany, Schwitzerland, Austria), is still in need of further development. At the moment German presence and activity is not very intense even within the *Association Européenne des Centres d'Éthique médicale*, the only organization which coordinates institutions directly involved in medical ethics and bioethics. However, the European Congress which took place at Bad Segeberg in October 1993 seems to prelude a future of stronger collaboration.

4.1. Centers of Research

The presence of some specialized institutions is also worth mentioning. These have initiated a long-term program in the field of medical ethics and bioethics. They occupy a middle space between traditional forms of university teaching and private research institutes. Most of them offer optional courses, and receive some support from resources outside the university for research. Undoubtly this "mixed" institution presents clear advantages.

The "Institut für Geschichte der Medizin" at the University of Freiburg i. Br. is among these new initiatives. It is currently directed by Prof. E. Seidler, a longstanding expert in ethical problems related to medicine.[47]

D. von Engelhard, who is active at Bremen, concentrates particularly on the study of the different ways in which health and medicine have been interpreted through history.

Recently a second Center was created at the University of Bochum directed by Prof. Sass and Viefhues. The Center publishes thematic notes on different issues[48] together with some translations from foreign literature. Peculiar to this institution is its bridge-function with the Anglosaxon and American world.[49]

Finally, the Center "Ethik in der Naturwissenschaften" operates at the University of Tübingen. The Center is directed by the Catholic moral theologian Dietmar Mieth, although this institution doesn't have any particular confessional character. Approximately ten researchers from different disciplines (scientific, philosophical and theological) collaborate with him. A vast congrss on procreative techniques organized by the Center in 1987 has, for the first time, stimulated a fruitful dialogue within different approaches to Bioethics in Germany.[50]

In Switzerland two institutes are active at the University of Zürich: the "Institut für Sozialethik" and the "Arbeitsstelle für Ethik". Other institutes operate within theological faculties at Freiburg i. Ue. and Luzern. The teaching of Bioethics is also part of the curriculum of theological ethics at Lausanne and Genève, as well as the curriculum of philosophical ethics at Basel and Freiburg i. Ue. In Austria a Center of medical ethics is in process of formation led by Prof. G. Virt.

4.2. The Teaching

The German world has just began taking its first steps in including the teaching of ethics as part of the curriculum of medical students. Traditional resistances are more or less evident and motivated. These emerge because physicians seem to have difficulty in recognizing to ethics the status of a discipline which is epistemologically an materially independent.

In Germany, Switzerland and Austria, almost every medical faculty promotes isolated attempts to reflect on medical ethics and biomedical issues. However, these initiatives -- symposia, interdisciplinary sessions, and doctoral dissertations -- do not yet form a regular teaching program coherently included within the medical curriculum. The trend of these institutions would appear to be moved by the intention of entrusting the teaching of ethics to trained physicians. This intention however, seems to meet with obstacles. First, the introduction of a new discipline appears to aggravate an already burdensome curriculum. Second, strong objections are leveled against entrusting a course in medical ethics to a physician.

5. Juridical and Social Structures

5.1. Ethics Committees

Ethics committees are relatively new institutions open to further developments.[51] Most important for these institutions seem their guarantees of independence. According to Roman law *nemo est judex in causa propria*. How can this fundamental principle be guaranteed within a field heavily dominated by emotions, or within structures like the scientific or the medical ones which are organized on the basis of a strict hierarchy?

Furthermore, it can be added that no criterium is available for defining something like ethical competence. Given the complexity of the situation, is it wise to take for granted the competence of a hospital chaplain? On the other hand, how to avoid the extreme of a so called "republic of philosophers"?

In conclusion, a middle ground has to be found between two extremes: experts operating exclusively on the basis of their professional competence, and institutional hierarchies whose judgement simply relies upon their authority.

5.2. Professional Organizations

All German speaking countries are characterized by some institutions (e.g. the *Ärtzekammer*), which have normative power on health care professionals. Characteristic to the German world is the fact that these institutions, having concentrated their efforts in organizing a common research at the level of professional ethics, represent a sort of "Magisterium", or a recognized authority in judging new medical practices.

In Switzerland, for example, the "Academy of Medical Sciences" (Akademie der medizinischen Wissenschaften) has an internal committee (zentralethische Kommission). Its function is to elaborate guidelines for specific issues (e.g. insemination, in-vitro fertilization, sterilization, euthanasia and lately also pre-natal diagnosis) by referring to the results of interdisciplinary work-groups. Once these guidelines are published, they become normative rules for health care professionals. Sanctions are provided for those who do not respect them. What we have here is a form of internal professional law with self-regulatory function.

Other important institutions are the "societies of experts" (Gelehrtengesellschaften). Their ethical function is to make possible a real confrontation and a dialogue among different parties in a situation of institutional equality.

Worth mentioning here are the "Academy for Ethics in Medicine" (Akademie Ethik in der Medizin) in Germany, and the "Swiss Society for Biomedical Ethics" (Schweitzerische Gesellschaft für biomedizinische Ethik). These institutions have proved themselves capable of judging different issues regardless of outside pressures. It is worthwhile stressing the neutrality of these institutions given the pluralistic environment and the condition of their financial support. In fact, only private generosity provides for scientific research through congresses and symposia.

5.3. Government Committees.

Government committees in German speaking countries have elaborated written documents on different concrete issues which have become paradigmatic during the last decade. Outstanding among these are the so called *Benda Report* in Germany,[52] and the *Amstad Report* in Switzerland.[53]

The issues at stake in these institutions are mainly concrete problems affecting the everyday life of patients, para-medical personnel, physicians and scientists operating in laboratories and research centers. Most of the literature deals with these "sub-discussions" related to concrete ethical issues.

6. Some Concrete Ethical Issues

6.1. The "Moral" Status of Animals and Plants

A first preliminary observation may be useful in order to understand the wide range of bibliographic literature dealing with questions like the moral "status" of animals and plants.[54]

Although contemporary discussion of this issue has begun in Anglosaxon countries, it has found a "fertile soil" in the German speaking world. Since the Enlightenment, German philosophy has confronted this issue in depth.[55]

The discussion has enlarged to the point of involving a wide range of questions. For instance, the sub-problem of consuming animal meat, establishing a balance in agricultural products between first and third world, the issue of animal experimentation and vivisection and the question of animals rights. Philosophy and theology seem more aware of the moral bound which relates humans to animals. The question of animal rights can be addressed ultimately in light of a global understanding of the relation between nature and humans.

6.2. Genetic Technologies

Major differences can be seen between German literature and literature from Latin as well as from Anglosaxon countries concerning generic technology in general (Gentechnologie). The massive breakthrough of genetic technologies has generated, in the German universe, a profound reflection on both their meaning and legitimacy.[56]

The literature on this particular issue tends to emphasize the element of discontinuity in genetic technology when confronted with technical progress as a whole. Insofar as this episode constitutes a qualitative step, it deserves an appropriate moral reflection. It is possible to find differentiated accounts of genetic technology at a specialized level more than at the level of popular literature. A distinction is made among different fields of application in the attempt to evaluate connections and potential effects of different sectorial practices.[57]

6.3. Procreative Techniques

Particular attention in German bioethical production has been given to procreative techniques.[58] It doesn't necessarily follow that this issue is the most urgent and important. The question is first of all addressed from a legal point of view. That is to say, to analyze concepts taken for granted before, e.g. paternity-maternity, family *etc.*, given the new procreative techniques. German legal traditions are particularly sensitive toward the stability of the institution of marriage, and therefore tend to see these new possibilities as a factor of institutional instability. The German-speaking world has immediately realized the importance of a regulative approach to these techniques. This implies not only a reflection of legal nature, but also of ethical and political character as well. The issues it touches upon range from the status of the embryo, the consequences of procreative techniques on the right to health in general (*i.e.*, sterility as "disease", pregnancy as "pathological state", *etc.*) to the questio of the relation between personal legitimate desires and interests of fundamental scientific research.

Secondly, an attempt can be found within German production to distinguish the problems related to heterologous insemination from those of in-vitro fertilization.

6.4. Prenatal Diagnosis

German speaking world is also attentive to the possibilities opened up by pre-natal diagnosis.[59]

The approach to the issue at stake is both legal and ethical In German speaking countries the discussion has been long and intense involving the interest of public opinion. In order to fully appreciate this discussion, it is important to take into account its particular background as well as the two different phases which characterizes it. The memory of eugenic experiments during the Third Reich[60] inevitably generates a negative feedback, especially in Germany, toward any medical attempt concerned with prevention of hereditary diseases. Nevertheless, new reasons have made ethical reflections and legal regulations in the field of prenatal diagnosis urgent. German reflection seems to be particularly concerned with the question of how far society can go in accepting handicaps which can be easily discovered thanks to prenatal diagnosis. On the other hand, what is invoked at this point is the right of the pregnant woman not to know, in spite of all psychological pressures. In the case of a particular genetic defect, genetic counseling is recommended before initiating the pregnancy.[61]

6.5. Abortion

The abortion issues has been the object of lively debate for centuries within medical practice.[62] New practices created by biotechnological possibilities have made the debate even more intense.[63]

In the last twenty years, however, the way of framing the moral issue has been moving away from the classical paradigm. The discussion has taken into account, on one hand, the question of the status of the embryo and the status of the fetus, on the other, the possibilities of prenatal diagnosis discussed above.

The recent reunification of Germany has added more intensity to the debate. In Switzerland the issue has re-emerged in the search for a new legal regulation for the 1990's.

6.6. Sterilization

The discussion of sterilization which had been very much alive in the fifties and sixties[64] and which sank into oblivion, has lately emerged with new force. Today the discussion centers on respect for the will of the man/woman who intends to undergo sterilization,[65] and no longer on the intrinsic legitimacy of the intervention as such. Two burning dimensions of the issue have been given much legal attention: the civic responsibility of the physician in the case of failure while performing a sterilization, and the question of whether it is legitimate to sterilize persons who are heavily mentally handicapped and do not live in a state of sexual reclusion.

6.7. Organ Transplantation

Ethical discussion on organ transplants has been active in German countries since the sixties,[66] but it has become evn more intense during the last years because of new reflections on the concept and the criterium of cerebral death.[67] The discussion centers on the issue of justice:[68] how and when should organs be transplanted given their scarcity? How is it possible to cope with the need for infrastructural resources, and with the increasing number od candidates?

6.8. Terminally Ill Patients

The issue of terminally ill patients resembles the above discussion on eugenism. The term "euthanasia" is a reminder of terrible theories and even more terrible practices during the Nazi regime. On the other hand, German language is characterized by a non-valuative use of the term euthanasia. This semantic shift was made possible by the influence of the Netherlands and Scandinavian countries, as well as by the distinction between passive and active euthanasia. The failure to appreciate this distinction, has been the cause of some misunderstandings.[69]

7. Some Global Evaluations

Leaving aside all unnecessary details, we can finally provide a general evaluation of German bioethical research within the context of the whole European debate. The attempt will be inevitably short, since it is not meant to be definitive.

First of all, the speculative inclination of philosophical and theological reflection should be noted. This feature prevents bioethics from becoming a transitory fashion or a discipline deprived of scientific seriousness. German scholars understand bioethics, not as a separate discipline with specific principles and methods, but rather as a particular chapter of ethics in general. Only the position of H. M. Sass seems different on this point. He refers to American models, and so tends to emphasize the peculiar professional dimension of the discipline.

Secondly, German research has been initially characterized by theological interest[70] but it has soon after included philosophers together with theologians. This promising relationship is open to further collaboration, and therefore is quite unpredictable in its future development. Even the contribution of law in this field is ethically and philosophically oriented thus confirming the specific mark of German legal science. On the other hand, Swiss and Austrian interest is more pragmatic although very much alive. The speculative approach of German legal scholars to bioethics has created, indeed, a literature which provides a useful frame for the political debate on new practices in genetics, biology and medicine. Finally, a lack of sensibility for a sociological interpretation of bioethical conflicts should be noted.

ENDNOTES

1. See W. van den Daele, *Menschen nach Mass?* (München: Beck Verlag, 1985).

2. I have given an account of the debate in the essay entitled "Momenti del dibattito tedesco sull'etica (1970-1985)," in *Religione e societa'* 1, (1986): 38-56.

3. A classical exposition of the ethical orientations of existentialistic philosophy can be found in H. Fahrenbach, *Existenzanalyse und Ethik* (Frankfurt: Klostermann, 1970).

4. One of the first bibliographical note in German informing on analytic ethics goes back to A. Pieper, "Analytische Ethik. Ein Überblick über die seit 1900 in England und America erschienene Ethik-Literatur," in *Philosophisches Jarbuch* 78, (1971): 144-176. Also, more recently A. Pieper, *Sprachanalytische Ethik und praktische Freiheit. Das Problem der Ethik als autonomer Wissenschaft* (Stuttgart: 1973); G. Grewendorf and G. Meggle, eds., *Seminar: Sprache und Ethik. Zur Entwicklung der Metaethik* (Frankfurt a. M.: Suhrkamp, 1974); R. Ginters, *Werte und Normen* (Düsseldorf: Patmos, 1982); F. von Kutschera, *Grundlagen der Ethik* (Berlin: Walter de Gruyter, 1982).

5. K. H. Ilting, "Hobbes und die praktische Philosophie der Neuzeit," in *Philosophisches Jahrbuch* 72, (1964): 84-102.

6. M. Riedel, ed., *Rehabilitierung der Praktischen Philosophie* (Freiburg i. Br.: Rombach Verlag, 1972-74).

7. See F. P. Hager, ed., *Ethik und Politik des Aristoteles* (Darmstadt: Wissenschaftliche Buchgesellschaft, 1972); O. Höffe, *Praktische Philosophie. Das Modell des Aristoteles* (München: Pustet, 1971); A. Kamp, *Die politische Philosophie des Aristoteles und ihre metaphysichen Grundlagen* (Freiburg: Karl Alber Verlag, 1985).

220

8. The German literature on "contemporary ethical crisis" is legion and cannot be referred to in all its extension. Apel's account of this crisis remains valuable, even after several years. See K. O. Apel, *Die Transformation der Philosophie* (Frankfurt a. M.: Suhrkamp Verlag, 1973). For the rehabilitation of the concept of virtue in Apel, see K.O. Apel, "Kein Ende der Tugenden," in *Frankfurter Hefte* 29, (1974): 783-794.

9. G. Bien, *Die Grundlegung der politischen Ethik bei Aristoteles* (Freiburg i. Br.: Alber Verlag, 1980).

10. See Ch. Zahlmann, ed., *Kommunitarismus in der Diskussion. Eine streitbare Einführung* (Berlin: Rotbuch Verlag, 1992); A. Honneth, ed., *Kommunitarismus. Eine Debatte über die moralischen Grundlagen moderner Gesellschaften* (Frankfurt: Campus Verlag, 1993).

11. See H. Albert, *Plädoyer für den kritischen Rationalismus* (München: Piper Verlag, 1971).

12. G. Pfafferott, *Ethik und Hermeneutik* (Königstein: Hain Verlag, 1981).

13. See K. Demmer, *Deuten und Handeln. Grundlagen und Grundfragen der Fundamentalmoral* (Freiburg i. Br.: Herder Verlag, 1985).

14. See, for instance, G. Grewendorf and G. Meggle, eds., *Seminar: Sprache und Ethik. Zur Entwicklung der Metaethik* (Frankfurt a. M.: Suhrkamp, 1974); O. Höffe, ed., *Einführung in die utilitaristische Ethik. Klassische und zeitgenössische Texte* (München: Beck Verlag, 1975); D. Birnbacher and N. Hoester, eds., *Texte zur Ethik* (München: Taschebuch Verlag, 1976); R. Ginters, ed., *Typen ethischer Argumentation* (Düsseldorf: Patmos Verlag, 1976); O. Höffe, ed., *Über J. Rawls' Theorie der Gerechtigkeit* (Frankfurt: Suhrkamp Verlag, 1977).

15. See, for instance, U. Wolf, *Das Problem des moralischen Sollens* (Berlin: Walter de Gruyter, 1986).

16. The debate on marxist ethics has found its first documentation in a collective volume: E. Angehm and G. Lohmann, eds., *Ethik und Marx* (Königstein: Hain Verlag, 1986). The debate on the so called austro-marxism -- a debate which took place at the beginning of the century -- is documented by R. De La Vega and H. Sandkühler, eds., *Marxismus und Ethik* (Frankfurt: Suhrkamp, 1974).

17. See for example, the synthesis of A. Pieper, *Ethik und Moral. Eine Einführung in die praktische Philosophie* (München: Beck Verlag, 1985). Also

the accurate introduction to ethical problems of F. Ricken, *Allgemeine Ethik* (Stuttgart, Kohlammer Verlag, 1983).

18. The literature on interdisciplinary work in theology is wide indeed. Among the many titles: J. B. Metz and T. Rendtorff, eds., *Theologie in der interdisziplinären Forschung* (Gütersloh: Mohn Verlag, 1971); H. Fries, "Konvergenzargumentation," in *Lexikon für Theologie und Kirche*, vol. VI, pp. 517-518; W. Schöllgen, *Konkrete Ethik* (Düsseldorf: Patmos Verlag, 1961); J. Gründel, "Die Bedeutung einer Konvergenzargumentation für die Gewissheitsbildung und für die Zustimmung zur absoluten Geltung einzelner sittlicher Normen," in *Wahrheit und Verkündigung* [Festschrift Schmaus] (München: 1967), pp. 1607-1630; D. Mieth, *Moral und Erfahrung* (Freiburg: Herder Verlag, 1977); Idem, *Die Spannungseinheit von Theorie und Praxis* (Freiburg: Herder Verlag, 1986); J. Blank and G. Hasenhüttl, eds., *Erfahrung, Glaube und Moral* (Düsseldorf: Patmos Verlag, 1982); W. Korff, "Die ethische und theologische Relevanz der Humanwissenschaften," in D. Mieth and F. Compagnoni, eds., *Ethik im Kontext des Glaubens* (Freiburg: Herder Verlag, 1978), pp. 157-185; H. Ringeling, "Christliche Ethik im Dialog mit der Anthropologie: das Problem der Identität," in A. Hertz, ed., *Handbuch der christlichen Ethik* (Freibur: Herder, 1978), Vol. I, pp. 474-518; Idem, *Ethik vor der Sinnfrage* (Gütersloh: Mohn Verlag, 1980), pp. 113-128.

19. See "Thesen einer Arbeitsgruppe der Societas Ethical über die Rolle der Ethik an den westeuropäischen Universitäten," in *Zeitschrift für Evangelische Ethik* 16, (1972): 67-168.

20. On this relation see H. W. Döring, *Technik und Ethik. Die sozialphilosophische und politische Diskussion um die Gentechnologie* (Frankfurt: Campus Verlag, 1988). For the relation to the life of medicine H. Piechowiak, ed., *Ethische Probleme der modernen Medizin* (Maiz: Grünewald Verlag, 1985).

21. As one of the many examples see *Genetik und Moral. Beiträge zu einer Ethik des Ungeborenen* (Mainz: Grünewald, 1985).

22. V. Eid and al., *Moraltheologisches Jahrbuch. Bioethische Probleme* (Mainz: Grünewald, 1989).

23. So the bibliographical bullettins on recent publications in medical ethics. Among many see J. Hübner, "Neue theologische Literatur zur medizinischen Ethik. Zur fundamentalethischen Diskussion," in *Theologische Rundschau* 48, (1983): 273-299. See also J. Hübner, ed., *Der dialog zwischen Theologie und Naturwissenschaft. Ein bibliographischer Bericht* (München: Kaiser Verlag, 1987); W. Becher, ed., *Medizinische Ethik in der evangelischen Theologie der Ökumene* (Frankfurt: 1979).

222

24. Informations on the state of the discussion are provided by F. J. Illhard, *Medizinische Ethik* (Berlin: Springer Verlag, 1985).

25. As a general introduction to these problems H. Schipperges, *Moderne Medizin im Spiegel der Geschichte* (Stuttgart: DTV/Thieme Verlag, 1970). Among other authors: B. Pfleiderer, *Krankheit und Kultur: eine Einführung in die Ethnomedizin* (Berlin: Reimer Verlag, 1985); H. Schipperges, *Homo patients: zur Geschichte des kranken Menschen* (Zürich: Piper Verlag, 1985); E. Sievers, *Natur als Weg: Thomas von Aquin und gesundes Leben* (Würzburg: Naumann Verlag, 1985). For a systematic interpretation of the changes of paradigms in medicine and clinical research, see the fundamental work of W. Wieland, *Strukturwandel der Medizin und ärztliche Ethik: philosophische Überlegungen zu Grundfragen einer praktischen Wissenschaft* (Heidelberg: Winter Verlag, 1986).

26. H. Schipperges and al., *Krankheit, Heilkunst, Heilung* (Freiburg i. Br.: Alber verlag, 1978); G. Groddeck, *Krankheit als Symbol* (Frankfurt: Fischer Verlag, 1983); K. Horn and al., *Gesundverhalten und Krankheitsgewinn* (Opladen: Westdeutscher Verlag, 1984); G. Overbeck, *Krankheit als Anpassung* (Frankfurt: Suhrkamp, 1984); B. Pfeiderer, *Krankheit als Kultur* (Berlin: Reimer Verlag, 1985); H. U. Deppe and M. Regus, *Seminar: Medizin, Gesellschaft, Geschichte* (Frankfurt: Suhrkamp, 1975); H. Schipperges, *Die Vernunft des Leibes. Gesundheit und Krankheit im Wandel* (Graz: Styria Verlag, 1984).

27. D. von Engelhardt, "Dauer und Wandel in der Geschichte der medizinischen Ethik. Ein Beitrag zur Prüfung des Paradigmawechselns des Thomas S. Kuhn in der Medizin," in *Ethik in der Medizin*, ed. U. Schaudraff (Berlin: Springer Verlag, 1987), pp. 35-44; Idem, "Betrachtungen zur Struktur der medizinischen Ethik," in *Wissenschaft-Technik-Humanität*, ed. A. J. Buch and J. Splett (Frankfurt: Suhrkamp, 1982), pp. 99-119; Idem, *Die inneren Verbindungen zwischen Philosophie und Medizin im 20. Jahrhundert* (Darmstadt: Wissenschafliche Buchgesellschaft, 1980).

28. See the recent edition of his works by P. Achilles: V. von Weiszäcker, *Gesammelte Schriften* [10 Voll.] (Frankfurt: Suhrkamp Verlag, 1986). Directly influenced by the reflection of von Weiszäcker are G. Knapp, *Mensch und Krankheit* (Stuttgart: Klett-Cotta, 1970), and F. Hartmann, *Ärtzliche Anthropologie. Das Problem des Menschen in der Medizin der Neuzeit* (Bremen: Schnemann Verlag, 1973).

29. S. Dressler, *Viktor von Weiszäcker medizinische Anthropologie und Philosophie* (Wien: Überreiter Wissenschaft, 1989); W. Rorarius, *Viktor von Weiszäckers Pathosophie* (Stuttgart: Thieme Verlag, 1991); S. Emonds, *Menschenwerden in Beziehung* (Stuttgart: Frommann-Holzboog, 1993); J. Rattner, *Krankheit, Gesundheit und der Artz* (München: Quintessenz Verlag, 1993).

30. J. S. Ach and A. Gaidt, eds., *Herausforderung der Bioethik* (Stuttgart: Frommann-Holzboog Verlag, 1993).

31. For the first type of literature see G. Altner, ed., *Kreatur Mensch. Moderne Wissenschaft auf der Suche nach dem Humanum* (München: DTV Taschenbuchverlag, 1973); S. Wehowsky, ed., *Schöpfer Mensch? Gentechnik, Verantwortung und unsere Zukunft* (Gütersloh: Mohn Verlag, 1985).

32. H. Jonas, *Das Prinzip Verantwortung. Versuch einer Ethik für die technologische Zivilisation* (Frankfurt: Suhrkamp, 1979). Also Idem, *Technik, Medizin und Ethik* (Frankfurt: Suhrkamp, 1985). For an analysis of the work of Jonas, see W. E. Meller, *Der Begriff der Verantwortung bei H. Jonas* (Frankfurt: Athenäum Verlag, 1988), and J. Römelt, *Verantwortung für das Leben* (Innsbruch: Resch Verlag, 1993).

33. It is evident here a polemical reference to Ernst Bloch.

34. See especially J. B. Metz, *Christliche Anthropozentrik* (München: Kösel Verlag, 1962), and more recently A. Auer, *Umweltethik. Ein theologischer Beitrag zur ökologischen Diskussion* (Düsseldorf: Patmos Verlag, 1985).

35. H. Jonas, *Das Prinzip Verantwortung*, p. 63-65.

36. Especially in the book *Technik, Medizin und Ethik*.

37. This concern for future generations is particularly strong in contemporary German ethical reflection. For a first introduction to the discussion see H. Kleger, "Gerechtigkeit zwischen Generationen," in *Archivs für Rechts-und Sozialphilosophie* 26, (1986): 147-190. Richer from a speculative point of view is the perspective developed by D. Birnbacher, *Verantwortung für zukünftige Generationen* (Stuttgart: Reclam Verlag, 1988).

38. See H. M. Sass, ed., *Medizin und Ethik* (Stuttgart: Reclam Verlag, 1989).

39. See H. M. Sass, "Methoden ethischer Güterabwägung in der Biotechnologie," in *Ethische und rechtliche Fragen der Gentechnologie und der Reprodutionsmedizin*, ed. V. Braun, D. Mieth and K. Steigleder (München: Schweitzer Verlag, 1987), pp. 89-110.

40. See for instance U. Beck, *Risikogesellschaft. Auf dem Weg in eine andere Moderne* (Frankfurt: Suhrkamp, 1986).

41. K. Lorenz, *Antriebe tierischen und menschlichen Verhaltens* (München: Piper Verlag, 1968); Idem, *Die Evolution des Denkens* (München:

224

Piper Verlag, 1983); H. M. Zippelius, *Die Vermessene Theorie* (Braunschweig: Vieweg Verlag, 1992); F. M. Wuketits, *Konrad Lorenz: Leben und Werk eines grossen Naturforschers* (München: Piper Verlag, 1990).

42. One has to think, for instance, of all the authors like Gehlen and Plessner who try to elaborate an ethics on the basis on empirical anthropology: A. Gehlen, *Der Mensch. Seine Natur und seine Stellung in der Welt* (Wiesbaden: 1978). Also W. Wickler and U. Seibt, *Das Prinzip Eigennutz. Ursachen und Konsequenzen sozialen Verhaltens* (Hamburg: 1977); W. Schulz, "Die Epoche der nichtspekulativen Anthropologie," in Idem, *Philosophie in der veränderten Welt* (Pfullingen: 1972), pp. 419-456.

43. See the editorial to A. Leist, ed., *Um Leben und Tod* (Frankfurt: Suhrkamp, 1990), pp. 9-64.

44. For an analysis of the debate between *Naturalism* and *anti-Naturalism* from the point of view of biological sciences see H. Mohr, *Natur und Moral. Ethik in der Biologie* (Darmstadt: Wissenschaftliche Buchgessellschaft, 1987).

45. B. Bujo, *Die Begründung der Sittlichen* (Schöning: Paderborn, 1984); W. Kerber, *Sittliche Normen. Zum Problem ihrer allgemeinen und unwandelbaren Geltung* (Düsseldorf: Patmos Verlag, 1981); B. Schüller, *Die Begründung der sittlichen Urteile* (Düsseldorf: Patmos Verlag, 1980).

46. F. Furger, *Was Ethik begründet. Deontologie oder Teleologie - Hintergrund und Tragweite einer moraltheologischen Auseinandersetzung* (Zürich: Benzinger Verlag, 1984).

47. See E. Seidler, ed., *Medizinische Anthropologie: Beiträge für eine theoretische Pathologie* (Berlin: Springer Verlag, 1984).

48. Zentrum für Medizinische Ethik Bochum, ed., *Medizinethische Materialien*.

49. See the splendid volume of H. M. Sass, *Bioethik in den USA. Methoden-Themen- Positionen* (Berlin: Springer Verlag, 1988).

50. V. Braun, D. Mieth and K. Steigleder, eds, *Ethische und rechtliche Fragen der Gentechnologie und der Reproduktionsmedizin* (Münchem: Schweitzer Verlag, 1987).

51. See J. Czwallina, *Ethik-Kommissionen* (Bern: Lang Verlag, 1987); A. Eser and H. G. Koch, eds., *Schwangerschaftsabbruch: Auf dem Weg zu einer Neuregelung* (Baden-Baden: Nomos Verlag, 1992); *Medizinische Ethik-Kommissionen. Aspekte und Aufgaben* (Münster: Vereinigung der Freunde der

medizinischen Fakultät der west. Wilhelms-Universität zu Münster, 1981); O. Gsell, "Medizinisch-ethische Kommissionen der Krankenhäuser der Schweiz," in *Schweitzärische Ärtzezeitung*, (1979): 1345-1350.

52. See the complete text under the title *In-vitro-Fertilisation, Genomanalyse und Gentherapie. Bericht der gemeinsamen Arbeitsgruppe des Bundesministers für Forschung und Technologie und des Bundesministers der Justiz* (München: Schweitzer Verlag, 1985).

53. *Expertenkommission Humangenethik und Reproduktionsmedizin. Bericht erstattet an das Eidg. Departement des Inneren und Eidg. Justiz- und Polizeidepartement* (Bern: Eidg. Gesundheitsamt, 1988).

54. Bibliographical references can be found in A. Bondolfi, "Tier 'rechte' und Tierversuche," in *Concilium* 25 (1989): 267-274.

55. For a global presentation of the issue from both an historical and a systematic perspective, see H. Sauer, *Über die Geschichte der Mensch-Tier Beziehung und die historische Entwicklung des Tierschutzes in Deutschland* (Giessen, 1983).

56. U. Steger, ed., *Die Herstellung der Natur* (Bonn: 1985); W. van den Daele, *Menschen nach Mass?* (München, Beck Verlag, 1985); Idem, "Technische Dynamik und gesellschaftliche Moral. Zur soziologischen Bedeutung der Gentechnologie," in *Soziale Welt* 37, (1986): 149-172; G. Altner, "Die Nutzungsziele der Gentechnologie unter der Perspektive von Umwelt- und Sozialverträglichkeit," in *Ethische und rechtliche Fragen der Gentechnologie und der Reproduktionsmedizin*, ed. V. Braun, D. Mieth and K. Steigleder (München: Schweitzer Verlag, 1987), pp. 213-223; A. Blankenagel, "Gentechnologie und Menschenwürde. Über die Strapazierung vom juristischem Sachverstand und gesundem Menschenverstand anlässlich eines ernsten Themas," in *Kritische Justiz* 20, (1987): 379-393; J. Radkau, "Hiroschima und Asilomar. Die Inszenierung des Diskurses über die Gentechnik vor dem Hintergrund der Kernenergie-Kontroverse," in *Geschichte und Gesellschaft* 14, (1988): 329-363; H. J. Münk, "Die christliche Ethik vor der Herausforderung durch die Gentechnik," in *Leben in der Hand des Menschen*, ed. J. Pfamatter and E. Christen (Zürich: Benzinger Verlag, 1991), pp. 75-178; A. Bondolfi, *Gentechnologie in der Medizin* (Genève: Folia Bioethica, 1992); *Gentechnologie aus ethischer Sicht*, ed. Nationalkommission Justitia et Pax (Bern: 1992); H. Halter, "Ist Gentechnologie des Teufels?" in *Verantwortung für das Leben*, ed. J. Römelt (Innsbruck: Resch Verlag, 1993), pp. 37-62.

57. An example of a very balanced approach can be found in K. Grosch, P. Hampe and J. Schmidt, *Herstellung der Natur?* (Frankfurt: Campus Verlag, 1990). For a juridical as well as socio-political account see I. Künzier, *Macht*

der Technik-Ohnmacht des Rechts? Regelungsbedarf und Regelungsmöglichkeiten in Bereich der Gentechnologie (Bern: Lang Verlag, 1990).

58. W. Meyhöfer and W. Künzel, eds., *Donogene Insemination* (Berlin: Springer verlag, 1988); M. Lanz-Zumstein, *Embryonenschutz und Befruchtungsethik* (München: Schweitzer Verlag, 1986); M. Honecker, "Genetische Eingriffe und Reproduktionsmedizin aus der Sicht theologischer Anthropologie," in *Zeitschrift für Theologie und Kirche* 84, (1987): 118-136; J. von Ins and P. Grossmann, eds., *Künstliches Leben-ärtzliche Kunst?* (Zürich: Verlag der Fachvereine, 1989); M. Rassem, "Zur Revolution der reproduktion," in *Zeitschrift für Politik* 36, (1989): 347-357; W. Selb, *Rechtsordnung und künstliche Reproduktion des Menschen* (Tübingen: Mohr Verlag, 1987); A. Eser, H. G. Koch and Th. Wiesenbart, eds., *Regelungen der Fortflanzungsmedizin und Humangenetik* (Frankfurt: Campus Verlag, 1990).

59. R. Baumann-Hölzle, *Human-Gentechnologie und moderne Gesellschaft* (Zürich: TVZ, 1990); R. Baumann, A. Bondolfi and H. Ruh, *Genetische Testmöglichkeiten* (Frankfurt: Campus Verlag, 1990); D. Beckmann and al., *Humangenetik-Segen für die Menschheit oder unkalkulierbares Risiko?* (Bern: Lang Verlag, 1991)

60. For a critical and historical reconstruction see P. Weingart, K. Bayertz and J. Kroll, *Rasse, Blut und Gene. Geschichte der Eugenik und Rassenhygiene in Deutschland* (Frankfurt: Suhrkamp Verlag, 1988).

61. See R. Baumann-Hölzle, A. Bondolfi and H. Ruth, eds., *Genetische Testmöglichkeiten*, op. cit.

62. German literature on abortion is legion. For the ethical discussion see A. Leist, *Eine Frage des Lebens. Ethik der Abtreibung und künstlichen Befruchtung* (Frankfurt: Campus Verlag, 1990). For the legal discussion A. Eser and H. G. Koch, *Schwangerschaftsabbruch: Auf dem Weg zu einer Neuregelung*, op. cit.

63. G. Amendt, *Die bestrafte Abtreibung* (Fulda: Fuldaer Verlag, 1988); H. Pötter, ed., *Die ungewollte Schwangerschaft* (Köln: Deutsche Ärzte Verlag, 1982); F. Böckle, ed., *Schwangerschaftsabbruch als individuelles und gesellschaftliches Problem* (Düsseldorf: Patmos Verlag, 1981).

64. See the detailed information of J. Gründel and H. G. Koch, "Sterilization" in *Lexikon Medizin Ethik Recht*, ed. A. Eser (Freiburg i. Br.: Herder Verlag, 1989), pp. 1102-1117.

65. F. Böckle, "Sterilization und Kastration," in *Handbuch der christlichen Ethik*, ed. A. Herz (Freibur: Herder, 1978), vol. II, pp. 46-53.

227

66. R. Egenter, "Die Organtransplantation im Lichte der biblischen Ethik," in *Moral zwischen Anspruch und Verantwortung*, ed. F. Böckle and F. Groner (Düsseldorf: Patmos Verlag, 1964), pp. 142-153.

67. A. Elsässer, "Organspende-selbsverständliche Christenpflicht?" in *Theologisch-praktische Quartalschrift* 128, (1980): 231-239; R. Löw, "Die moralische Dimension von Organtransmantation," in *Scheidewege* 17, (1987/88): 16-48; W. Ruf, *Organverpflanzung aus katholischer Sicht* (München: 1971); A. Bondolfi and al., *Ethik und Transplantationsmedizin* (Comano: Alice, 1993); R. Greinert and G. Wuttke, *Organspende. Kritische Ansichten zur Transplantationsmedizin* (Freiburg: Lamuv Verlag, 1993).

68. See A. Bondolfi, "Allokationsprobleme in der Transplantationsmedizin," in *Zeitschrift für ärztliche Fortbildung*, (1993): 547-551.

69. A. Auer, H. Menzel and A. Eser, *Zwischen Heilauftrag und Sterbehilfe* (Köln: Heymann Verlag, 1977); U. Eibach, *Recht auf Leben-Recht auf Sterben* (Wuppertal: Brockhaus Verlag, 1977); V. Eid, *Euthanasie, oder soll man auf verlangen töten?* (Mainz: Grünewald Verlag, 1984); F. Furger and K. Koch, *Verfügbares Leben?* (Freiburg: Imba Verlag, 1978); A. Eser, ed., *Suizid und Euthanasie als human- und sozialwissenschaftliches Problem* (Stuttgart: Enke Verlag, 1976).

70. H. Ringeling, *Leben im Anspruch der Schöpfung* (Freiburg: Herder Verlag, 1988); K. Demmer, *Leben in Menschenhand* (Freiburg: Herder Verlag, 1987); E. Schockenhoff, *Ethik des Lebens* (Mainz: Grünewald, 1993).

Chapter 7

THE OUTLINES OF ITALIAN BIOETHICS

Adriano Bompiani

Introduction

Describing the contribution of Italian authors to the development of bioethics and understanding how our culture has experienced bioethics in recent decades (especially the past one) is no easy endeavor[1]. In any case, it entails recognizing the persistence of a notable "vagueness" in many aspects of the problem.

What is bioethics, a "movement" or a "discipline"? What are the goals of bioethics? To whom is it directed? What are its principles, what are its strategies, and from what sources does it derive? What is the relationship between bioethics and traditional medical ethics? What is its relationship with environmental ethics?

There is no doubt that the initial message expressed by Italian bioethics was that of a movement soon tempered by the necessity to thoroughly investigate the "contents" of the message itself with scientific exactness.

1. Italian Bioethics: Between "Movement" and "Institution"

Situated in the middle of this "parabola," Italian thought is working to delineate gradually the "fields" and the "significances" of bioethics. From this work, a more rigorous foundation of the epistemological framework is expected to emerge.

1.1. Fields and Meanings

From the point of view emphasizing *content*,[2] there are at least three fields that make up the realm of Italian bioethics:

a) the field regarding the relationship between life and ethical values in reference to applications of bio-medicine (in continuity with medical ethics);

b) the field relating to the relationship between life and ethical values in the more general panorama of life sciences;

c) the field regarding the relationship between living conditions on earth and Man's new dimensions of responsibility relating to all forms of life and future generations.

From the point of view emphasizing *form*,[3] bioethics tends to be considered as a branch or a sub-discipline of ethical knowledge, from which it receives its basic epistemological statute. As such, bioethics derives its justification and orientation from its subordinate relationship to ethical knowledge. The question of "form," other than being decisive in methodological structure, influences the *significance* that is attributed to bioethics. The opinions in Italy on this matter are very articulated; in any case, these are the most emphasized aspects:

a) the legitimization within the bioethical sector of the conviction that the management of progress is not only a scientific issue, but that it must also be dealt with through reasoned ethical reflection;

b) the strengthening of a rational foundation for ethics by elaborating parameters of reference and ethical evaluation that are easily communicated, plausible, and coherent;

c) the determination, within the context of pluralism in ethical opinion, of priorities in order to restore the contents of public and individual ethics, so that they are integrated and compatible with one another.

1.2. Aspects of Cultural Elaboration

Regarding cultural elaboration in bioethics, the Italian situation seems to be characterized by the fervent engagement of spokespersons from diverse cultural extractions. There were many meetings and debates at all levels of "quality." It must be stated that initiatives stemming from Catholic culture[4] have been until now the most coordinated, although the secular culture has vigorously entered the debate within bioethical research.[5] There is constant dialogue between these two different cultural points of view. In some cases, the dialogue is heated and the positions are irreconcilable; in others, however, there is the possibility for compromise. The examination of a few important chapters in bioethics will demonstrate the different positions.

The commitment to adequate cultural elaboration was undertaken in the eighties through the activity of certain scientific centers and institutes. These centers and institutes played an important role in the field of bioethical research and in the creation of numerous initiatives.

Here is a list of the most active centers and institutes that, above and beyond the activity of single scholars, contribute to the transmission of the "bioethical message" and to its systematic, in-depth examination.

The Center for Bioethics at the Sacred Heart Catholic University of Rome, Department of Medicine and Surgery - Founded in 1985, the Center is currently directed by Elio Sgreggia, holder of the bioethics chair. This chair was instituted at the Catholic University's Department of Medicine in the academic year 1983-84. In the same department, a post-graduate course in bioethics began in the academic year 1989-90. This course is open to all who hold degrees in either medicine, biology, philosophy, law, or theology. Moreover, Director Sgreggia's center organizes, within the Catholic world, numerous standing training activities, the most important of which is the residential course in bioethics.

Publications: Medicina e Morale is a bimonthly review of bioethics, deontology and medical ethics and is directed by E. Sgreggia. The Center for Bioethics also edits the series "Scienza, Medicina, Etica" published by Vita e Pensiero. The following numerous monographs have been published: A. Serra, G. Neri (ed.) *New Genetics, Man and Society*, Milan 1986; E. Sgreggia (ed.) *The Gift of Life*, Milan 1987; S. Mancuso, E. Sgreggia (ed.) *Treatment of Conjugal Sterility*, Milan 1988; A. Bompiani, E. Sgreggia (ed.) *Organ Transplants: Technological Progress, Ethical Aspects, and Legislative Prospects*, Milan 1989; M.L. Di Pietro, E. Sgreggia, *The Transmission of Life in the Teachings of John Paul II*, Milan 1989; L. Antico, E. Sgreccia (ed.) *Elderly Creativity*, Milan 1989.

Theoretical Approach: The Center tends towards what E. Sgreccia defines as "ontologically rooted personalism." With this idea, the Center clearly tends towards Thomistic philosophical tradition. "It is in this tradition that Man is considered in his 'being' and in his ontological value, for what he is and is defended from every power of exploitation and every ideology."[6]

Politea, the Center for Research and Training in Politics and Ethics - This is a secular center that has been active since 1983, the year of its foundation, in biomedical research. The Center is home to various groups: a research group coordinated by Sebastiano Maffettone, interested in proposing a public environmental philosophy; a group for social policies directed by Paolo Martelli and Elena Gramaglia; a theoretical seminar on economics and philosophy, coordinated by Lorenzo Sacconi; and, finally, more directly relevant to bioethics, a research group coordinated by Maurizio Mori and composed of moral philosophers, lawyers, and physicians with a program that includes study seminars, research, and document collection. The group organizes debates and meetings. The last meeting aroused a great deal of interest nationally and discussed "Bioethics: Moral and Political Questions on the Future of Man" (Rome, March 29-31, 1990).

Publications: Every quarter, Politeia publishes *Notizie di Politeia*, with the goals of spreading and commenting on cultural and scholarly initiatives, along with furnishing services for research.

Theoretical Approach: Having surpassed the historicist and Marxist conceptions which had been dominant in Italy until recently, Politeia appeals to a particular vision of the liberal-democratic tradition in which modern societies are understood to be the outcome of individuals' free and rational choices. "Politeia proposes the study of institutions and public policies of the pluralist democracies, and, towards this end, privileges methodological individualism as the theoretical tool to formulate reform proposals of the collective decision making procedures according to criteria of effectiveness, efficiency, and equity. On these issues, Politeia intends to foster civil and scientific debate, to set up initiatives, instruments and research institutes, and to begin communication, training, and education" (From Art. 3 of Politeia Constitution).

The H. San Raffaele Scientific Institute, Didactic Branch, University of Milan - The defining characteristic of the approach to bioethics as practiced in the Institute is tied to the attempt to integrate, from the ethical-humanistic point of view, the study of medicine. This goal is sought through the "School of Medicine and Human Sciences." The director of the School is Paolo Cattorini, who has the dual qualification of physician and philosopher.

The most important occurrences in the School's annual cycle include the following: the instructive-educational *Meetings*, the monograph *Seminars*, including the *Conventions* that San Raffaele organizes and oversees, such as "The European Day of Bioethics," which this year reached its fifth edition. There is also the Medical Ethics and Bioethics *Week*, lead by professor Manuel Cuyas, and *Conversations in Bioethics* that occur every two weeks.

Publications: the series "Medicina e Scienze Umane" which includes *Essays on Medicine and Human Sciences* and *New Essays on Medicine and*

234

Human Sciences, a collection of the issues covered in the first teaching cycle from 1984-85; *Sanare Infirmos*, a journal of the Institute appearing every four months; *Kos*, a bimonthly review of science and ethics.

Theoretical Approach: the basic objective is the ethical-humanistic integration of the study of medicine. This goal is pursued in two ways: first through "education with an anthropological approach;" second, through "clear methodological awareness."[7]

The Center of Bioethics of Genoa - The Center was founded in 1984 on the initiative of university instructors from many disciplines and areas of research, ranging from philosophy to law, and from medicine to the social sciences. Currently, the Center is directed by Luisella Battaglia. With a secular orientation, the Center proposes the study of the following issue areas: medical ethics, problems relating to "the right to life," animal rights, and the protection of the environment. The Center's activities are divided into various areas and include seminars, training courses, and study conventions.

Theoretical Approach: the approach to bioethics as proposed and practiced by the Center is characterized by the need not to restrict its attention only to human life, but to include in its reflection *everything that is alive* and, by extension, to the environment in which these various forms of life occur. The Center of Bioethics of Genoa has tried to take into consideration the specificity of this sphere of research by confronting not only bioethical medical issues, but also environmental and animal bioethical issues.[8] The following conventions were dedicated to environmental problems: "Day of environmental ethics," Naples 1989, in cooperation with the "Istituto Suor Orsola Benincasa;" "Ethics and Environment," Genoa 1988, in cooperation with the Museum of Natural History; "The Dark Mirror: Animals in the Imagination of Man," Genoa, November 1990.

The International Center for the Study of the Family - The Center confronts bioethical problems from the point of view pertinent to their physiognomy, *i.e.*, the point of view of the family. The Center's conventions and contributions are of great interest, even if they are centered on this particular perspective. The credit goes above all to the director of the Center, S. Spinsanti, one of the most renowned scholars of biomedical ethics in Italy. He had the merit of opening bioethical reflection with stimulating approaches, such as the "anthropological" framework of medicine and the "transpersonal" framework.[9]

The most important series of intervention into the bioethical debate by Spinasti's Center were the following: the first was the Symposium on Hospital Ethics Committees, held in Milan on March 23-25, 1986,[10] organized together with the hospitalary order of San Giovanni di Dio (Fatebenefratelli); the second, centered more on the family, was the convention "Birth, Love, and Death," which explicitly introduced the family into bioethical problems; in fact, "Ethics of Life and Family" was the subtitle of the convention.[11]

Italian Association of Bioethics, Chair of Anthropology, University of Florence - Founded in 1987, the Association is presided over by Brunetto Chiarelli.

Publications: The Association's official organ is *Problemi di Bioetica*, a journal whose framework reflects the make-up of the Association. In fact, the journal intends to be a meeting-place for reflection and debate on all the issues inherent in the area generally defined as "bio-ethical," *i.e.*, medical ethics and environmental ethics. The explicit purpose of the journal is to integrate different approaches in this field of knowledge without ideological or methodological presuppositions.

Theoretical Approach: This association is open to different approaches. However, it inclines towards a strain of thought that, in the understanding of an ethical fact, tends to emphasize investigations and scientific acquisitions of ethology, social anthropology, and sociology. These investigations, undertaken in those three closely connected "sectors" by scholars of such authority as B. Chiarelli, V. Melotti, and A. Oliverio, lead to statements that entail ethics' foundation *on natural basis*. These statements can be expressed as follows:

a) the development of the evolutionary school of thought increasingly suggests that the uniqueness of Man's physical, cultural, and historic development be considered from its natural basis. Natural sciences, just as much as humanistic sciences, furnish precious elements that indicate there is no conflict between the recognition of Man's nature as an animal species and his uniqueness as a cultural animal.

b) Ethics, based on this natural perspective, is seen as a biological characteristic of Man that developed through natural selection. Despite their biased differences, all ethical systems represent organized responses to fundamental human needs. The moral values that they carry with them and emphasize function as ways to favor the survival and reproduction of the populations to which they apply. These moral values are, in their totality, an ideological superstructure selected for its indirectly positive effects on the genetic fitness of society's members.[12]

Center for Bioethics, Gramsci Institute, Rome - Some time ago, the Gramsci Institute began an intense internal debate among scientists, moral philosophers, legal scholars, sociologists, and politicians about problems in bioethics. The first external demonstration of this activity was the convention in March of 1988 on "Questions of Life, Science, Ethics, and Law."[13] The success of this convention led to the formation of the "Center for Bioethics."

Theoretical Approach: The center recognizes that bioethical problems require an extension and democratization of the debate; moreover, it recognizes the principle of free choice in ethics. Finally, it states that decisions on bioethical matters involving "social" aspects must not be left up to market criteria.[14]

The Ethical and Medical Project of the Lanza Foundation, Padua - The project "Ethics and Medicine" is one of the areas in which the Lanza Foundation's activity takes place. The persons in charge are Paolo Benciolini, full professor of legal medicine at the University of Padua, together with Giorgio De Sandre, director of the Institute of medical pathology at the University of Verona, and Giuseppe Trentin, professor of moral theology at the Theological Faculty of Northern Italy. The research is coordinated by Corrado Viafora.

The Project, started in 1988, had the following goals in its first three years:

1) the achievement of a survey of trends and tendencies in bioethics at an international level;

2) the initiation of a "bioethics workshop" that would offer the possibility of on-going training;

3) the preparation of a bioethics archive that would gradually become a center for documentation;

4) the putting together of the research undertaken by the Group with the initiatives and outlooks of other national and international Centers for Bioethics.

The achievement of the goal that the Group "Ethics and Medicine" believes to be fundamental (*i.e.*, the creation of a bioethics training workshop) was entrusted to the "Interdisciplinary Seminar." The thematic itinerary covered until now includes a survey of bioethics began by F. Böckle and A. Autiero, who followed up on the following seminars: *Ethics and Medicine: what parameters of judgment?* (December 3/4, 1988), *The Patient as Partner: Ethical Problems of Experimentation and Consent* (April 15, 1989), *Ethical Problems in Gynecology: Prenatal Diagnosis* (December 2, 1989), *Ethical Problems in Intensive Therapy: Treatment and Excessive Treatment* (March 3, 1990), *The Relationship that Heals: Ethical Problems in the Doctor-Patient Relationship* (March 12, 1990). For 1991, two seminars are foreseen: *Ethical Problems in Pediatrics* and *Ethical Problems in Geriatrics*. The seminars should thoroughly investigate the ethical problems

238

in the treatment of long-term juvenile patients and long-term elderly patients. On the edges of the interdisciplinary seminars, the reflection was primarily dedicated to the elaboration of a body of instruments aimed at aiding bioethical judgments and evaluations. Two instruments in particular were put in place: the first dealt with the establishment of a model for discussion; the second dealt with the formulation of a procedural protocol for the teaching and discussion of the "cases."

Theoretical Approach: The Project fully assimilates the fumdamental acquisitions of bioethical sensibility: *e.g.*, the need to deal ethically with bioethical progress, the need of a rational ethical foundation, and the practice of an interdisciplinary approach. Moreover, the Project shares now universally accepted principles in bioethical literature, such as the principles of autonomy, charity, and justice. Such principles, interpreted in the light of *Christian-influenced personalism*, receive more intense significance from this particular anthropological paradigm. These principles also translate respectively into the principles of dignity of the human being, global care, and solidarity.

The Project's basic presupposition is the conviction that, in the current phase of bioethics, it is certainly necessary to distinguish principles and norms. But it is also necessary to create Groups that act as "Training workshops," capable of putting into action ethical conscience as the indispensable factor in dealing with bioethical progress, both through dialogue and comparison.

The emphasis of the merits of these recently founded institutions should not make one forget that in Italy the task of bringing together ethical values and medicine was preceded by a long cultural elaboration on the in-depth examination of medical ethics.

This line of thinking regarding in-depth examination is joined by the particular tradition of Catholic medical ethics. This tradition, because of its continuity and the great human energies that it mobilized and motivated, must be particularly taken into consideration.

Out of basic principles that inspire the cultural elaboration of Catholic medical ethics, the following ones emerge: *fraternity* and *charity* as reference points in the doctor-patient and nurse-patient relationship; the *redemptive* significance of suffering and illness; the conception of the human life as *sacred* and the assumption of modern medicine as an enterprise at the *service* of the life and health of the human being as a *whole*.

These principles were sustained in Italy and made its own also from the "pastoral" aspect by the "Association of Italian Catholic Doctors." The Association was founded immediately after the Second World War due to the interest of Pope Pius XII, who was actively involved in the moral evaluation of the emerging medical technologies. The Association distinguished itself through the series of national Congresses[15] organized by Monsignor Fiorenzo Angelini and by the Association's leaders from the 1950's until today.

Even beyond these demonstrations, the contributions of Christian-influenced "laymen" have been numerous and valuable. They include figures such as Gedda, Stabilini, De Francisci, De Virgilio, Teodori, Beretta Anguissola, Manni, Polli, and, above all, Jandolo, the author of many balanced and insightful publications of ethics and medical deontology for doctors and nurses.[16]

This "corpus" of Catholic medical tradition constitutes the organic construction of a model of medical ethics that has strongly impressed its "presence" also onto the emerging Italian bioethical thought of the last decade. On the other hand, a series of questions have come to this tradition from the recent bioethical debate. It is held that when moral reflection independent of theology is distinguished (*i.e.*, a purely "rational" ethic), it appears detrimental to start from primitively deontological positions. However, what would be closer to reality of medical praxis would be the adoption of a "teleological" approach, based not so much on adherence to certain principles, but rather only on the evaluation of consequences. Moreover, the development of a morally pluralistic society would render the construction of a unitary medical ethic increasingly problematic. This is why ethical normativity in the medical field must be "reduced" to the dual deontology of the civil and penal law codes.

If these requests express the terms of the new difficulties that ethical reflection must face and if it is right to express the conditions of "correct" health-care praxis in "secular" terms, then the Catholics' reply seems well-founded and reasonable. The Catholic response emphasizes how the "solidarity" shown to the patient is much richer with the presence of a community and how the support offered to the physician himself is richer in the exercise of "values" that go well beyond individual moral integrity determined by the observation of deontological codes and of laws.

2. From Medical Ethics To Bioethics: The Determining Factors in the Italian Socio-Cultural Context

The stimuli to new research programs and effective, new instruments started by various bioethics centers stem from a phenomenon that involves the entire arena of socio-cultural life in our country: a growing *demand for ethics*[17] that has found particular expression through the field of bioethics.

However, to understand the current demand for ethics in its depth and uniqueness that has been grafted onto bioethical reflection, we must take into account some phenomena that constitute determining socio-cultural factors in the passage from traditional medical ethics to the new approach of bioethics. Let us examine three factors in particular: the process of the *socialization* of medicine, the emergence of a new *subjectivity* centered on the "rediscovery of the body," and the urgency of responsible management of *research* and experimentation.

2.1. The Process of Medicine's Socialization in Italy

The development of systems of "State Social Securities" (the Welfare State) in almost all Western countries following World War II has now reached advanced forms of socio-health services that protect individual and communal health. It is true, however, that health services do vary greatly among Western nations. This gradual development, occurring in step with the expansion of medical technology, has given rise to serious ethical questions, particularly the following:

a) how to reconcile the individual's increasing "desire" to take advantage of enjoying higher levels of health (in the largest sense of the word) with the necessity to pursue the "real" health needs of each person;

b) how to reconcile resource distribution among the various health sectors relative to the increasingly higher costs of the exercise of medicine on one hand, and the production of national resources on the other;

c) what space (resources, organization, personnel, *etc.*) to dedicate to treatment practices and so-called preventive practices;

In all the "systems," the answers to these questions have been of necessity only partial. The balance between them has incited passionate and continuing debate both in legislatures and in public opinion. This occurred with particular fervor in our country and has frequently assumed the form of a clash between political groupings.

After this necessary introduction, the "ethical aspects" inherent in the Italian case can be distinguished: first, in the social development of medicine, then in the difficulty of managing the national health service, and finally in the problem of allocating economic resources in health.

2.1.1. The Ethical Dimension of the Social Development of Medicine

The well-known process cannot be described in this forum. But it must be remembered that the ethical valence of the various subjects did not always emerge with the proper emphasis, at least in the first phase. In this phase, the consideration of sociological aspects[18] primarily directed at popularizing an instructional message to health personnel prevailed. This occurred in the light of a growing socialization of the organization of medicine's practice.

The "ethical valence" began to emerge more securely during the preparation and approval in Parliament of the so-called Health Reform Law of

December 23, 1978, no. 833 on the "Institution of the National Health Service."[19] In its basic principles, the old logic of conceiving of health as the result of a single, isolated medical intervention gave way to a new conception of health. This new understanding saw health as the process of prevention, treatment, recovery, and rehabilitation with an eye to the person's social and psycho-physical well-being. Thus, medicine moved from concentrating on treatment to focusing on prevention. Another ethically important fact is that the entitlement of the right to health was returned to the citizen as such and not as the member of a certain social category. This approach counters any discrimination, since all citizens are equal and have the same rights and duties in relation to health and preventive treatment.

If health is everyone's right and a communal good, then it demands the involvement, the responsibility, and participation of everyone. The State realizes that health's requirements must have a clear and adequate response within the social community, the territory in which the citizens habitually live and work. The assignment to the municipalities of the health service's administrative functions (accompanied by the acknowledgement of direct forms of intervention by citizens through voluntary service) clearly confirms this participatory orientation. In the general policy framework of the Health Reform, as one can see, ethical aspects are unquestionably present.[20]

2.1.2. The Ethical Dimension of the "Crisis" of the National Health Service

Why does the Italian health situation not correspond to that hypothesized by the general policy framework described above? The widespread belief is that the system inaugurated in Italy degenerated, in many places, because of many factors, including the following: first, the political parties' *occupation* of the health system's administrative ranks, with the assignment of persons specifically unprepared to manage the health services; second, the *bureaucratization* of every welfare procedure; and, third, the *insensitivity* to suffering on the part of health workers.[21]

Regarding "bureaucratization," this is a "technical" aspect adopted by all "Welfare State" nations which are the direct distributor of services. The ten-year anniversary of the National Health Service's establishment gave rise, in addition to recurring controversy, to more accurate studies on these aspects.[22] Moreover, the bureaucratization phenomenon in our country derives, according to some,[23] from moral thought that has ancient roots. This thought, on one hand, still perceives public services as gifts, favors, or donations. On the other hand, it conceives of such services as an anomaly, exercised concretely for this or that person, but not in the interest of all. Obviously, this raises the question of how to propagate a public ethic, based on principles of rational altruism, in health procedures.

The subject of the ethical dimension of the health "crisis" would not be complete without also mentioning the universally difficult *integration* of social services with health services.[24] We should also mention the well-known issue of "behavioral illnesses" in modern society which are linked to sexual promiscuity, the use and abuse of drugs, cigarettes, alcohol, and so on. Finally, we should refer to the lively consumer "movement" that in various forms (e.g. the Court of Patients' Rights, the institution of a so called Civic Defender) is increasingly pushing for an active presence in the oversight of the services' administration. In fact, this movement has already obtained, in some regions, such oversight laws.

2.1.3. The Ethical Dimension of Economic Resource Allocation in Health Services

We are faced with the following problem: the development of socialized systems of medicine and state-sponsored health care, as well as increasingly sophisticated and expensive biomedical technologies, have inevitably driven the cost of health services up in industrialized countries, including Italy. This leads to the *central* problem of the responsibility of resource allocation to the health sector (to the detriment of others) and *indirectly* to the problem of individual and collective responsibility on the qualitative level and on the cost of health care (*i.e.*, the optimal use of resources).[25]

"Technical" analyses of possible solutions are numerous, but these solutions are not analyzable in this forum.[26] The analyses consist of a series of rationalization processes that attempt, on one hand, to distinguish between "needs" and "desires" and, on the other, to guarantee services that are not only effective and efficient, but also equitable.[27]

The solution to the different problems is not simple. In fact, the balance between two opposing sides is always subject either to administrative modifications because of the budgetary situation or to popular "pressures." Moreover, economists generally complain of the medical profession's unwillingness to assume responsibility for the problems of the health sector, while many voices, in various settings, have risen against the expensive "medicalization" of every part of life and the excessive development of health industries. This conflict, which is based on "substantial" data, will never be completely resolved, but it should be regulated.

Let us take as a given that as medicine progresses, it becomes more difficult and costly to treat the patient. At this point, we should state that no patient should never be denied treatment based on "public utilitarian ethics," which rest on the cost/benefit principle. Instead, every effort must be made to prevent illness and maintain good health. The measures adopted on these matters (health education, mass screening, *etc.*) have, indeed, clear ethical implications.[28]

2.2. The Emergence of a New Subjectivity Centered Around the "Rediscovery of the Body"

The evolution of traditional concepts of "corporality" took on particular importance during the years we have been examining. This evolution also occurred in Italy in Catholic moral-theological thought[29] as well as in philosophic-legal thought.[30] Obviously, bioethics is strongly involved in this reflection.

It should be made clear that *feminism* strongly influenced the Italian debate on these issues. Feminism certainly stimulated a re-evaluation not only of traditional ideas about a woman's role in society, but also on the more general understanding of "corporality." But we must leave to other scholars a more detailed understanding of the concept of corporality,[31] and at this time, consider the "feminist movement's" repercussions on bioethics.

The response of the most thoughtful and knowledgeable groups to the instances of emancipation seems not to reside in practical approaches to the free use of one's own body. Rather, it resides in the attempt to go beyond soul/body dualism through the concept of *subject-body*. The subject-body is no longer an *object*, and as such, it is capable of expressing women's personality at the same level of man. It is well-known that these conceptions have already had strong repercussions in those sectors of bioethics concerned with the evaluation of abortion in cases of unwanted pregnancies. In all (Western) countries, including Italy, the introduction of more or less broadly permissive laws on the termination of pregnancy received a strong impetus from this new vision of "female coporality." This occurred not only during parliamentary debate, but also during the cultural one that in each country preceded, accompanied, and followed the legislative decision.

It is appropriate to point out, however, that what was specific about feminism was not only the principle of a woman's "free choice," it was also, more generally, the intense feeling of suspicion that feminism had towards what it saw as an infuriating male monopoly, *i.e.*, the medical profession. With the strategic vision favoring, in every case and circumstance, redress from persistent male domination, an ethical conception developed that impacts on many problems in bioethics. These problems include, abortion (naturally), sterilization, psychological treatment of women, medical coverage of the elderly, public health structures relating to childbirth, return of childbirth to the home and participatory methods of delivery, the use of amniocentesis for sex selection, and models of doctor-patient relations in a culture (and profession) traditionally dominated by sexism.

The advent of new reproductive technologies has brought about much puzzlement. Above all, in recent years, attitudes have been rather ambivalent. The most responsible groups accept the development and rational use of the new reproductive technologies. Such development and use, however, is subject to ethical limits including not only free choice, but also the safeguarding of the mother's health, the existence of an environment that favors the development and growth of the unborn child, and the refusal to manipulate the embryo.

The issue of "decision" remains open. Should it be up to the woman only, or should it have a reciprocal dimension in the interest of the unborn? The evolution of the entire question, from "equality" to "reciprocity" was the subject of the most recent Catholic, as well as "moderate secular," thinking.

It is worth noting that feminism's "specificity" (the struggle for emancipation) did not only deal with the issue of corporality. Feminism's most enlightened groups contributed to bioethical issues concerning nature and consequently, ecological questions. Nature has generally been symbolized as feminine, even in Western cultural traditions; many times, analogies have been drawn between masculine possessive attitudes towards the world and towards women.

The pragmatic position of certain feminist groups extends, according to a clear and realistic outlook, to the conception of nature. This type of feminism has become the advocate of nature's close interdependence with humanity's development and has sought the fair and moderate use of natural resources. It has also sought the strict prohibition of any technology that could pose a risk to the environment (*e.g.*, even the peaceful use of nuclear fusion).

2.3. The Urgency of Responsible Management of Research and Experimentation

The issue of responsible management of research and experimentation is perceived as increasingly urgent. This stems from the fact that we see scientific research *invading* all areas of life, which feeds hope as well as fear.[32] The subject is of fundamental importance in bioethics with its strict connection from its very origin, to technologies of experimentation.[33] Therefore, we must examine, in particular, the issues of clinical experimentation and genetic experimentation on humans.

2.3.1. Clinical Experimentation

Italian writers have actively participated in the definition of the concept of "experimentation," both in its technical and legal meaning.[34] Many authors, including Italians, make a distinction between "therapeutic experimentation" and "non-therapeutic experimentation." These two different cases are important when debating the lawfulness and legality of experimentation.

1) When the direct, personal interest of a passive subject in therapy is small, the availability of that person's body for experimental purposes is governed by various legislative rules that strongly limit the reach of Article 50 of the Penal Code on the Consent of the Right bearer. Thus, the "scientific," "biological," or "non-therapeutic" experimentation on human beings must be considered unlawful. The one performing such experimentation could be prosecuted in the following instances: a) when such experimentation is undertaken without (or even against) the consent of the passive subject, or when such consent is "invalid" because of natural or legal incapacity, or if the consent is extorted through violence, threats, suggestion, or obtained by trickery; b) when, despite the subject's valid consent, the experimentation violates "the law," "public order," or "sound morals;" c) if such experimentation leads to "a permanent decrease in physical integrity" (in our opinion, also including "mental integrity"). This

includes not just a "permanent" lessening of personal integrity in the medical-legal sense, but any harm to and appreciable functional impact on the person; d) when, judging from the above-mentioned permanent harm, it is possible to reconstruct what occurred with enough certainty (in penal evaluation) to constitute a crime of bodily harm that is punishable, perhaps not through regular legal channels, but rather officially or through censuring such behavior (*i.e.*, not necessarily legally, but deontologically).

2) Instead, when the passive subject has a direct, personal interest in experimentation (when such experimentation can provide tangible benefits for the passive subject's life, health, or integrity), Article 5 of the Civil Code and the duly punishable crime of bodily harm, no longer seem to apply. When there is good cause and it can be recognized as "necessary " (not always possible, for example, the case of aesthetic surgery), it is allowed to surpass the limits we discussed earlier. In fact, the real danger of serious harm to the subject (especially if it is death) makes even his or her consent unnecessary. Of course, this must be "proportional to the danger faced by the subject."

Therefore, at such times, the preeminent and contingent "clinical" ("therapeutic") interest allows for ample possibilities of experimental actions, especially if the "case" appears treatable in no other way. The one performing such experimentation, however, must still respect those fundamental ethical premises stated above. Any violation of those premises could easily lead to professional conduct that is not only deontologically censurable, but also illegal.

In the context of experimentation, the idea of "informed consent" has particular value. This idea implies the right to accept or refuse experimentation. For valid consent, the subject must have the capacity to act. This means that the person must be of legal age, and must not be either in an incapacitated state according to the law, or be in a state of psychological compulsion. In such full legal expression, informed consent can conflict with "experimental techniques" that could be necessary in order to provide scientific proof. This is valid above all for randomized experiments, with drugs and placebos, conducted according to "single-blind" or "double-blind" methods.

Many clinical researchers refuse *a priori* these distinctions between "drug" and "placebo." They see the experiment under the dual concept of "experimental drug - known drug," which is entirely different both legally and morally, although it equally presents the problem of "informed consent." The orientation of persons in Italian bioethics is rather unified in this matter.

Finally, we should keep in mind some deontological elements which are absolutely important for both therapeutic and non-therapeutic experimentation:

a) experimentation on a human being must respect the moral and scientific principles that are at the base of human medicine; such experimentation must also be preceded by preliminary assessments in other valid areas.

b) any experimentation must be performed by scientifically qualified persons and under the supervision of a highly skilled doctor;

c) the professional goals must be proportional to the risks of the experiment;

d) particular care must be exercised in the undertaking of experiments that could alter the subject's personality.[35]

2.3.2. Genetic Experimentation on Humans

This is the area of medicine in which experimentation on humans raises the most delicate questions. Up until a short time ago, ethical problems in medicine came from new frontiers in techniques of resuscitation or organ transplant. However, concern has recently centered on the new area of human genetics. For some, the emerging positions seem comparable; for others, they seem wide apart.[36] Let us consider two fields in which genetic engineering can be applied: clinical diagnostics and therapy.

Genetic Engineering's Application to Clinical Diagnostics - Thanks to gene cloning techniques and other methodologies, it is possible to study the entire genetic legacy of complex organisms, including human beings.

Techniques for the diagnosis of some extremely specific and delicate infectious diseases were developed. The promising results began to be realized with the early diagnosis of some neoplasias with the identification of "oncogenes." The most important progress, however, was obtained through DNA-based diagnostic "probes" in the identification, during the fetal stage, of hereditary diseases. This possibility extends abortion into the field of eugenics, which today is now dramatically possible. Such ethical problems are extremely important and have been confronted more than once in Italy.[37]

The diagnosis of metabolic diseases can also occur during the subject's childhood. This has opened the way to problems such as whether or not it is useful to "inform" the patient (the parents) at such an early time of conditions that could worsen during the course of the disease, when the eventual manifestations are years, or even decades away.

Moreover, delicate ethical problems stem from the diagnostic use of genetic engineering techniques for possible social discrimination.

Genetic Engineering's Application to Therapy - Obviously, "therapeutic" applications must be distinguished from all other possible ends. The question clearly is one of great moral sensitivity, even considering only therapeutic prospects. The therapeutic goal is to introduce into the genetic legacy of human cells DNA sequences that in some measure correct the genetic alterations present there.

Somatic or germinal cells can be acted upon. In the first case, an attempt is made to "cure" the effects that derive from the genetic anomaly; in the second, an attempt is made to practice a radical "genetic therapy" that, by repairing the genetic malfunction, prevents the transmission of the "negative" trait.

The first strategy is undergoing trial, despite the undeniable technical difficulties that still must be surmounted. Such trial is being done on illnesses that derive from genetic anomalies which alter the production of vital, yet simply regulated enzymes, such as hypoxantintransferase, purinucleoside transferase, and adenosindeaminase. Other more difficult efforts involve the correction of hemoglobin anomalies. The possibility of correcting, *in vitro*, some types of abnormal cellular clones (*e.g.*, medullary cells) and putting them back into the affected organism so that the healthy cells balance the sick ones, must be considered real. However, such a procedure is still in the first stages of actual application.

In any case, any fanciful "optimism" must be rejected, since, in animal and human cells, we are a long way away from seeing the nomotrophic integration of foreign DNA in high percentages and having the cells function.

Radical "genetic therapy" on germinal cells is not being pursued today. This is because of the complexity and the "responsibility" currently connected to the use of experimental technologies. It seems we can discern a kind of "moratorium" on human genetic material tacitly followed by researchers while waiting for more substantial experimental progress.

But there are also deeper ethical motives that should be considered. In the actual state of the techniques, corrective "therapy" will have a "causal," *i.e.*, positive, effect only on a few germinal cells relative to the entire number treated in such a manner. This leads to the necessity of differentiating healthy "products" (embryos) from unhealthy ones, which means a very high level of prenatal selection must occur.

3. The Bioethical Debate in Italy: the Distinction between Ethical Order and Legal Order

After having presented the fundamental *topoi* of Italian bioethics' cultural elaboration and identified the factors that determine its roots in the fabric of society, we would like to address the current debate by referring to some of the major issues that have been confronted. From the point of view of content, this last decade's debate seems to have been focussed on two central themes:

a) ethical issues that come up at the *beginning* or the *end* of human life;

b) ethical issues that come up within the relationship between human life and *life in nature* in its entirety.

Condensed in this way, the debate reveals a constant reference to the conception of "life." Related to the evolution of such an important factor in bioethics, two directions in particular can be distinguished. As for the first central theme, the direction that it takes seems to be toward the tendency to *concentrate* the value of life on quality, rather than holding to the conviction of life's unconditional value. The direction that the second central theme takes seems to be toward the tendency not to *restrict* the concept of "respect for life" to Man alone, but to *broaden* it to every living thing.

We intend to present the debate on these two themes by first discussing the "medical" theme and then the "ecological" one. The perspective in which we present the debate is one of the relationship between the ethical order and the legal order, which is a subject that particularly concerns bioethics.

Today in this relationship, the following definitions prevail:

a) *ethical order*: a system of norms prescribing certain behavior within a certain society. The principle of ethical norms is that of the individual conscience as the final arbiter of judgment, even of the dominant social code;

b) *legal order*: a society organized through norms whose effective observation is guaranteed by an authority. The principle of legal norms is the organization of society, and more specifically, the organization of strongly pluralist societies.

In sum, it seems we can say that the objective of ethical norms is to make the person who observes them *good*, while that of legal norms is to render the society that they organize *right*. This explains the "non-coincidental" transfer between the moral and legal spheres in modern society, which is resolved in extreme cases by the institution of the "conscientious objection."

Given these premises regarding the distinction between ethical order and legal order, it is possible to understand the positions assumed by the various tendencies that meet in the "bioethics movement." In the current Italian debate, there are numerous and contradictory assertions on the subject. Let us list some, by way of example:

I. a) Scientific research cannot be stopped by legal regulation.

   b) Scientific research must be put under the control of society when it becomes dangerous or contrary to the dignity of Man.

II. a) Treatment for sterility must be allowed, regardless of the consequences, through artificial insemination of unmarried persons and homosexual couples.

   b) Such insemination must be prohibited in any sterility treatment.

III. a) A person has the right to ask for the suspension or the denial of treatments (even with the so-called last will and testament); the person has the right to obtain technical help to end his or her own life.

   b) Life is sacred and cannot be left, except under the application of proportionality of treatment.

These are fiercely contradictory statements that at the moment do not seem easily reconcilable. To account for how the bringing together of these positions that is currently occurring in Italy in more detailed terms, given the definition of legal criteria inspired by shared ethical criteria, we must consider the two central themes already discussed. As for issues posed at the beginning and end of life, we should refer particularly to the debate on legal regulation of assisted procreation techniques and on regulation of the "control of one's own death." Regarding, instead, ethical issues relative to the relationship between human life, and the life of nature in its entirety, we should refer to ethical questions in environmental policy and to the problem of animal "rights."

3.1. Ethical Order and Legal Order in the Reflection on Assisted Procreation

One of the most important chapters of "biomedical ethics" deals with the evaluation of techniques that "implement" human fertility's "potential" or substitute mechanisms that, because of various pathological causes, are not functioning well enough to aid reproduction in the spontaneous conditions of human procreation.[38] The techniques included in this chapter were devised with a therapeutic goal in mind. But it must be said that, next to these rigorous "therapeutic indications" which legitimized the use of such techniques, there developed a "radical" tendency. This tendency considered some of these techniques to be absolutely, unquestionably applicable according to the subject's choice, even when the subject was healthy and able to procreate naturally. Such ideas gave rise to procreative "procedures" that were believed preferable to "natural" ones.

This vision, held to be a "right" by some, intensely involved legal thought. It could have been no other way, with the presentation of new legal cases concretely connected to the use of reproductive technology. In fact, the topic is one of the most debated in the Italian ethical-legal literature.[39]

The debate became especially in-depth and extensive, although deep differences remain between the various legal cultures of the individual authors. The consideration of the issues regarding the unborn's rights and protection of its interests, beyond the members of the couple, is present and well developed.

In general, the legal admissibility of "therapeutic" procedures prevails when they are conducted by experts under the proper control of suitable public institutions. The ban on alternative methods of procreation when there are no medically justifiable reasons is also legally admissible. Moreover, this ban is not espoused by some legal scholars, though they are only a small, minority group. However this group has managed to influence some recent legislative proposals.

As to the use of various methodologies, the principle criterion for judgment is not only the referral to "informed consent," but also the "dignity of Man." With some qualification, the "question" of the embryo's protection returns to this idea. Generally, the prohibition on any embryonic manipulation and the ban on any "commercialization" has been confirmed (such as renting the uterus, or the selling of sperm). The issue of the use or donor's sperm (or eggs) has been hotly debated; some consider this issue to be a "residual hypothesis."

3.1.1. Teleological and Deontological Argumentation on the Evaluation of Techniques of Assisted Procreation

We are faced with a subject corrupted at its base by strategies that, having forgotten the "therapeutic" valence of these techniques, end up turning to the most maximalist solutions. Confronted with such problem, the request for legislative rules is nearly universal. In "secular" thought, "therapeutic justification," -- a teleological argument -- is emphasized, while in "Catholic" thought the proper mode of procreation -- a deontological argument -- is accentuated.[40] From whatever perspective the subject is met, the question of the "technical" modes[41] is certainly considerable for legal regulation purposes. It seems appropriate to examine the following considerations:

a) As is known, artificial procreation is achieved through two ways: either through the use of a single technique designed to remove or surmount the obstacle, or, in other cases, through the use of various, harmonized techniques, one after the other. It must acknowledged that some of these techniques have reached a high degree of reliability, but others have not.

FIVET, for example, still has low yield percentages and the same is true for GIFT. In every case, each one of these techniques retains, strictly speaking, its own "specific" directions for use. Thus, there is continuous technological progress in these areas. As in all fields of biomedicine in which surgical procedures are required, the instruction of "specialized" and well-trained operators leads to better reliability and safety for the woman. This is also an "ethical" goal that legislative proposals emphasize in particular. However, in this case it does not seem possible (neither to us nor to others) to make the "effectiveness/efficiency" argument the only parameter of ethical evaluation.

b) The choice of the most appropriate technique to the case in question undoubtedly constitutes -- even leaving aside Catholic moral theology's considerations -- a deontological-ethical argument. The tendency to surpass those criteria of "proportionality," that were adopted at the start of the experience with reproductive technology, is occurring for various reasons, even in some Italian centers. These criteria were adopted to focus all possible technical means on providing a better result in the least amount of time, independent of ethical demands (*e.g.*, the protection of extra embryos). This was justified by the cost/benefit principle, typical of social utilitarian ethics. Some of the goals of such utilitarian ethics were to provide access to services for the most number of people per unit of work time and to diminish the subject's discomfort and obligations.

Therefore, the evaluation of the entire body of instructions, *i.e.*, allowable conditions and contraindications in these methodologies' application (initially very rigorous and analytical), is undergoing an about-face in its perspective.[42]

c) As we have already seen, the possibility of an "overflow" of these reproductive techniques from the "therapeutic" area (even loosely interpreted) into the area of "unnecessary option," is becoming increasingly likely.

The "sex selection" of future embryos is the most noted case of such an overflow. This is so because sex selection occurs not to prevent the transmission of a genetic illness linked to the sex chromosomes, but rather because of other, unnecessary reasons. In such a case, the technique of sperm selection (before in vitro fertilization) can be used. Through modern methods (not yet perfected) of concentrating the sperm carrying "X" or "Y" chromosomes, the "probability" of conceiving a male or female can be increased. However, sex determination of the "early embryo" (before implantation) with diagnostic techniques now appears immanent. This raises the possibility of the adoption of criteria that permit the determination of who survives and who does not, denying the uterine "transfer."

d) Even leaving aside such drastic situations, the grave ethical problem of "extra embryos" remains. They result from therapeutic in vitro fertilization techniques that produces excess embryos because of technical reasons (the difficulty of performing new cycles of ovarian stimulation and gathering the oocites, the required availability of embryos that have no problems in their very first phases of development, etc.). Many of these embryos are "scientifically" destined not to be transferred to the uterus.[43]

Italian theological-moral and medical-moral thought has dedicated itself fully to this problem. The expected loss of individual human life, which is considered viable if transferred to the uterus, is judged by most as unacceptable and a grave "intrinsic" barrier to the acceptance of FIVET, although this is not the only barrier. Nevertheless, there are those who believe that putting all the embryos obtained in vitro back into the uterus goes a long way towards mitigating moral responsibility in such procedures. Many Italian practitioners, biologists, and some secular moral philosophers agree with this idea. Others believe that "embryonic loss," which also occurs in nature, is a price that must be paid, at least in the current phase of technological development; for them, such loss does not affect the positive "end" which is the attempt at therapy.

e) It is well-known that Catholic moral theology acknowledges the physical and moral naturalness of coitus as the only legitimate expression of sexual union and activity between a man and a woman. Of course, such activity must take place within a monogamous and indissoluble matrimony.

In Italian Catholic moralist thought, there have been some who have voiced reservations about the full legitimacy of this vision of sexual ethics. They consider the *finalization of love* (for the good of the possible unborn child) of all the actions of a person who undergoes reproductive treatments, to be important. These reproductive treatments include homologous FIVET (the so-called "simple case") in determined conditions of otherwise irreversible female sterility.

Homologous insemination (with sperm from the husband) and GIFT (or similar techniques of gamete positioning, not in the Fallopian tubes, but in the peritoneum) escape moral theologians' negative judgment, provided that they follow normal conjugal acts. In fact, in these techniques, there is no third-party participation in the direct "production" or later destiny of the embryos. Thus, the entire procedure falls under the rubric of "aid to nature," which is exactly in what "assisted procreation" consists.

The restrictive criteria of Church teaching is strongly contested in Italy, as well, by currents of secular moral philosophy[44] and by numerous legal scholars and medical practitioners in the field.

f) The current writings on Catholic ethics express grave reservations regarding the use of donor semen, both for live and in vitro fertilization. These reservations are expressed above all because of inherent concerns regarding the stability of the family and the proper rasing of children. A strong current of secular moral-philosophic thought, along with a substantial share of the Italian medical class, see no particular "moral" problem with the use of donor semen, as long as such procedures occur within the limits of explicit consent and effective health regulation ("authorized" procedures with certain conditions determined by the state).

g) To complete the analytical framework, we must acknowledge the broadening of the specter of doctors' ethical references in modern society. This is substantially due to the plurality of value systems taken into consideration. A greater "heterogeneity" has come about in professional ethics, relative to the "traditional" model based on strict standards of the assumption of responsibility grounded in personal convictions. Instead, the moral responsibility for decisions has been transferred to the one petitioning the doctor for treatment.

It is the affirmation of "services on demand" that, if they follow certain "procedural" and contractual rules, is considered deontologically "legitimate," even if not ideologically shared by all. In today's society, this "loss" of ethics in medicine appears more and more frequently. In its place, we see a "technological service" that is deemed deontologically valid, even though it is ethically ambiguous.

Finally, also in Italian society, it is believed that this represents a decisive stimulus to the development of methods of artificial reproduction. This is the feasible benefit in a field where the "hope" of fertility outweighs the serious economic sacrifice necessary to achieve it.

3.2. Ethical Order and Legal Order in the Reflection on the "Control of One's Own Death"

Italy, like almost all Western countries, has for some time been wrestling with the problem of the "control of one's death." The "modern" approach to this problem comes from, as is known, the so-called refusal of *aggressive treatment*. This is the refusal of methods and procedures by excessively "technologized" medicine with the goal of achieving "survival on earth," ignoring the desires and suffering of the patient.

This aspect of the problem, presented in an emotional form to the public, has ended up distorting any objective perspective. There is no longer any unbiased view on ethical aspects related to the limits of the "disposability of one's own life," or to the limits of the "duties to protect the life of others," which were questions originally entrusted to the medical profession.

However, the deepest justifications for the problem meet in the following factors: the *secularization of society*, the fall of the idea of life's *sacred* value, the refusal of any suffering, and the move towards ever increasing *efficiency* that marginalizes anyone who cannot compete. In certain cases, such as so-called "neonatal euthanasia" (because of grave defects, for example), we are dealing with a "selection." This selection is fed by the family's fear of confronting such a terrible problem and by the dreadful prospects regarding the child's future.

The ethical and legal discussions in Italy have contributed much to the debate.[45] After the publication of the "Declaration on Euthanasia" by the Congregation for the Doctrine of the Faith (1980), a wide reflection on the matter began in Catholic moral theology. This reflection revived during the government bill "Fortuna's" presentation in Parliament and more recently, during the approval of European Code of Medical Ethics ("Principles of Medical Ethics," approved January 6, 1987).[46] "Secular" Italian thought is also very much interested in this subject.[47]

The document "Principles of European Medical Ethics," recently approved on January 6, 1987, was presented to the Italian press as favorable to passive euthanasia and provoked a brief debate. In reality, it was a reaffirmation of already codified principles in medical ethics. In fact, the deontological code states in Art. 43 that "in no case, even if requested by the patient, will the doctor perform any treatment aimed at reducing the mental or physical integrity of the patient, or any actions which shorten the life of the patient. Any action aimed at deliberately causing the death of a patient is contrary to medical ethics."

3.2.1. Ethical and Legal Positions in the Current Debate

In an outline, the opinion that definitions of euthanasia are controversial and have been worn-out is gaining ground. It would be better to abandon such definitions in favor of legally defined "cases."

a) In any case, as for the concept of active euthanasia (*i.e.*, "deliberate" and conducted with means that bring a rapid end to the subject's life, without suffering), we must state that the law, in accordance with broadly prevalent moral opinion, forbids the use of *direct* and *intentional* means to bring on death. This is true even if the patient makes a request to die.

b) The same is not true for passive euthanasia, that includes at least two variables: the deliberate omission of useful therapy (thus, it is not seen as "active") and the idea of "letting nature take its course." However theoretically well-differentiated these ideas may be, there are many practical difficulties in "objectively" distinguishing the reach of the two cases in the real world. Moreover, we must distinguish "omissions" on a conscious and consenting patient from "omissions" on an unconscious or unaware patient.

In short, the following items meet:

- the rejection of etiological therapies in cases where the clinical conditions show no hope (practically, starting from cases covered by formulas of "living wills" if the patient has agreed, whether or not the patient is in a coma);

- the rejection of resuscitory therapy in particular clinical circumstances ("do not resuscitate" orders) with or without the patient's consent;

- the suspension of resuscitory therapy ("detach" the tubes or the respirator);

- the administration of analgesics in such a dose and quantity as to bring about unconsciousness. This is done with or without a specific request by the patient (and with or without informing the relatives) in anticipation of the patient's entry into the last stages before death. In this manner, the patient dies (cardiac arrest) without regaining consciousness (so-called invasive analgesic therapy);

- the administration of "tranquilizers" or analgesics in such quantities so as presumably not to interfere with the spontaneous loss of consciousness in the final stage before death.

This illustration demonstrates how it may be inappropriate to speak indiscriminately of "passive euthanasia" for each of these eventualities. It also demonstrates how the ethical-legal characterization (both moral and legal responsibility) differs in the various cases.

3.2.2. The Principle of Proportionality of Treatment

In many people's opinion, the only solution to the difficult health problems in the terminal stages of illness is in the principle of *proportionality of treatment*. Above all, it is evident that a "right not to suffer uselessly" exists. But this right is very clear to the doctor, who has always given analgesic treatment when necessary and has interpreted his own precise professional duty in the light of "science" and "conscience." For this reason, many doctors feel the issue of a "right not to suffer" should be taken for granted. Therefore, if one includes euthanasia (easy, painless death) as part of this, euthanasia becomes a "false problem."

Moreover, it must be confirmed that legal and medical doctrines are in agreement regarding the acknowledgement, even today, of the principle "*voluntas aegroti suprema lex.*" This principle, applied to the case in question, does not allow the doctor to go against the "informed" will of the patient, nor to deceive or coerce the patient. Therefore, when the doctor judges, in full honesty and "objectivity," that the patient has entered the "terminal stage," the abstention from (or suspension of) therapy "disproportionate to the circumstances" seems to be required, if expressly requested by the patient. In obedience to such a desire, "redundant" therapies would become relentless treatments. On the other hand, therapeutic efforts, even to the very end, must not be withheld if this is expressly requested by the patient.

In general, the majority holds to the principle that in any case, the doctor cannot abandon the criteria, today in force, of the legal obligation to utilize any "therapy proportional to the case." Sometimes, however, this is a difficult judgment.[48] This is a deontological norm that has always been in force, and even up to today, has never been questioned.

On a more general ethical level, however, it is recognized that there is much to be done for better care in the last stages of illness, both in the organization of services and in the use of health personnel. An on-going "presence" must be offered to terminally ill patients; caring concern and human thoughtfulness must take the place of health workers' frequent "abandonment." Much has already been stated on these aspects and the important activity now is to create conditions in health organization so these needs can be satisfied.[49]

3.3. The Ethical Order and the Legal Order in the Debate on Environmental Policies

According to authoritative opinion,[50] until the end of the 1970's, the Italian publishing industry was rather belated, relative to other countries, in discussing the ecological crisis of the modern era. This negative judgment, which was valid at that time, has been moderated by the activities of "environmental movements" (growing in number, such movements have followers and political leverage up to the referendum level, which they successfully managed). Above all, the negative judgment has been mitigated by the outline, in recent years, of a mature ethical reflection on environmental problems, both on the theological-moral level and the secular level.

Leaving aside the so-called "animal question," (that must be examined separately because of the subject's breadth), the ecological problems to be considered under an ethical rubric are numerous. Such problems fall into the following, approximate framework:

a) the "ecological crisis'" prognosis and therapy; almost everyone agrees on the diagnosis, but they diverge on its gravity and on how to remedy it;

b) the behavior of individuals in environmental protection (including maturity of ecological awareness, the determination to act in an ecologically sound manner, *etc.*)

c) the ethical-social engagement of single communities and governments to act in an ecologically sound manner; this brings with it problems on the local, national, and world scene (according to the political decision levels, but with an integrated responsibility); these problems include the use of available natural resources, the balancing of development between "rich" and "poor" nations in order to achieve the sound use of environmental resources, the proper disposal of refuse, the correction of already present environmental damage, *etc.*;

d) the conservation of particular environments and vegetable and animal species on their way to extinction, *etc.*

Other questions hang over these issues, which in and of themselves require much thought and ethical reflection. The other questions are inherent to the ever-increasing need of energy for development and to the so-called "nuclear alternative" proposal, which many countries have put into practice. In reality, one can see that at least a part of Catholic writings on ecological ethics concerns itself with this particular problem. This issue is considered a "boundary case" and proposes a alternative and up-side down global conception of ways of living.[51]

These positions, converging with those of many "ecological movements" and "secular" writers,[52] have certainly carried much weight, even in determining the favorable outcome of referendums for the prohibition of nuclear energy in Italy. Recent Italian theological reflection seems to be broader. It examines, in depth, human and Biblical values regarding the concept of "*dominium terrae*," as other, mainly Evangelical Christian-trained authors, have fully discussed.[53] Even among "secular" scholars, treatment of this topic has gradually become more prevalent.[54]

3.3.1. The Terms of the Problem in the "Theological and "Secular" Positions

Two positions seem to stand out on this question. Please note, however, that there has been serious simplification among the positions taken by various authors and that excessively analytical elements of argumentation have been eliminated as much as possible. These positions are:

a) First, one which we could say is of *theological* origin. This position has had to face the accusations of some secular thinkers who felt that the Judeo-Christian religious foundation was at the basis of Western Man's violent attitude towards nature. Modern reflection, however, finds a much more complex origin of such an attitude.[55]

In the sphere of the "theological position," it is recognized that biblical doctrine made a decisive contribution to the secularization of nature. However, it did not make any ethical justifications for the pollution and destruction of nature. Appeals were made, from time to time, in the patristic and medieval age, to the duties toward a creation waiting for the "good steward," *i.e.*, Man (e.g. Hugo of Saint Victor, Benedetto da Norcia, Francis of Assisi, *etc.*).

The "intrinsic" development of Western theological thought (Protestant and Catholic) was deepened, both during the Renaissance and the modern periods. Moreover, it was recognized that the passing of the line exalting the direct creationistic dimension, in the "image of God," of Man, certainly influenced the consideration of the relationship between Man (whose intellect is exalted) and

Nature (which is perceived as increasingly subordinate thanks to ever-more inventive technology).

A renewed ecological sensibility is affirmed. It is based on a "radical" vision, in which the redeeming of the world in its intrinsic goodness is outlined. It also proposes a categorical imperative based on the "ethics of responsibility," of "justice."

b) The second position, more clearly *secular* and leaving out religious values in its argumentative framework, brings out certain aspects that we will attempt to summarize.

First of all, it is nearly everywhere recognized that it is permissible to "broaden the sphere of moral consideration beyond the confines of interhuman relations and to define a system of moral rules to follow when and if our behavior has repercussions on the life and conditions of non-human beings not produced by Man."[56]

But at this point, first of all, we can distinguish those who contest, at their root, every hypothesis of "human dominion over nature." They believe in the necessity and urgency of a new ethical conception that grounds moral value in natural objects through ecological notions such as the "bioethical pyramid," "interdependence of (living and non-living) beings," and the "equilibrium of nature." It also presumes a normative concept and of "knowledge" rooted in nature itself and in its spontaneous evolution.

This trend, while small, is tenaciously supported by environmental organizations and "groups." We can define this trend, strictly speaking, as "environmental ethics." Such groups tend to extend to the environment the concept of the "subject of rights."

Others believe that it is not necessary to create new ethics, since traditional "doctrines" can be applied (of course expediently), to the environment as well. It is thus a question of elaborating coherent ethical constructs, that both justify the protection of the "values" at stake, and are capable of suggesting normative guidelines with a positive environmental effect. In particular, the *utilitarians* place value on, beyond its purely "pragmatic" aspect, interest in considering the consequences of humans' actions on the environment beyond a strictly anthropomorphic point of view; they take into account the "state of things" even from the viewpoint of other species and of the "well-being of the bioethical community" taken as a whole.

The *contractualists*, for whom morals have a rational foundation in the form of a "pact" or "contract," now acknowledge that moral relations can be established between a moral agent (with free will) and "objects" or "living things" without a will. They wonder if, next to social justice, there does not also exist a kind of "bioethical justice," for which, as Mary Midgely wrote, "it is the contract that has a place in morality, not vice-versa." In any case, we must add that ethical reflection related to the environment seems still to encounter difficulties regarding completed theorization.[57]

3.3.2. Normative Aspects of the Debate

Even the normative process advances with difficulty, despite the incessant appeals from every arena. It is recognized that these difficulties are inherent to numerous factors, such as:

a) the "planetary" nature of the problem, that gives a particular complexity and range to any proposal of intervention;

b) the necessity that any solution does not slow the development of emerging countries, and, if possible, reduces the distance between industrialized countries (hyperconsumers of environmental goods) and poor countries (that are led to use primary resources in an unplanned and tumultuous manner), rather than stopping the development of the latter, to preserve the ecology of the former;

c) the necessity that certain fundamental ethical requirements are respected within the framework of the dignity of every person in every country.

In this context, even the continued cries about demographic growth, the progressive desertification of the planet and so on cannot bring about ethically acceptable solutions, such as forced sterilization or the maintenance of forests.

On the other hand, the right to education for responsible procreation is recognized. This limits demographic growth through voluntary means, and is freely accepted and proper to the dignity of Man in the first case and in the second case, through the proper development of agricultural technology adequate to halt desertification through exhaustion of the topsoil.

Even in technologically advanced countries, certain people champion effective and coherent engagement in environmental impact evaluations and in analysis of risks and of costs/benefits. These appear, even under an ethical profile, as suitable tools for the rational, "methodological" definition of environmental problems. At any rate according to Moroni, two dimensions will have to be taken into account:

- knowledge gained through scientific research, particularly regarding ecology, about how nature works;

- Man's biological and cultural reality, his belonging to nature and his emergence from it through awareness and responsibility for its management and for the entire environment.

3.4. Ethical Order and Legal Order in the Debate on Animal Rights

One of the most interesting chapters in bioethics is the reflection on the human-animal relationship in an ethical setting. This topic is of particular interest to those "movements" of "the protection of animal rights" that, under various emotional tendencies and with various goals, have emerged in modern society. It is undeniable that Western society, in its entirety, has had no particular ethical problems up until a short time ago, in its relationship with the animal world, despite examples of great spirituality in the approach to such relations (examine for example, the case of St. Francis). Additionally, we also see, in the second half of the nineteenth century during the full fervor of "scientific positivism," the so-called antivisectionist movement.[58]

Currently, even the human-animal relationship on the ethical level has undergone notable and positive evolution. This is related to a different, global ethical sensitivity and to a reconsideration of ethical problems. In the Western world, for many centuries Catholic ethical thought has been decisive in this sector as well. This stems from theological and doctrinal foundations that were well-codified and derived from a long tradition.[59] This tradition, which remained stable for centuries, was greatly modified beginning with the theorization of a new image of the world by the new discoveries in geography and (above all) in physics by Galileo and Newton, and regarding the animal world, codified by Descartes. He clearly explained the mechanistic condition of living organisms; this meant that animals were "automatons," without language or sensation, be it pleasure or pain.

Descartes' affirmation opened the way (or perhaps already reflected?) contemporary indifference to animals' pain and above all to the possible industrialization of their production and reproduction.

3.4.1. Contemporary Italian Catholic Reflection on Ethics

Let us present some ideas for reflection. It is recognized that human responsibility must be reconsidered as a responsibility for the entire ecosystem and responsibility for life must be responsibility for every form of life. The common good, that the ideology of profit must fit into, must be understood as "common" not only in an "intraspecies" (only human beings) sense, but also in an "interspecies" sense (Autiero).

The phenomenon of the forced rearing of many animal species must be censured as a meaningful "test" from which a cultural hinterland full of immorality emerges: forced rearing is the expression of dominion over nature and animals that is part of an oppressive and despotic logic (Mattai).

Regarding animal experimentation, we can affirm that, in a conception of animals as tools in relation to Man, there are no ethical problems with such procedures. However, such a conception is unacceptable because non-human living beings, beyond their utilitarian value, have value in and of themselves. This does not lead to the refusal and opposition of any form of animal experimentation; this would renounce the great benefits that might derive from such procedures for all of humanity. It is rather a question of finding the right humane solution. As the correct laws regarding human experimentation were created, so must also an ethical code regarding animal experimentation be elaborated. It is not enough that there are already available measures to avoid useless suffering. We must ask the question whether or not Man has the right to dispose of the integrity and life of animals as he sees fit (Lorenzetti).

Regarding animals' "patentability," we should take a very thoughtful stance. Some ask if we are heading towards an industrial model of life. Faced a more generalized request for patents on living things, is it legitimate to wonder: what will the consequences of a similar practice be for the future of humanity? Based on what criteria can we judge if they will be positive or negative? We can discuss the reasons of those who accept (or fight for) such patentability and those who deny it on principle and not only because the same could occur with humans. If we do discuss these reasons, we can see that the issue of the patentability of animals should not be over-dramatized, but neither should it be avoided and trivialized. The possibility of indiscriminate and generalized patentability carries risks; the first is the risk connected with the latent philosophy of a precise industrial model that leads, potentially and inadvertently, to attributing value to life only as a tool. At the moment regarding the issue of animals' patentability, there seem to be more doubts and questions than satisfactory answers (Trentin).

3.4.2. "Secular" Reflection and the Problem of Animal "Rights"

Italian moral philosophers have been active on this matter,[60] in keeping with the thought developed by certain philosophers (Singer, Midgley) of the English-speaking world. We intend to examine the animal/human relationship outside of any pietism, thus going beyond the radical ontological diversity that, in the past, dominated on the basis of "scientific" argumentation. These elements that such an investigation is based on are the following:

a) comparative neurophysiology which demonstrates the real similarity of animals' neurophysiological functions to those of humans;

b) the human mental life, which is rooted in an emotional structure largely common to other species;

c) compared ethology, which demonstrates significant elements of continuity between the behavior of animals and humans;

d) the increased awareness that the survival of our species in the world, can only be assured by looking after the survival of others;

e) the (philosophical-ethical) revision of the concept of "justice," extended in its contractualistic sense beyond interhuman relations;

Through the assumption of a "libertarian or emancipationist ideology" or of an "ecologist philosophy," a theorization of animal rights has been reached; this has found some followers in Italy as well. The libertarian ideology poses a parallel between animals' condition and slavery; "specie-ism" is made equal to racism or sexism. The moral community must be extended to all sentient beings.

Moreover, the most fervent animal rights activists support the principle that not all humans are persons (or possess such characteristics in a very limited manner, such as those who are brain-damaged, those in a comatose, vegetative state, the mentally retarded, fetuses, and "if we chose, even newborns") and that not only humans are persons.

The ecological philosophy redirects the "animal question" to the broadest ecological discourse (Man/environment relationship).

However, prevailing opinion, while accepting that humans and animals belong to the same "bioethical" community (together, therefore with plants) bound by reciprocal interests, does not accord to animals the dignity of being "subjects of rights." Such opinions do emphasize humans' responsibility and "duties" to animals. Moreover, the innate predisposition to favor one's own species is recognized as a *general* ethological characteristic; this idea does, however, refuse "specie-ism" as an index of uncontrollable and irresponsible anthropocentrism.

In a technical sense, animals are denied entitlement to rights, but they are owed certain duties from humans.

This does not prevent, in language's "approximation" that characterizes modern society, one from writing that "the use of a notion of subjective rights and the attribution of rights to animals would constitute a psychologically very effective legal tool for their protection (Castignone)."

Conclusion

The essential elements that we have outlined demonstrate how, also in Italy, during the twenty years from 1970-1990, a systematic reflection on bioethics occurred. So that this new refection can continue to develop in the coming years, it must take more directly into account the typical phenomena of our cultural context and this includes:

a) the tendency, when confronting ethical problems, to set the "Catholic" approach against the "secular" approach. This tendency naturally has an impact on emerging bioethical reflection.

b) a certain resistance on the part of world of Italian health care, to the legitimization of ethics in the biomedical field, since it is presumed that the "right" behavior dictated by "professional deontology" exhausts the entire field of normativity in medicine.

Faced with these two central problems, it seems to us that the proper solution lies in the direction of a more rigorous epistemological distinction between the levels involved in bioethics; this means distinguishing, not separating the legal order and ethical order and distinguishing, not setting against one another an effective deontological plan from the broadest and most well-founded ethical plan.

273

ENDNOTES

1. In this paper I will provide only general information in the form of "notes." The argument, however, requires a more systematic approach. For a more documented version of the outlines of Italian bioethics, see the first of the "Quaderni di Bioetica" (1991) edited by the "Lanza Foundation" of Padua. For an approach to Italian bioethics, see the article of M. Mori, "Per una bibliografia italiana sulla Bioetica," *Prospettive Settanta*, no. 1 (1987). Also, Italian manuals edited so far can be consulted, particularly the wide bibliography in C. Viafora, *Fondamenti di Bioetica* (Milano: Ambrosiana Editrice, 1989), pp. 324-342. This international selection contains significant references to Italian bioethics literature.

2. Although the reflection and production of Italian authors has been particularly attentive to the field of bio-medicine (see the manuals of Perico, Sgreccia, Tettamanzi, Spinsanti, Leone, Viafora, as well as the contributions of Scarpelli and Mori etc.) a wider approach can be found in recent publications with the inclusion of other sectors (see Bartolomei, Battaglia, Castiglione, Chiarelli).

3. So Scarpelli: "Bioethics is ethics insofar as it relates particularly to the phenomena of organic life, body, procreation, development, maturity and aging, health, illness and death. It cannot be considered a discipline which is in itself autonomous and independent even if within the frame of ethics. Indeed, the term bioethics covers focal interests as well as new problems related to advances in biological knowledge and technology. Yet, an adequate in-depth analysis of these new issues cannot fail to refer them to fundamental ethical attitudes concerning the human being as soul and body, spirit and matter, or if preferred, organism capable of actions as well as meaningful and symbolic interactions which exceed biology's field of inquiry," U. Scarpelli, "La Bioetica. Alla ricerca dei principi," *Biblioteca della Liberta'* 99, (1987), p.7.

4. Particularly significant are the manuals of bioethics variably grounded upon Christian inspired personalism edited in the last years: G. Perico, *Problemi di etica sanitaria* (Milano: Ancora, 1985); E. Sgreccia, *Bioetica. Manuale per Medici e Biologi* (Milano: Vita e Pensiero, 1986); S. Spinsanti, *Etica bio-medica*

274

(Milano: 1987); D. Tettamanzi, *Bioetica. Nuove sfide per l'uomo* (Casale Monferrato: Piemme, 1987); S. Leone, *Lineamenti di Bioetica* (Padova: Medical Books, 1987); C. Viafora, *Fondamenti di Bioetica* (Milano: Ambrosiana, 1989). For a more clear theological reflection, see the wide treatments of bioethics in moral theology treatises of Italian theologians: L. Lorenzetti, ed., *Trattato di Etica Teologica* (Bologna: Dehoniane, 1982), the part edited by A. Autiero and G. Mattai in "Medicina e Societa'," vol. III; T. Goffi and G. Piana, eds., *Corso di Morale* (Brescia: Queriniana, 1983: in particular the remarkable contributions of S. Spinsanti, "Vita Fisica" (Cap. IV), "Corporeita'" (Cap. II) in the Vol. II dedicated to personal ethics. For an interpretation of echological issues in ethical perspectives, see in the same Vol. II: A. Autiero, "Essere nel mondo. Ecologia del bisogno." Also E. Chiavacci, *Morale della vita fisica* (Bologna: Dehoniane, 1979. From a theological perspective impressive is the attention to bioethics given by "Rivista di Teologia Morale," directed by L. Lorenzetti and edited by Dehoniane of Bologna.

5. From a secular perspective, see M. Mori, ed., *Questioni di Bioetica* (Roma: Editori Riuniti, 1988); A. Di Meo and C. Mancina, eds., *Bioetica* (Bari: Laterza, 1989). Also M. Mori, "Bioetica: concetti, teorie, problemi," *Notizie di Politeia* 16, (1989): 29-43; U. Scarpelli, "La Bioetica alla ricerca dei principi," *Biblioteca della Liberta'* 99, (1987): 7-32, followed by the writings of Mori, Lecaldano, Castiglione, Jori; E. Gadler and B. Chiarelli, "Analisi e problemi della Bioetica in Italia," *Problemi di Bioetica*, no. 6 (1990): 7-33; A. Tagliavini, "Bioetica: una prospettiva multidisciplinare," *Rivista di Filosofia*, no. 2 (1989): 299-310; M. Bianca, "Etica e Bioetica: valori umani e valori naturali," *Problemi di Bioetica*, no. 1 (1988): 43-49. See finally M. Mori and U. Scarpelli, eds., "Diritto alla vita," monographic issue of *Rivista di Filosofia*, (1983).

6. E. Sgreccia, *Bioetica. Manuale per Medici e Biologi* (Milano: Vita e Pensiero, 1986), p.41.

7. See P. Cattorini, "Profilo della Scuola di Medicina e Scienze Umane. Educare ad un'intenzione antropologica," *Sanare Infirmos* 3, (1988): 19-23.

8. See M. Mori, ed., "Eutanasia come problema," *Quaderni della Societa' di Letture e Conversazioni Scientifiche* 8, (1987). See also the first National Convention organized in 1986 by the Center for Animal Rights. The Convention's proceedings were edited in 1987 by S. Castiglione and L. Battaglia.

9. See S. Spinsanti, *Guarire tutto l'uomo. La medicina antropologica di V. von Weizsäker* (Milano: Paoline, 1988); "Rispettare la vita in tutte le sue forme," *Famiglia oggi* 33, (1988): 8-14.

10. See the Proceedings in S. Spinsanti, ed., *I comitati di etica in ospedale* (Milano: Paoline, 1988).

11. S. Spinsanti, ed., *Nascere, amare, morire* (Milano: Paoline, 1989). The particular perspective from which the convention has dealt with the theme is evident in the following statement of Spinsanti: "The introduction of the family in the bioethical debate has the advantage of contrasting the tendency to seek refuge in ideological shortcuts, as well as in the crisis situation occasioned by the cultural transition thus shifting away from traditional ethical parameters of behavior. The scholars gathered to this convention on birth, love and death -- indeed, human events of the most profound ethical meaning -- have pointed to a univocal and global solution. In the family it becomes possible not only to protect life, but also to take care of it. Deprived of the fundamental structure of reciprocity which the family guarantees, human life loses the qualitative character which makes it promising."

12. See B. Chiarelli, "Storia naturale del concetto di etica e sue implicazioni per gli equilibri naturali attuali," *Problemi di Bioetica*, no. 1 (1988): 51-58; V. Melotti, "Etica ed etologia," *Problemi di Bioetica*, no. 6 (1990): 35-48.

13. See the proceedings in A. Di Meo and C. Mancina, eds., *Bioetica* (Bari: Laterza, 1989).

14. See "Dossier" no. 1, Centro di Bioetica Istituto Gramsci, July 1990, p. 3.

15. It may be meaningful to review the themes of these conventions: "The mission of the physician today," Rome, January 1946; "Individual medicine and collective medicine," "The search for God in medicine," Rome, 11 April 1947; "The human person from the point of view of medical science," Padua, 16-19 October 1948; "Contemporary problems in the profession," "Medical and moral problems in marital life," Rome, 3-5 September 1959; "Medical problems in marriage and in the family," Bologna, 17-19 October 1952; "Work and medicine," Rome, 5-8- December 1954; "Human relationship in the profession," Bari, San Giovanni Rotondo, 6-9 May 1957; "Spiritual life and health," Catania, September 1959; "The continuing education of the physician," Genoa, 28-30 October 1961; "Diagnosis and therapy in today medicine," Florence, 29-31 October 1961; "Preventive medicine," Castellamare di Stabia, 27-29 October 1967; "The irregular childhood," Padua, 9-12 October 1970; "The defence of life," 1974; "Against violence in medicine," 30 October- 1 November 1976; "Medicine is for life," Assisi, 1979; "The physician in service of life," Rome, 1-5 October 1982; "Medicine for peace civilization," Venice, 17-20 October 1985; "Quality of medicine for quality of life," Florence, 17-20 October 1988.

16. Among the most important works of C. Jandolo: *L'etica al letto del malato* (Roma: Armando Editore, 1990); *L'approccio umano al malato. Aspetti psicologici dell'assistenza* (Roma: Armando Editore, 1979); *Introduzione all'etica clinica* (Roma: Luigi Pozzi, 1990).

17. For an interpretation of such a request, see the volume *Etica oggi: comportamenti collettivi e modelli culturali*, ed. Fondazione Lanza (Padova: Gregoriana, 1989).

18. See, for instance, the series "Societa' e Salute" directed by G. Berlinguer and A. Seppilli, as well as the volumes published in the series "Sociologia della Medicina" edited by G. Maccacaro and A. Martelli.

19. For an analysis of the ethical valence of the debate on Health-Reform, see A. Autiero and G. Mattai, "Medicina e Societa'" in *Trattato di Etica Teologica*, ed. L. Lorenzetti, Vol. III, pp. 281-288.

20. The reflection on the ethical aspects of the National Health Service has been gradually extended to various academic institutions. Laudable in this sense is the effort of the Italian Institute of Social Medicine directed by Reale. Many "secular" scholars participate in this reflection. They emphasize the importance of a *daily sanitary ethics* thus shifting the attention from "limit-cases" raised by advanced biotechnologies to normal problems of health care -- which are often forgotten by the public opinion -- emerging from mass pathologies. Praiseworthy in this sense is the effort of G. Berlinguer. For an approach to this interpretation of bioethical reflection, see G. Berlinguer, "Bioetica quotidiana e Bioetica di frontiera" in *Bioetica*, ed. A. Di Meo and C. Mancina, pp. 5-18.

21. These aspects are analyzed from an ethical point of view both in some Manuals (see, for instance, S. Spinsanti, C. Viafora, S. Leone) and in articles. Noteworthy, in particular, G. De Sandre, "A servizio di chi sono i servizi sociali e sanitari?" in *Il rispetto delle persone nei servizi sociali e sanitari* (Padova: Fondazione Zancan, 1986), pp.9-40.

22. See M. Rossanda and I. Peretti, eds., "Il bene salute fra politica e societa'," *Democrazia e diritto*, no. 6 (1988).

23. This is the position of F. Alberoni and S. Veca, *L'altruismo e la morale* (Milano: Garzanti, 1989).

24. On this problem, see F. Villa, ed., *L'integrazione annunciata: teoria e realta' nelle relazioni fra sociale e sanitario* (Milano: Vita e Pensiero, 1989).

25. On the issue of the sanitary economy and its ethical implications, see A. Bompiani, "Il medico come regolatore della cultura della salute e dell'uso dei

servizio sanitari," in *La regolazione sociale del sistema socio-sanitario*, ed. V. Ghetti (Milano: Franco Angeli - Fondazione Smith-Kline, 1985); E. Sgreccia, "Economia e salute: considerazioni etiche," *Medicina e Morale* 34, (1986): 31-46. The remarkable contribution of various foundations and cultural associations -- like the foundation Smith-Kline presided over by Sen. Prof. Lombardini and directed by V. Ghetti -- to the evaluation of sanitary needs from the point of view of organization and costs is worth mentioning. See in particular A. Maynard, ed., *Pubblico e privato nei sistemi sanitari* (Milano: Franco Angeli - Fondazine Smith-Kline, 1986); G. Muraro, ed., Problemi finanziari del servizio sanitario nazionale (Milano, Franco Angeli - Fondazione Smith-Kline, 1987).

26. Among other contributions, see G. Clerico, "Redistribuzione e controllo del consumo sanitario," *Economia Pubblica* 20, (1990): 43-48; P. Donati, "Il sistema socio-sanitario come apparato di controllo dei bisogni di salute nel Welfare State," in *La regolazione*, ed. V. Ghetti.

27. On the criteria of "effectiveness" "efficacy," and "equity," see A. Bompiani, "Il medico come regolatore."

28. We agree with Sgreccia that "ethics is called in question in the case, for example, of sanitary education, prevention of diseases, and speculations on pharmaceutical products. Ethics is called in question also in the discussion on cutting health care services for terminally ill patients, selecting patients for treatment, guiding the distribution of free cures, or defining the burden of treatment for the elderly. Yet, in all these cases, the ethical principle emerging as a reference point is not always an absolute value, but rather, it rests upon the evaluation of cost/benefit analysis," E. Sgreccia, "Economia e salute."

29. In particular S. Spinsanti, "Verso una teologia sistematica del corpo," *Medicina e Morale*, no. 1 (1983): 5-11. Pope John Paul II has also provide an authoritative impulse to a systematic theology of the body with his catechesis on the book of Genesis: Giovanni Paolo II, *Teologia del corpo* (Roma: Paoline, 1982).

30. See F. D'Agostino, ed., *Diritto e corporeita'* (Milano: Jaka Book, 1984); L. Lombardi-Vallauri, "Promozione e protezione della vita: Funzioni e limiti della legge," in *Nascere, amare, morire. Etica della vita e famiglia oggi* (Milano: Paoline, 1989), pp.125-142; S. Rodota', "Per un nuovo statuto del corpo umano," in *Bioetica*, ed. A. Di Meo and C. Mancina, pp. 47-69.

31. See S. Acquaviva, *In principio era il corpo* (Roma: 1977). For an overview of the meaning of the body in contemporary cultural movements, see S. Spinsanti, *Il corpo nella cultura contemporanea* (Brescia: Queriniana, 1983). The importance of the new understanding of the body in the biomedical field is

analyzed by C. Ventimiglia, "Il corpo fra ambivalenza e simbolismo," *Transizione* 14, (1989): 83-120.

32. On the question of the autonomy and responsibility of science, see P. Cattorini, ed., *Scienza ed etica nella centralita' dell'uomo* (Milano: Franco Angeli, 1989).

33. This aspect is highlighted by A. Autiero, "Legittimazione etica della ricerca biologica," *Rivista di Teologia Morale* 75, (1987): 37-46. The contribution of Italian reflection on experimentation can be found in specific chapters of various bioethics manuals dedicated to this issue: E. Sgreccia (IV, Bioetica e genetica; XII, Bioetica e sperimentazione sull'uomo; XV, Bioetica e tecnologia); S. Spinsanti (II par. 3, L'uomo e la natura; VIII, Ricerca e sperimentazione con esseri umani); D. Tettamanzi (II, Uomo responsabile della vita umana; IV, Ingegneria genetica e interrogativi etici; VII, Interventi su embrioni e feti umani); C. Viafora (VII, Ricerca e sperimentazione su soggetti umani; VIII, La sperimentazione genetica umana; XIII, Diagnosi prenatale: contro ogni forma di automatismo selettivo; XIV, Le nuove tecniche procreatiche: interrogativi etici); S. Leone (VII, Tecnologie riproduttive; X, Sperimentazione); G. Perico (IV, Il consenso del malato e potere decisionale del medico; IV, Sperimentazione clinica).

34. Among the many contributions, see G. Federspil, "Metodologia scientifica," *Medicina e Morale*, no. 3 (1985): 501-507; A. Bompiani, "La sperimentazione clinica dei farmaci: stato attuale del problema normativo e proposte di riforma," *Medicina e Morale*, no. 2 (1982): 93-134; G. Dell'Osso, ed., *Responsabilita' e progresso medico* (Milano: Giuffre', 1984); A. Bellelli, *Aspetti civilistici della sperimentazione umana* (Terni: 1989); "Il contratto sociale delle tecnologie," *Transizione* 14, (1989); D. Mongiano, "Responsabilita' morale degli scienziati: panorama delle concezioni epistemologiche contemporanee," *Medicina e Morale*, no. 2 (1989): 233-271.

35. A clear framework on experimentation, from a legal and medical perspective, is offered by P. Benciolini and A. Aprile, "Il conflitto tra interessi della comunita' e del singolo," In *Etica e deontologia in Medicina: contributi per una riflessione* (Padova: Cleup, 1988), pp. 57-68. Having made a clear distinction among the different modes of experimental activity in medicine, these authors deal primarily with the question of the lawfulness of experimentation. Giving special attention to therapeutic experimentation, they identify the basis for the legitimization of the phenomenon in the conception of a "right to health" stated in the art. 32 of Italian Costitution. In light of such a conception it becomes clear that therapeutic experimentation can be considered legitimate once no other effective means is available. Unlike therapeutic experimentation, pure experimentation does not seem to be clearly legitimized by the legal system. Indeed, the law 833/78, art. 2, no. 7 mentions "guidelines for experimentation"

as one of the goals of the National Health Service. Yet, in the present situation any experimental activity and its modalities are left to the discretion of the competent administration and to medical deontology. On the contrary, according to our authors, the field of experimentation should be regulated with a special law. In order to outline a law capable of solving the conflict between the community's interests on one hand (indeed a wide legitimization of experimentation would greatly benefit the community) and individual's interests on the other (that is the respect of autonomy) it is necessary to refer to both the basic principles of our constitution, i.e the principle of respect for *person* and the principle of *solidarity*. Once free consent is guaranteed, "being available for others" in experimental projects should always be assured even when a certain amount of risk is present.

36. In the Italian publications as well as in the debate in general issues related with genetic experimentation are treated together with issues on experimentation with embryos. For the contribution of the "Catholic area," see A. Serra, "Interrogativi etici dell'ingegneria genetica," *Medicina e Morale* 24, (1984): 306-321; "Verso la manipolazione genetica dell'uomo? Premesse, prospettive e problemi, I," *Civilta' Cattolica*, no. 1 (1985): 431-444; "Verso la manipolazione genetica dell'uomo?, II," *Civilta' Cattolica*, no. 1 (1985): 550-562; E. Brovedani, "L'ingegneria genetica. Aspetti scientifico-tecnici," *Aggiornamenti Sociali*, (1986): 517-534; "Le applicazioni dell'ingegneria genetica. Dalla biotecnologia alla terapia genetica umana," *Aggiornamenti Sociali*, (1986): 605-619; A. Bompiani, "Problemi biologici e clinici aperti dall'ingegneria genetica, dall'inseminazione artificiale e dalla fecondazione in vitro con embryotransfer nella specie umana," in *Manipolazioni genetiche e diritto*. Proceedings XXXV Convention Unione Giuristi Cattolici (Milano: Giuffre', 1984); C. Cirotto and S. Privitera, *La sfida dell'ingegneria genetica. Tra scienza e morale* (Assisi: Cittadella, 1985); L. Lorenzetti, "Etica e manipolazione genetica," *Il Mulino* 34, (1985): 471-483; see also the supplement to the issue no. 4 (1989) of *Medicina e Morale* which introduces an important document of the Center of Bioethics - The Catholic University of Rome, "Identita' e statuto dell'embrione umano." From the perspective of secular moral philosophy, see A. Aurisicchio, "Sulla questione dell'ingegneria genetica," *Prospettive Settanta* 1, (1987): 73-101; L. Terrenato, "Bioetica e genetica," *Problemi di Bioetica* 2, (1988):47-48; F. Zucco, "Responsabilita' etica e ricerca scientifica: il caso della mappatura del genoma," in *Bioetica*, ed. A. Di Meo and C. Mancina, pp. 217-230. From a more "technical" perspective, see L. Lombardi-Vallauri, "L'embrione umano fra Bioetica e biogiuridica," in P. Cattorini, ed., *Scienza ed etica nella centralita' dell'uomo*; S. Rodota', "Diagnosis, secrecy, destiny," in *Diagnosis and prediction. The human genome sequensing: ethical issues*. International Conference on Bioethics (Rome: Class Inten. Ed., 1988); S. Rodota', "Regole, valori, diritti," *Transizione* 13-14, (1989); A. Lisitano, "La manipolazione genetica," in *Diritto e corporeita'*, F. D'Agostino, ed. One must remember that

the issue of "experimentation on embryos" has been a matter of reflection for the Committees istituted by the Minister of Health Degan (Commissione Santuosso) and Donat-Cattin (Commissione Polli). Finally, the Italian delegates to the European Parliament (C. Casini, F. Foschi, and E. Parodi) have played an important role in the proposition of guidelines on this matter. The political activity of these delegates has led to the approbation of the "Rothley Report" on March 16, 1989. An important debate took place also at the level of national Parliament (Chamber of Deputies, see Martinazzoli and others, 1989).

37. An overview of the different positions on the evaluation of prenatal diagnosis was provided by the interdisciplinary Seminar of the Lanza Foundation on December 2, 1989 (Proceedings' publication forthcoming).

38. This chapter of bioethics has been defined by the term "assisted technical procreation" (term which seems a reduction when referred to some of the techniques) in order to differentiate these procedures from "genetic engineering" (which is completely different). The simplification of the language by those who are not specialists, is very often a source of misunderstanding. Some others use the term "artificial reproduction." In so doing they mean to include those techniques which manipulate insemination, and which are part of a larger chapter of the physiopathology of human reproduction concerning spermatic and embryonic selection as well. However, it seems more appropriate to refer the term "assisted artificial procreation" to every intervention which implements "natural" processes, whereas the term "artificial reproduction" denotes the substitution of natural processes through a human intervention.

39. The debate on artificial insemination from an ethical and legal point of view was triggered at the end of the '40s by the news that many American soldiers had been sending home their sperm to impregnate their wives. Ten years later the debate intensified as a consequence of two famous judicial cases, one in Rome (1956) (the sentence in *Giurisp. it.*, 1957, pt. I, sez. II. col. 218 ss. with the important critical comment of A. Trabucchi, *Fecondazione artificiale e legittimita' dei figli*), and the other in Padua (1958) (*Giurisp. it.*, 1959, pt. II. col. 84 ss; also the sentence of the tribunal in *Il foro italiano*, 1959, pt. II, col. 81 ss). Six important contribution of S. Lener on the argument appeared in various issues of the periodical *Civilta' Cattolica* in 1959. Systematic studies are due to F. Santosuosso, *La fecondazione artificiale della donna* (Milano: Giuffre', 1961); *La fecondazione artificiale umana* (Milano: Giuffre', 1984); A. Trabucchi, "Fecondazione artificiale," *Diritto Civile* (Novissimo Digesto italiano, 1962); V. Lojacono, "Inseminazione artificiale," in *Enciclopedia del Diritto*, p. 751 ss.; G. Valensin, *Fecondazione artificiale e naturale della donna* (Milano: Giuffre', 1959). From a juridical-ethical perspective, see L. Rossi, *Morale sessuale in evoluzione* (Torino: Gribaudi, 1967); *Problemi di morale oggi* (Assisi: Cittadella, 1971); L. Leuzzi, "Il dibattito sulla inseminazione artificiale nella riflessione

medico-morale in Italia nell'ultimo decennio," *Medicina e Morale* 22, (1982): 343-370; G. Alpa, "Appunti sull'inseminazione artificiale," *Rivista critica di diritto privato* 3, no. 2 (1985): 333-348; *Procreazione artificiale e interventi nella genetica umana* (Padova: Cedam,1987). On the in-vitro fertilization, see -- from an ethical-juridical perspective -- F.D. Busnelli, "Il diritto e le nuove frontiere della vita umana," *Iustitia* 42, (1985): 263-283. Also should be mentioned the important conventions of the "Unione Giuristi Cattolici Italiani."

40. From the perspective of the Catholic faith, the child is a "gift;" see Congregation for the Doctrine of the Faith, *Instruction on Respect for Human Life in its Origin and on the Dignity of Procreation*, 1987). The child is a gift both in its origin (*i.e.*, in the reciprocal intra-conjugal and trans-conjugal donation of husband and wife who thus participate to the act of creation), and in its structure of meaning (the child is a "person" not the "object" of the parents). Without denying these presuppositions, the reflection of some Catholic moral theologians on this matter is more nuanced. Interesting contributions can be found in a special monographic issue of *Rivista di Teologia Morale* (1986). The "secular" reflection seems to emphasize more the "therapeutic justification." Considerations on the morality of the means are remarkably different from those emerging in the Catholic literature. For an overview on the different positions see, C. Viafora, *Fondamenti*, pp. 226-234.

41. For the sake of clarity, here is a list of the "techniques" and their abbreviation: AIH - Artificial Insemination Husband; AID - Artificial Insemination Donor; FIVET - In-vitro Fertilization, Embryo Transfer; IVF-ET - In-vitro Fertilization, Embryo Transfer; TEST - Tubal Embryo Stage Transfer; GIFT - Gamete Intrafallopian Transfer; PROST - Pronuclear Stage Tubal Transfer; ZIFT - Zigote Intraffalopian Transfer; GIPT - Gamete Intraperitoneal Transfer; GIFTP - Gamete Intraprossimal Fallopian Transfer.

42. In the beginning in-vitro fertilization with embryo transfer (FIVET) was exclusively practiced on sterile women. According to Testart and other gynecologists sterile women today make up only half of the "clients." The other half is made of women who have difficulty in conceiving, and therefore recur to these sophisticated methods in order to shorten the time required for more traditional cures. Meanwhile, the chances of success for artificial fertilization matches those of natural fertilization thanks to the freezing of embyos. The tendency to turn to artificial techniques, therefore, is likely to increase with the enhancement of technology. Since only 20% of sterile couples can solve the problem of sterility with therapeutic means of any nature it may be said that the "pressure" on the physicians to use artificial techniques will increase. The hope - - on the side of those dealing with the problem of sterility -- is that a new "technique" will eventually bring about a definite solution.

43. Angelo Serra states that a survey done in 1985 on 62 centers -- out of 200 which were asked to answer a questionnaire -- has brought to the following results: only 7,993 zygotes out of 14,585 obtained in the laboratories of the above 62 clinics could be transferred to the maternal uterus. Of these, only 1,369 eventually resulted in a pregnancy, whereas 6,624 embryos were lost. Yet, the total number of born babies is even lower, *i.e.*, only 600, that is 7.5% of the implanted zygotes, and only 4.1% of the zygotes available. Crio-conservation techniques can guarantee the immediate survival (2-3 years) of non-transferred embryos. Yet, such a technique -- although useful in the case of a differed transfer or of a second pregnancy -- does not entirely solve the problem at hand.

44. See, for example, M. Mori, "La questione biologica e la morale cristiana. Un'analisi filosofica dell'Istruzione Ratzinger," *Transizione* 9, (1987).

45. The term euthanasia (sweet death, death without pain) has, in time, undergone a shift of meaning. Today's ethical and legal debate no longer defines the concept of euthanasia as "serene death," or as the medical effort to "ease the pain" (such a therapeutic effort being called analgesia or "pain therapy"). Even the term "indirect euthanasia" -- referring to the risk/fact of (indirect) life shortening due to the use of drugs which in itself (i.e. directly) are intended for therapeutic/analgesic reasons -- is not appropriate. The definition proposed by the Congregation for the Doctrine of the Faith on May 5, 1980 seems more appropriate: "Euthanasia means an action or an omission which in its nature, or in its intention causes death, and whose end is to eliminate any pain." Therefore, death is caused by an action or by the omission of an action which is due, and is capable of sustaining life. The intention is to avoid pain, and the means employed is to cause death. From a legal point of view, the distinction between "active" and "passive" euthanasia is still frequently used. While the former refers to any kind of painless killing, the latter covers only those omissions to act which result in failing to administer necessary drugs to "terminally ill" patients thus hastening their death. As for active euthanasia, it should be stated that to eliminate a human life constitutes -- and will always constitute -- a serious crime independently of the reasons which motivate such an act. Yet, from a penal perspective it has been suggested that this case be tried differently than a simple murder by highlighting the patient's consent or request. Euthanasia can be further classified as "euthanasia of terminally ill patients," "neonatal euthanasia," and "social euthanasia." The first type is the only one taken into account by legal projects.

46. From a moral theological perspective, see *Eutanasia. Il senso del vivere e del morire umano*. Proceedings of the XII National Congress of Italian Moral Theologians, Florence, 1-4 April 1986 (Bologna, Dehoniane, 1987); G. Piana, "La questione dell'Eutanasia: significati culturali e valutazione etica," *Credere oggi* 5, (1985): 75-84; D. Tettamanzi, *L'Eutanasia - L'illusione della buona morte* (Casale Monferrato: Piemme, 1985); A. Autiero, "Vivere la morte.

Per una rivisitazione del tema del morire," *Civilta' Cattolica*, no. 1 (1983): 348-356; L. Lorenzetti, "Eutanasia: decodificare la domanda," *Il Regno Attualita'* 29, (1984); P. Montini, "Eutanasia nella stampa italiana," *Rivista di Teologia Morale*, (1986). See also the Congress on "Death and dying" (46. Corso di studi cristiani) organized by Cittadella of Assisi. Some of the papers presented at the Congress can be found in *Rocca*, among which G. Piana, "Nel cuore del mistero," *Rocca*, no. 6 (1988): 34-38. The Catholic medical culture has been actively involved in the definition of death as well as in the issue of care for terminally ill patients. See, for instance O. Corli, ed., *Una medicina per chi muore. Il cammino delle cure palliative in Italia* (Roma: citta'Nuova, 1988); M. Barni, "Considerazioni sulla Eutanasia," *Federazione Medica*, (1985), p. 5 ss. From the point of view of philosophy of law, see the contribution of V. Vitale, "L'antigiuridicita' 'strutturale' del suicidio," in *Diritto e corporeita'*, ed. F. D'Agostino, pp.121-145; F. D'Agostino, "L'Eutanasia come problema giuridico," in *Eutanasia. Il senso del vivere e del morire umano*, pp. 47-65.

47. M. Mori reminds in his bibliographical survey that contributions on "death and dying" from a secular point of view appeared in *Bollettino della societa' italiana di tanatologia* (1979-1982) edited in Milan by E. Grappiolo and G. Di Mola. For an analysis of different concenptions of death in medical thought, see F. Mondella, "Morte naturale e longevita' come progetto utopico della medicina," *Minerva Medica* 72, (1981): 2123-2127. For a more theoretical analysis from a non-religious perspective, see the essay of E. Pattaro, "Presupposti metafisici e metaetici di un'etica della responsabilita'" in the issue already quoted of *Rivista di Filosofia*. Also the issue no. 7 of *Quaderni della societa' di letture e di conversazioni scientifiche*, ed. M. Mori (Genova: 1986) is dedicated to the theme "L'eutanasia come problema." The issue contains contributions of L. Lombardi-Vallauri, S. Maffettone, L. Battaglia, S. Castiglione, R. Ottolenghi, G. Imbraguglia on the essay of M. Mori, "Eutanasia: un'analisi chiarificatrice e una proposta etica." In this essay M. Mori maintains the lawfulness of euthanasia as a form of "rational assisted suicide." S. Maffettone has dealt with the issue of euthanasia in his paper at the Congress of Politeia on November 1986: S. Maffettone, "Valori individuali e scelte pubbliche nelle questioni di accesso alla vita," in *Un'etica pubblica per la societa' aperta*. Proceedings of the International Congress of Politeia (Milano: 1987), pp. 198-209; see also M. Mori, "Sacralita' e disponibilita' della vita: per un'analisi delle prospettive generali sottese alla moralita' dell'eutanasia," in *Un'etica pubblica per la societa' aperta*, pp. 237-242. These positions have been maintained in the recent Congress of Politeia (Rome 1990).

48. The line between aggressive therapeutic treatment and the continuation of an adequate reanimation treatment is very thin especially when the possible result of such a treatment is uncertain. The possibility for an organism or for a single organ to recover is largely unknown. Yet, some cases of

284

unexpected and surprising recovery, although very limited in number, justify, in our opinion, an interventionist attitude ("in dubio" to act). Moreover, a distinction should be made between patients with acute pathologies (for instance, politrauma, shock, acute intoxication) -- in these cases an "aggressive" treatment should be used -- and patients with chronic pathologies. In the last case it is possible to analyse every element, both diagnostic and prognostic, in order to act in the best possible way and with respect to the dignity of the person even when refraining from useless and disproportionate therapies. So for example, it is a common opinion (although not a rigid general rule) that in the case of irreversible chronic pathologies -- such as chronic enlarged cardiopathy in terminal stage, some serious cerebral vascularpathologies, the terminal stage of chronic respiratory insufficiency, epatic insufficiency and terminal stage neoplasia -- it is better to refrain from further therapies when there is no rational hope that the organ in question will recover.

49. See Di Mola, ed., *Cure palliative. Approccio multidisciplinare alle malattie inguaribili* (Milano: Masson Editore, 1987).

50. See, for example, A. Bondolfi, "Pubblicazioni di etica ecologica: il 'dominum terrae' in discussione," *Rivista di Teologia Morale* 49, (1981): 127-134.

51. So, for instance, the position of G. Mattai, "Problemi ecologici e bioetici a confronto con l'esperienza di un nuovo modello di sviluppo," *Rivista di Teologia Morale* 36, (1977): 573-605.

52. G. B. Zorzoli, *Proposte per il futuro: scelte energetiche e nuovo modello di sviluppo* (Milano: Feltrinelli, 1975); G. Nebbia, "I conti sbagliati del programma nucleare," *Mondoperaio* 10, (1976): 67-75; D. Paccino, *L'imbroglio ecologico* (Torino: Einaudi, 1972); V. Pallottino, *I pericoli dell'atomo* (Milano: Rusconi, 1977); F. Prattico, *La qualita' sociale* (Bari: Laterza, 1986).

53. See, for example, the outline of A. Autiero, "Custodire la creazione. Linee di etica ecologica," *Rivista di Teologia Morale* 81, (1989): 99-113.

54. See among many the contributions of M. Acanfora, "Fra la catastrofe del 'totale' e l'esigenza del 'globale'," *Problemi di Bioetica*, no. 5 (1989): 13-23; S. Bartolommei, "Di alcuni problemi in etica ambientale," *Problemi di Bioetica*, no. 3 (1989): 61-65; F. Campagnari, "Rischio del nucleare," in *Paure dell'uomo* (Vicenza: Rezzara, 1989); I. Ferrari, "Alterazioni irreversibili dell'ecosistema," in *Paure dell'uomo*; L. Conti, *Questo pianeta* (Roma: Editori Riuniti, 1983); A. Forbice, ed., *La sfida ecologica* (Milano: Franco Angeli, 1986); A. Moroni, "I fondamenti scientifici dell'etica ambientale," *Problemi di Bioetica*, no. 4 (1989(: 23-49; G. Ruffolo, *La qualita' sociale* (Bari: Laterza, 1986); A. Sacchetti,

Sviluppo o salute: la vera alternativa (Bologna: Patron, 1981); E. Tiezzi, *Tempi storici, tempi biologici* (Milano: Garzanti, 1984).

55. According to Moroni, the roots of the conflict between nature and Man are more universal and ancient than the Judeo-Christian religion. These roots must be found in another common denominator which has fueled an attitude of aggression and exploitation toward nature, and also toward human society independently of geographic location or religion. One must think: a) of the attitude toward nature which developed in the populations of the Mesolithic as they faced the sudden lack of food caused by the general warming of the climate and the fauna's move toward the North. These populations "rebelled" against nature forcing it to produce food; so with the Neolithic, agriculture and cattle-breeding were born; b) of the way in which the great Eastern Civilizations related to the environment causing the expansion of large desert areas; c) of Greek rationalism (Man the measure of everything), or Roman pragmatism. These two cultures which had a great influence upon humanity were born and grew outside the Judeo-Christian orbit; d) of an incoherent cultural adaptation of the Biblical message through expressions of Greek and Roman culture. It cannot be denied that the Biblical model was subjected within the Western context to different, and not always coherent interpretations; e) of the mercantilist culture in the XIII century; of the concept of Man in the Renaissance; f) of the philosophy of the Enlightenment in the XVIII century; of the culture of unlimited economic growth sustained by powerful technology which has led to the exploitation of natural resources and ecological processes. Such a culture has reduced not only nature, but also every manifestation of life to disposable goods, thus favoring a mentality of death and nihilism. See A. Moroni, "I fondamenti scientifici dell'etica ambientale," *Problemi di Bioetica*, no. 4 (1989): 23-49.

56. S. Bartolommei, "Di alcuni problemi di etica ambientale," *Problemi di Bioetica*, no. 6 (1989): 61-65.

57. For a useful approach to issues of environmental ethics, see the introductory document to the first International Conference on *Ethics and Environmental Policies*, organized by the "Lanza Foundation" and by the "Human Dimensions of Global Chance Program" at Borca di Cadore from August 30 to September 1, 1990. The Document, entitled *Environmental ethics, theory, politics, practice*, written and edited by C. Poli and P. Timmerman, will be published together with a selection of the Conference material. The Conference highlighted the following areas among those which should be taken into account by the research in the field: - the use of the concept of health and integrity in the evaluation of ecological welfare; - the interrelation between ethics, economy, and environment; - the development of an ethical focus in ecological education; - the analysis of the ethical implications, and of potential conflicts generated by the rapid increasing interest toward the environment in some social groups, especially

286

the business community and the public; - the estimate of values in the process of ecological evaluation (VIA); - the role of ethics in the economic and ecological interests of developing countries.

58. One has to remember the Italian contribution of B. Miraglia, *Contro la vivisezione degli animali* (Napoli: 1884); V. Montesperelli, *Contro la vivisezione animale* (Roma: 1890); A. Corsetti, *L'intelligenza degli animali bruti e i doveri dell'uomo* (Roma: 1890); A. Agabiti, *Il problema della vivisezione. Tortura degli animali e scempio di coscienze* (Roam: 1910).

59. See in the issue no. 82 (1989) of *Rivista di Teologia morale* the contributions of F. Battazzi, "Gli animali creature di Dio;" A. Autiero, "Una nuova etica per il rapporto uomo-animale;" G. Mattai, "Gli allevamenti forzati;" L. Lorenzetti, "Sperimentazione animale;" G. Trentin, "Brevettabilita' degli animali;" F. Compagnoni, "Etologia e morale."

60. See in particular S. Castignone, "Osservazione sui diritti degli animali," in *Un'Etica pubblica per una societa' aperta*, pp. 228-230; S. Castignone, ed., *I diritti degli animali. Prospettive bioetiche e giuridiche* (Bologna: Il Mulino, 1985); L. Battaglia, "La questione dei diritti degli animali," *Prospettive Settanta* 9, no. 1 (1987).

CONTRIBUTORS

CORRADO VIAFORA was born in 1950. He graduated with a degree in philosophy from Naples in 1974, and studied pedagogy and theology successively. He taught philosophy in several lyceums, and collaborated with FIRAS in the course "Education for Professionals on the Assistance to Senior Citizens" from 1979-1982. He has taught ethics since 1980 for professional nurses at the Civic Hospital of Padua. This teaching experience gave birth to his *Etica Infermieristica* (Milano: Ambrosiana, 1986). His other book, *Fondamenti di Bioetica* (Milano: Ambrosiana, 1989) deals with issues pertaining specifically to biomedical ethics. Since 1988, he has coordinated the research of the Lanza Foundation group "Ethics and Medicine", and especially has organized interdisciplinary seminars on ethics and medicine as well as "International Bioethics Conferences". He teaches *Foundations of Bioethics* since 1989 at the School of Gynecology and Obstetrics and at the University of Padua. In addition to the two books already mentioned his publications include:

"Sofferenza e morte, 'scandalo' dell'esistenza umana. Il pensiero filosofico occidentale di fronte al problema della sofferenza e della morte," in *Credere Oggi* 5, (1985): 15-32.

"Umanizzare la nascita, la malattia e la morte. Problemi e prospettive," in *Credere Oggi* 6, (1987): 98-112.

"Per una morte degna dell'uomo. Orientamenti etici nella cura dei malati terminali," in *Giornale Italiano di Terapia Antalgica*, Suppl. no. 1, pp. 10-18.

"Il feto ha diritto alla vita? Considerazioni critiche in margine al seminario organizzato da 'Politeia'," in *Ginecologia Clinica* 2, (1989): 83-89.

"La Bioetica e la vita umana nascente: problemi e prospettive," in *La vita: nuove frontiere per la politica* [Atti del Convegno organizzato dal Movimento Femminile della Democrazia Cristiana, Abano Terme, 2 aprile 1989] (Abano Terme: Reprint, 1989), pp. 47-56.

"Il paziente come 'partner': problemi etici nel campo della sperimentazione," in *Bollettino Ordine dei Medici di Padova* 3, (1989): 17-18.

"Bioetica e ginecologia. Contributi alla definizione di un modello argomentativo, in *Ginecologia Clinica* 2, (1990): 138-140.

"Contraccezione e salute: un problema solo medico?" in *Ginecologia Clinica* 34, (1990): 247-254.

DAVID ROY is one of the most prestigious names associated with North American bioethics. This Scottish born scholar has taught medical ethics for a number of years at the Mc Gill University in Montreal, and Lavall University. He completed mathematical studies at St. John's University, New York, The Case Technological Institute, and Western Reserve University, Cleveland. Later, he moved to the field of philosophy and theology, receiving professional degrees from both the Gregorian University in Rome, and Tübingen University in Germany. He is known in the field of bioethics because of his prolific publication of articles in the most prestigious international journals. In addition, during the late Seventies and early Eighties, he directed *Cahiers de Bioéthique* which is a series of monographs whose first issue was *La Bioéthique* (1979). He is also the director of the *Journal of Palliative Care*, as well as *Synapse* which is an interesting journal on biomedical ethics. The most authoritative title held by David Roy is as founder and chairman of the *Center for Bioethics* of the *Institute of Clinical Research* of Montreal. The Center was founded in 1976, and is one *of Clinical Research* of Montreal. The Center was founded in 1976, and is one of the leading Centers of bioethics. The fact that he is part of a leading research institute of Canada contributes indeed to the appeal and the mature quality of bioethical reflection in that institute. In addition to being chairman of the *Center for Bioethics*, David Roy also plays important consulting roles in ethics committees of different hospitals, research institutes and other entities. He was consultant for the *Clinical Ethics Committee* at the *Hospital Royal Victoria*, Montreal, from 1982 to 1985. He has been part of the group working on the distribution of sanitary resources activated by the *Conseil de Recherches médicales* in Canada since 1984. Since 1987 he is a member of the *Bioethics Committee* of the *Hotel Dieu*, Montreal. Also since '87, he is part of the *ad hoc* committee on pre-natal diagnosis for the institute of Toronto of the *Canadian Foundation for Cistic Fibrosis*. He has participated on the work of the committee on AIDS which was formed by the Health Ministry and Social Services of Quebec, an has been the official representative of the Canadian Government during international congresses on bioethics. David Roy is member of the *International Academy of Philosophy and Science*. His academic training as well as his cultural role qualify him as having a great capacity for synthesis.

Among the numerous publications which run parallel to his intense professional activity, some are especially noteworthy:

"Promesses et dangers d'un nouveau pouvouir," in *Cahier de bioéthique I. La Bioéthique* (Quebec: Les Presses de l'Université Laval, 1979), pp. 81-102.

"La biomédicine aujourd'hui et l'homme demain. Point de départ et directions de la bioéthique," in *Le Supplément* 128, (1979): 59-75.

"L'enseignement de l'éthique medicale," in *Journal de médicine légale, droit médicale* 6, (1982): 723-732.

"Développements biomédicaux et dilemmes éthiques: l'histoire récente," in *Église et Théologie* 6, (1982): 283-294.

290

"Médicine, éthique, anthropologie," in *Traité d'anthropologie médicale: l'istitution de la santé et de la maladie,* ed. J. Dufresne, F. Dumont and Y. Martin (Montreal: Presse de l'Université de Quebec, 1985), pp. 1189-1217.

"Death, Dying and the Brain," in *Critical Care Clinics* 1, (1986): 161-172.

"Controlled Critical Trials: An Ethical Imperative," in *Journal of Chronic Disease* 3, (1986): 159-162.

"Ethical Principles in Surgical Research," in *Principles and Practice of Research: Strategy for Surgical Investigator,* ed. H. Troidl and al. (Heidelberg: Springer Verlag, 1986), pp. 118-131.

"Ethics in Clinical Research and Clinical Practice," in *Clinical and Investigative Medicine* 4, (1986): 283-289.

"Ethics in Palliative Care," in *Journal of Palliative Care* 1, (1987): 3-4

"La legge del dolore," in *Prometeo* 21, (1988): 80-87.

"Fetal Therapy: Ethical Considerations," in *Biomedical Ethics and Fetal Therapy,* ed. C. Nimrod, G. Griener (Waterloo: Wilfried Laurier University Press, 1988), pp. 59-66.

"Ethics and Aging: Trends and Problems in Clinical Setting," in *Ethics and Aging: the Right to Live, the Right to Die,* ed.J. E. Thornton and E. R. Winkler (Vancouver: The University of British Colombia Press, 1988), pp. 3-40.

"HIV Infection and AIDS: Ethical Issues," in *AIDS: A Perspective from Canadians* [Background Papers] (Ottawa: Royal Society of Canada, 1988), pp. 315-331.

"Ethique clinique: des cas aux fondements," in *Bioéthique. Méthodes et fondements* [Proceedings of the X Interdisciplinary Colloquium of Philosophy Society of Quebec], ed. M. H. Parizeau (Montreal: 1989).

"Ethics and Medical Genetics," in *Ethics and Human Genetics. A Cross-Cultural Perspective,* ed. D. Wertz and J. Fletcher (Berlin: Springer Verlag, 1989), pp. 119-140.

"Cancer Care: Toward a Global Ethics," in *Journal of Palliative Care* 3, (1989): 3-5.

"The Health and Life Sciences: Where is the Ethics for our Knowledge and Power?" in *Ethics and Technology: Ethical Choices in the Age of Pervasive Technology*, ed. J. Nef, J. Vancerkop and H. Wiseman (Toronto: Wall and Thompson, 1989), pp. 113-118.

"Humanity: The Measure of Palliative Care Ethics," in *Journal of Palliative Care* 3, (1989): 3-4.

"Ethical Issues in the Treatment of Cancer Patients," in *Bulletin of the World Health Organization* 4, (1989): 341-346.

WARREN THOMAS REICH was born in Peterson (New Jersey) in 1931, and received his doctorate in moral theology in 1962 at the Gregorian University of Rome with Josef Fuchs. He did his post-doctoral fellowship at the University of Würzburg; has been Visiting Professor at the University of Tübingen; and was a Fellow of the National Humanities Center. He went to Georgetown University (Washington, D.C.) in 1971 when its Center for Bioethics was first established. In 1977 he established the Medical Humanities Program at the Georgetown University School of Medicine where he has been the Director of the "Division of Health and Humanities" from 1980. He originated the *Encyclopedia of Bioethics Project* of which he is the Editor-in-Chief.

Some publications of Warren Reich are among others:

"Medical Ethics: The Contemporary Context," in *Chicago Studies* 11, (1972): 279-293.

"The Right to Life: Can We Decide," in *Clinical Proceedings-Children's Hospital National Medicine Center* 29, (1973): 265-286.

"Quality of Life and Defective Newborn Children: An Ethical Analysis," in *Decision Making and Defective Newborn: Proceedings of a Conference on Spina Bifida and Ethics*, ed. C. Swinyard (Springfield: Charles C. Thomas e Co., 1978), pp. 489-511.

"Codes and Statements Related to Medical Ethics," in *Encyclopedia of Bioethics*, ed. Warren T. Reich, pp. 1721-1815.

"Infants: Public Policy and Procedural Questions," in *Encyclopedia of Bioethics*, pp. 732-742.

"Infants: Ethical Perspectives on the Care of Infants," in *Encyclopedia of Bioethics*, pp. 724-735.

"Quality of Life," in *Encyclopedia of Bioethics*, pp. 829-840.

"Ethical Issues Related to Research Involving Elderly Subjects," in *Gerontologist* 4, (1978): 326-337.

"Philosophy of Medicine," in *A Guide to the Culture of Science, Technology and Medicine* (New York: Macmillan Free Press, 1980).

"In vitro Fertilization and Embryo Transfer: Public Policy and Ethics," in *Science and Morality*, ed. D. T. Zallen and C. D. Clemens (Lexington, Mass: 1982), pp. 10-54.

"Organ Transplantation International Perspective: Ethical Aspects," in *National Humanities Center Newsletter*, (1984): 20-28.

"Bioethics in the 1980: Challenges and Paradigms," in *Biomedical Ethics: A Community Forum*, ed. H. M. Sonheimer (Syracuse: State University of New York, 1985), pp. 1-35.

"Prolongation of Life," in *Dictionary of Christian Ethics*, ed. J. F. Childress (Philadelfia: Westminster, 1985), pp. 351-352.

"Perche' i Comitati etici? Una valutazione dei diversi modelli," in *I Comitati etici ospedalieri*, ed. S. Spinsanti (Milano: Paoline, 1987).

"Models of Pain and Suffering: Foundations for an Ethics of Compassion," in *Pain*, ed. J. Brihave, F. Loew and H. W. Pia, *Acta Neurochirurgica*, Supplementum 38, (1987): 117-122.

"Caring for Life in the First of It: Moral Paradigms for Perinatal and Neonatal Ethics," in *Seminars in Perinatology*, (1987): 279-287.

293

"Experiential Ethics as a Foundation for Dialogue between Health Communication and Health Care Ethics," in *Journal of Applied Communication Research*, (1988): 16-28.

"Speaking of Suffering: A Moral Account of Compassion," in *Soundings*, (1989): 83-108.

"La compassione in un'etica della vita centrata sulla famiglia," in *Nascere, amare, morire: etica della vita e famiglia, oggi*, ed. S. Spinsanti (Milano: Paoline, 1989), pp. 187-206.

"The Word 'Bioethics': Its Birth and the legacies of those Who shaped It," *Kennedy Institute of Ethics Journal* no. 4, (1994) 319-335

"The Word 'Bioethics': The Struggle over Its Earliest Meanings," *Kennedy Institute of Ethics Journal* no. 5, (1995) 19-34

JEAN-FRANCOIS MALHERBE is currently Professor of Medical Ethics and Anthropology at the University of Sharbrooke and at the University of Montreal (Canada). Already a Professor of Philosophy of Medicine at the Catholic University of Louvain (Belgium), is one of the most representative figures of European bioethics. To his initiative is due the creation in 1983 of the "Center of Bioethical Studies" of Bruxelles. The Center pursues a specific research in the field of philosophy of medicine on issues which have a great bioethical relevance: i.e. the ethical normativity of the concept of "quality of life", the concept of health, the distinction between normal and pathologic, as well as other more radical issues related with the concept of Man involved in the practice of the biomedical sciences. J. F. Malherbe has been also the director of one of the Center's initiatives, the Seminars of specialization on "Ethics and Philosophy of Medicine". These Seminars are directed, in particular, to health care professionals. The goal is to stimulate in health care operators an effective and creative preparation to ethical discernment in their profession. Yet, the Center is not only meant to be an institution dedicated to research and to the formation of health care operators, rather a place of information open to the people. For this reason, the research programs of the Center are always related to initiatives of public animation. These initiatives take place both in parallel with research, such as in the case of programs like "The ethics of nursing care" and "The care of dying patients", and in a phase subsequent to more technical research like the Seminar "Medicine and procreation". The intention to be open and to involve many people in dealing with bioethical issues explains another of Malherbe's initiatives: the creation of a research on "Ethics, Health, and the Third World". Finally, Malherbe has been the secretary of the "European Association of Medical Ethics Centers". This organization was founded in 1985 on the initiative of the Bioethics Institutes of Barcellona, Bruxelles and Maastricht, and now it involves thirty European Centers. As for the scientific production, Malherbe is known in the bioethical literature as the Director of "Catalysis", a collection of interdisciplinary contributions selected for their quality of rigor and originality. Among his publications the following are worth mentioning:

La Philosophie de Karl Popper et le positivisme logique (Paris: PUF, 1976).

"La neutralité axiologique est-elle un critère de scientificité?" in *Spécificité des sciences humaines en tant que sciences*. Colloque de l'Académie Internationale de Philosophie de Sciences, Trento, 4-7 May 1978 (Bruxelles: Office International de Librairie, 1979), pp. 183-210.

Epistémologies anglo-saxonnes (Paris: PUF, 1979).

"Autoproduction et responsabilité de l'homme. Remarques sur l'articulation de l'éthique et du biologique," *Revues de questions scientifiques* 153, (1982): 485-505.

"L'émergence de la norme médicale. Le cas de l'insémination artificielle avec donneur" in J. F. Malherbe and D. Delaisi de Parceval, "L'émergence des normes," *Cahiers du CREA* 3, (1984): 485-505.

"L'embryon est-il une personne humaine?" *Lumiére et Vie* 172, (1985): 19-31.

"Les valeurs en conflit en matière pré-et néonatale et leur perception," in *Désordres prénataux et problèmes de néonatologie*. FIUC Symposion, ed. J. F. Malherbe, H. Wattiaux and L. Dingemans (Bruxelles: 1985), pp. 10-34.

Le langage théologique à l'age de la science (Paris: Cerf, 1985).

Esquisses puor une philosophie de la santé (Louvain-la-Neuve: Ciaco, 1985).

Engendrés par la science: enjeux éthique des manipulations de la procréation (Paris: Cerf, 1985). In collaboration with E. Boné.

"Le concept de santé: hypothèse de définition à partir du concept d'autonomie," *Cahiers des Sciences Familiales et Sexuologiques* 10, (1986): 185-194.

"Le risque d'alienation dans l'art médicale," in *La responsabilité éthique dans le développement biomedicale* [Colloque de l'Académie Internationale de Philosophie des Sciences, Bruxelles, 23-28 April, 1984] (Louvain-la Neuve: Ciaco, 1987), pp. 343-352.

Pour une éthique de la médicine (Paris: Larousse, 1987).

"Le statut personnel de l'embryon. Essais philosophique," in *Débuts biologiques de la vie humaine: des chercheur chrétiens s'interrogent* (Paris-Louvain-la-Neuve: L'Harmattan-Ciaco, 1988), pp. 103-120.

Le citoyen, le médecin et le sida, l'exigence de vérité (Louvain-la-Neuve: Ciaco, 1988). In collaboration with S. Zorrilla.

"L'uomo di fronte alla problematica del normale e del patologico," *Kos* 37, (1988): 9-19.

"Éthique et fécondation in vitro," *Louvain Médicale*, no. 7 (1988): 497-502.

"La bioéthique à l'hospital," *Louvain Médicale*, no. 9 (1988): 497-502.

"I comitati di etica in ospedale, un luogo di sviluppo dell'autonomia," in *I comitati di etica in ospedale*, ed. S. Spinsanti (Milano: Paoline, 1988), pp. 103-120.

"La medicalizzazione della vita e la resistenza della Parola," in *Nascere, amare, morire*, ed. S. Spinsanti (Milano: Paoline, 1989), pp. 5-29.

Born in 1941 in Madrid **DIEGO GRACIA GUILLEN** is a Professor of History of Medicine at the Universidad Complutense. He is also a member of the "Consejo Superior de Investigaciones Cientificas" and an academic of the "Real Academia Nacional de Medicina". Thanks to his expertise in both medicine and philosophy, Gracia has established his authority in the bioethical literature with a rigorous scientific production. A wide international breath together with a close connection to the Spanish tradition -- whose contribution especially in the fields of medicine and medical anthropology is noteworthy -- constitute a peculiar aspect of this production. A figure of exceptional relevance in the interdisciplinary field of medicine and medical anthropology is Pedro Lain Entralgo, undoubtedly the most significant representative of Spanish medical humanism. A disciple of such an extraordinary figure, Diego Gracia is the successor of Lain Entralgo on the Chair of History of Medicine in Madrid. In this position Lain Entralgo has taught for thirty six years without interruption. From 1972 to 1975 Gracia has contributed, together with his teacher, to the *Historia Universal de la Medicina*, a monumental work of seven volumes. Among other contributions of Gracia in the field of "Humanidades Medicas" -- of which Lain Entralgo has been the pioneer -- can be found in the following works: J. L. G. De Rivera, A. Vela and J. Aran, eds., *Manual de Psiquiatria* (1979); J. L. Peset, ed., *Enfermidad y Castigo* (1984). He has co-authored *Ethics of Diagnosis* (1984), and he has published in the same year *Historia del Medicamento*. Finally, he is the Director of "Jano Humanidades Medicas". From the point of view of his philosophical formation, Gracia was under the influence of another great figure of contemporary Spanish culture, i.e. the philosopher Xavier Zubiri, of whom he has been a friend and a collaborator in his last years of life. Gracia has published different works on some aspects of Zubiri's philosophy, among others *Voluntad de Verdad. Para leer a Zubiri* (Barcellona: Editorial Labor, 1986). He also collaborates to the critical edition of the Master's posthumous writings. From

1972 Gracia directs also the Philosophical Seminar of the "Sociedad de Estudios y Publicaciones", today Foundation Banco Urquijo. The reflection of D. Gracia in the field of bioethics is engaged at two different levels: a characteristic and original historical approach to bioethical issues on one hand, and a search for foundations in bioethics on the other. The first volume of his *Tractado de Bioetica* (Madrid: Eudema, 1989) is dedicated to the foundational question, while the second volume *Bioetica Clinica* is forthcoming. The *Tractado* reflects contents and methods of the Master in bioethics -- the first in Europe --which D. Gracia directs at the Universidad Complutense. Other works of Diego Gracia:

"El aborto en la historia," in *Vida Nueva*, (1983): 14-19.

Etica de la calidad de la vida (Madrid: Fundacion SM, 1984).

"Medicina social," in *Avances del saber* 5, (1984): 179-233.

"Persona y Comunidad: De Boecio a Tomas de Aquino," in *Cuadernos Salmantinos de Filosofia* 11, (1984): 63-106.

"Cuestiones filosoficas sobre la genesis humana," in *Jano*, (1985): 32-41.

"Es el niño un ser enfermo?" in *Jano*, (1985): 801-814.

"Etica de la calidad de la vida," in *Jano*, (1985): 45-56.

"Historia de la etica medica," in *Etica y Medicina*, ed. F. Vilardel (Madrid: Espasa Calpe, 1985): 25-65.

"Los derechos de los enfermos," in *Dilemmas eticos de la medicina actual*, ed. J. Gafo (Madrid: Ediciones de la Universidad Pontificia Comillas, 1986), pp. 43-87.

"Bioetica, una nueva disciplina academica," in *Jano*, (1987): 68-75.

"El nacimiento de la clinica y el nuevo orden de la relacion medico-enfermo," in *Cuadernos Hispanoamericanos*, (1987): 269-282.

"Introduccion a la bioetica," in *Leciones de bioetica* (Valladolid: 1987), pp. 11-13.

"Spain from the Decree to the Proposal," in *Hastings Center Report* 17, (1987): 29-32.

"La Medicina en la historia de la civilizacion," in *Dolentium Hominum* 7, (1988): 65-72.

"Poblacion, desarollo y calidad de la vida," in *Razon y Fe*, (1988): 409-420.

"Problemas filosoficos de la ingenieria genetica," in *Manipulacion genetica y moral cristiana* (Madrid: Fundacion Universitaria San Pablo, 1988), pp. 55-119.

"L'umanita' di fronte al pericolo sangue," in *Famiglia oggi* 41, (1989): 21-25.

"Los Medicos y el SIDA. Problemas eticos de la asistencia medica a los enfermos de SIDA," in *EL SIDA: un reto a la Sanidad, la Sociedad y la etica. Dilemmas eticos de la Medicina actual n. 3*, ed. J. Gafo (Madrid: Publicaciones de la Universidad Pontificia Comillas, 1989), pp.113-127.

"Primum non nocere". El principio de no-maleficencia como fundamento de la etica medica (Madrid: Real Academia de Medicina, 1990).

ALBERTO BONDOLFI was born in 1946 in Canton Ticino (Switzerland), and studied philosophy and theology at the University of Fribourg. An Assistant Professor in the Moral Theology Institute of the same University for several years, from 1979 he has been a Researcher and a Professor at the Institute of Social Ethics at the University of Zürich. Bondolfi's activity is strictly related to the German and the Italian cultural environment besides, of course, the Swiss one. He collaborates with many Italian journals and initiatives, and lately he has been in contact with Eastern Europe as well.

The function of "mediation" is a characteristic feature of Bondolfi's personality. This is true not only for of his cultural activity but also for his church denomination, Bondolfi being the only Catholic Professor in a Protestant theological Institute. He has been the Chairman of the European Conference of

"Justitia et Pax" and is now a member of the homonymous National Commission. In the specific field of bioethics, Bondolfi is the only "lay" member (i.e. non-physician) of the Central Ethical Commission of the Swiss Academy of Medical Sciences. Moreover, he is the Chairman of the Swiss Society of Biomedical Ethics. The Swiss Society of Biomedical Ethics was founded in 1989 as an interdisciplinary body with the goal of promoting bioethical reflection Switzerland. From February 1990 the Society has published a bulletin entitled *Bioethica Forum.* The reflection of Bondolfi deals in particular with two clusters of issues: i.e. the relation ethics-law, and "animals rights". In light of contemporary bioethics tendency to reduce in one way or the other the question of the relation between morality and law, Bondolfi underscores the complexity of such relation. Indeed, he criticizes not only the attempt to practically identify morality and law, but also the position barring the law from any reference to a particular ethical code. Bondolfi's presupposition in dealing with the issue of animal rights is the conviction that the relation human being-animals is crucial to improving just relations among humans. Numerous are the publications in different fields of ethics. Among the most important are the followings:

Teoria critica ed etica cristiana (Bologna: Dehoniane, 1979).

"Novita' di etica medica: rassegna di pubblicazioni estere sul problema dell'eutanasia e della morte," in *Rivista di Teologia Morale* 12, (1980): 307-323.

"Etica Politica," in *Corso di Morale*, ed. T. Goffi and G. Piana (Brescia: Queriniana, 1983), vol. 4, pp. 84-180.

"Medizin zwischen Fortschritt und Verantwortung: eine sozialethische Überlegungen," in *Reformatio* 32, (1983): 231-235.

" 'Autonomie' und 'autonome Moral'. Untersuchungen zu einem Schlüsselbegriff," in *Concilium*, no. 2 (1984): 167-174.

"La riforme du droit pénal èn matière sexuelle. Quelques remarques éthiques autour d'un thème controversé," in *Studia Philosophica* 44, (1985): 182-189.

Pena e pena di morte (Bologna: Dehoniane, 1985).

"Momenti del dibattito tedesco sull'etica (1970-1985)," in *Religioni e Societa'*, no. 2 (1986): 38-56.

"Ethische Überlegungen zum Problemkreis In-vitro-fertilisatio und Embryotransfer," in *Schweizerische Kirchenzeitung* 155, (1987): 66-69.

"Lo sviluppo sociale dell'individuo e delle istituzioni sociali nella scuola di Habermas," in *Rassegna di Teologia* 28, (1987): 252-269.

"Aspetti etico-sociali della sterilita'," in *Rivista di Teologia Morale* 20, (1988): 63-73.

"Ethische Aspekte der AIDS-Information und Prävention," in *Sozial und Präventivmedizin* 33, (1988): 345-347.

"Ethische Erwägungen nach dem AIDS-Schock," in *Schweizerische Kirchenzeitung* 33, (1988): 428-430.

"Aspetti etico-giuridici ed etico-politici nelle biotecnologie," in *Testimonianze* 10, (1989): 66-105.

"Bibliografia scelta sulla discussione attorno ai 'diritti degli animali'," in *Rivista di Teologia Morale* 29, (1989): 107-123.

"Diritti degli animali ed esperimenti con gli animali," in *Concilium*, no. 3 (1989): 158-171.

Malattia, eutanasia e morte (Bologna: Dehoniane, 1989).

"Rapporto uomo-animale. Storia del pensiero filosofico e teologico," in *Rivista di Teologia Morale* 21, (1989): 57-77.

"Sistemi politici," in *Nuovo Dizionario di Teologia Morale*, ed. F. Compagnoni, G. Piana and S. Privitera (Milano: Paoline, 1990), pp. 1254-1262.

ADRIANO BOMPIANI was born in Rome in 1923. He was chair of the Obstetric Gynecology Department at the Policlinico Gemelli Hospital in Rome. His research activity, contained in over two hundred publications, dealt mainly with the development of gynecological endocrinology and perinatal medicine. Of particular interest in the international arena of endocrinology are his studies on the physiopathology of metabolism during pregnancy, as well as his contributions to the definition of dysplastic genetic syndromes of the female genitalia. In the area of perinatal medicine, A. Bompiani was one of the first in Italy to develop methods of steroid detection to determine the welfare of the fetus in utero. Moreover, his contribution in the fields of uterine collagen's biochemistry and electronic microscopy are at the very cutting edge of these fields.

For many years, Bompiani was president of the Italian Association of Obstetric Psychoprophylaxis, and between 1972-82, was also president of the Italian Association for the Study of Fertility and Sterility. During this time, he contributed greatly to the development of psychological preparation for women facing pregnancy and childbirth. Today, almost all regional laws recognize this psychological preparation as medical coverage that every patient has a right to have. Then, in 1976, he began his parliamentary activity. In the Health and Education Senate Commissions, he made a decisive contribution in the form of numerous bills, and through participation in the debate on the problems of health and university reform. In this dual context, he paid particular attention to the training of personnel, to the reform of research hospitals, to the laws pertaining to rehabilitation of the handicapped and the drug-addicted, to the adjustment of laws regarding the testing of pharmaceuticals and to the laws regarding transplants. Nominated president of the Senate Health Commission, Bompiani initiated and completed, between October 1983 and August 1984, an in-depth investigation on the implementation status of the law of December 23, 1978, No. 883 of the National Health Service. He shouldered the burden of reporting on the proposed health regulation law, examined between 1984 and 1985, that became

302

state law No. 595/1985. This law is of fundamental importance for the evolution of national health care. Additionally, on March 30 1990, he was nominated president of the National Bioethics Committee. Of course, Bompiani has given much thought to bioethical issues. Among his writings:

"Il ginecologo, l'aborto e l'obiezione di coscienza," *Medicina e Morale*, no. 1 (1978): 1-11.

"Aspetti medici della Legislazione dell'aborto," *Quaderni di Justitia* 25, (1972): 23-49.

"L'obiezione di coscienza. Storia parlamentare dell'art. 9," *Medicina e Morale*, no. 3 (1978).

"La sperimentazione clinica dei farmaci: stato attuale del problema normativo e proposte di riforma," *Medicina e Morale*, no. 2 (1982): 95-134.

"Liberta' e condizionamento nella ricerca biomedica," *Prospettive nel mondo* 48, (1980): 27-32.

"Embryo transfer. Gli aspetti tecnici della fecondazione in vitro e dell'embryo transfer umano," *Federazione Medica*, no. 1 (1984): 5-13.

"E' orrenda la prospettiva di un utero in affitto," *Famiglia oggi*, no. 11-12 (1984): 24-27.

"La protezione della vita nelle diverse fasi dello sviluppo prenatale," Paper read at the Seminar on *The Family*, 14-15 april 1984, Cadenabianca.

"Panorama della ricerca biomedica italiana e problemi della ricerca farmaceutica," *Cronache Farmaceutiche*, no. 4 (1984): 1-8.

"Riforma psichiatrica oggi," *Anime e Corpi* 116, (1984): 675-700.

"Eutanasia e diritti del malato in fase terminale," *Presenza Pastorale*, no. 5-6 (1985): 77-119.

"Evoluzione del servizio sanitario nazionale," *Organizzazione Sanitaria*, no. 6 (1985): 3-51.

"Medico, servizio sanitario, economia," *Medicina e Morale*, no. 4 (1985): 691-716.

"Problemi biologici e clinici aperti dall'ingegneria genetica, dall'inseminazione artificiale e dalla fecondazione in vitro con embryo transfer nella specie umana," *Justitia*, no.1 (1985): 33-86.

"Valore dell'informazione e della comunicazione," *Medicina e informatica*, no. 2 (1985): 11-17.

"La fecondazione in vitro: passato, presente, futuro," *Medicina e Morale*, no. 1 (1986): 79-102.

"Comitati etici e tutela dei diritti del malato nel dibattito attuale in sede legislativa italiana," in *Dalla Bioetica ai comitati etici. Prospettive e compiti. Manuale operativo*, ed. C. G. Vella, P. Quattrocchi and A. Bompiani (Milano: Ed. Ancora, 1988), pp. 101-128.

"La revisione della legge 644/1975 concernente la disciplina dei prelievi da cadavere ai fini di trapianto terapeutico," in *Trapianti di organo*, ed. E. Sgreccia (Milano: Vita e pensiero, 1989), pp. 85-131.

INDEX OF NAMES

It is a privilege to present to the U.S. reading public and bioethics scholars this volume on bioethics in several parts of the world. It offers a distinctive collection of culturally and intellectually diverse perspectives that are of mounting importance as the field of bioethics becomes more and more internationalized.

The essays are not designed to offer a substantive advancement of bioethical scholarship, but to present a rich portrayal of this field of learning in a variety of mentalities and cultures, and in this way to promote international and intercultural dialogue in bioethics.

Bioethics outside the United States deals with a somewhat different range of issues and methods. It offers critique of the initial U.S. orientation on bioethics, while utilizing some of the same rule-based analysis so common in the U.S. More significantly, one finds in the bioethics that has been developed in other countries distinctively different moral mentalities and intellectual approaches that are instructive for the rethinking of bioethics in the U.S.

Although the word and the field of bioethics were first spawned in the United States, their cousins in other countries are clearly a distinctive and forceful branch of the family that deserves to be better known in the country of origin. Thus it will be helpful to U.S. scholars to have available to them in English translation the essays found in this volume on bioethics in French-speaking, German-speaking, Dutch-speaking, Spanish-speaking, and Italian-speaking countries, placed in dialogue with chapters on bioethics in English-speaking countries.

(From the *Preface* of Warren T. Reich)